HDTV
High-Definition Television
2nd Edition

Stan Prentiss

TAB Books
Division of McGraw-Hill, Inc.
Blue Ridge Summit, PA 17294-0850

SECOND EDITION
FIRST PRINTING

© 1994 by **TAB Books.**
TAB Books is a division of McGraw-Hill, Inc.

Library of Congress Cataloging-in-Publication Data
Prentiss, Stan.
    HDTV : high-definition television / by Stan Prentiss.—2nd ed.
        p.   cm.
    ISBN 0-8306-4296-X   ISBN 0-8306-4295-1 (pbk.)
    1. High definition television. I. Title.
    TK6679.P74 1993
    621.388—dc20   92-43819
                                                            CIP

Acquisitions editor: Roland S. Phelps
Production team: Katherine G. Brown, Director
                Lisa M. Mellott, Typesetting
                Ollie Harmon, Typesetting
                Sue Kuhn, Typesetting
                Jana L. Fisher, Typesetting
                Patsy D. Harne, Layout
                Nancy K. Mickley, Proofreading
                Jodi L. Tyler, Indexer
Design team: Jaclyn J. Boone, Designer
                Brian Allison, Associate Designer   4323
Paperbound cover design: Graphics Plus, Hanover, Pa.   EL1

Contents

10 Field testing *213*

11 System audio improvements and the fateful decision *276*

12 Reported improvements to the four remaining digital systems in 1993 *283*

Acknowledgments

The author of this HDTV publication is both beholden and very much obliged to the many engineers and executive/advisory personnel from the terrestrial television and cable television industries both in the U.S. and Canada for the wealth of excellent design and test information made available through the Advanced Television Service, Advanced Television Systems Committee, The Electronic Industries Association, the many working parties of the ATSC and the Federal Communications Commission (from which most of this publication directly derives). Especially we are indebted to ATS Chairman Richard Wiley, Peter M. Fannon, ATTC, and Brian James, CableLabs for their enormously helpful editorial and advisory contributions. Also, Maureen Peratino, Hector Davis, and William Hassinger of the Federal Communications Commission. Without these individuals and their supporting associates, the historical, technical, and management programs included and developed in this publication could never have been conceived and matured. There's always considerable research, paraphrasing, and some direct quotations involved. Authors don't materialize such highly technical and informative intelligence out of the wild blue or spongy sod. Originators are our thoroughly appreciated sources and support.

The following, therefore, are due equivalent recognition for their considerable contributions: Jules Cohen, MSTV & consultant; Mark Richer, PBS; Paul Hearty, ATEL; Robert Hopkins, ATSC; Terrence Smith, Sarnoff Research; Woo Paik and Robt. Rast, Gen. Instrument; John Henderson and Jack Fuhrer, Hitachi America; Bob Keeler and Eric Petajan, AT&T Bell Labs.; Tom Gurley and Bruce Miller, ATTC; Robert Plonka and Robert Davis, Harris; Ron Lee, John Taylor, Wayne Luplow, Carl Eillers, Zenith; George Hanover, EIA; Edmund Williams, PBS & Field Test for ATV; Lynn Claudy, NAB; Aldo Cugnini, Philips; Yozo Ono, NHK; Birney Dayton, nVision; Chuck Slack, Dave MacDonald, Jeffrey O'Neal, James McGoffin, Robert Oblack, Roger Crooks, Tektronix; Tak Tsang, Ron Williamson, Michael Marino, John Fluke Mfg.; Tim Dehne, Holly Reams, National Instruments; Jerry von Behren, Winegard; Lance Piper, Cometic Antennas; Dale Sherrill, Comm/Scope, Inc.; Duffy Paul, Channel Master. And to all the others who have aided in many obvious or indirect ways to the final product, another barrel of thanks!

Introduction

Combined with the first edition of *HDTV: High-Definition Television*, this second edition describes and details one of the greatest and most challenging episodes in our electronic history—that of gracefully departing in a few years from the system set up by the National Television Systems Committee (NTSC) in 1953 and now entering the world of digital television crafted by and for the U.S. and Canada, in addition to the rest of the world, which must follow our remarkably developed standard, becoming mandatory here some 15 years after acceptance by the Federal Communications Commission (FCC) of a specific system scheduled for approval late in 1994. Temporarily, HDTV and NTSC must coexist on separate channels, but as available radio frequency spectrum shrinks, HDTV will supplant today's simulcasts, bringing vastly improved video, color, and audio programming to us all.

The first edition of HDTV described and illustrated in detail the many proponents who either submitted ideas, or wished to offer analog (signal processing) transmitting and receiving equipment somewhat advanced over our NTSC of today. Then, Zenith Electronics Corp. presented a hybrid analog and digital system with further advantages over NTSC. Soon, General Instrument/DigiCipher/MIT proposed their versions of two all-digital systems followed by the David Sarnoff Consortium, to which Zenith and telephone partner AT&T quickly responded. Now, all competing HDTV electronics have become completely digital, almost doubling resolution and definition of NTSC and ensuring significant technical advances over alternate systems here and abroad.

To complete our full chronology of this massive HDTV development, the second edition details the electrical, regulatory, and political aspects of our digital acceleration so that all can understand the FCC's specific selection of the system or combination of systems already described in this book. The waiting and struggling is now over and America once more has the golden opportunity of once again becoming the leader in consumer electronics. Regardless, after millions of dollars have been allocated and spent, all of North America has contributed mightily in the effort, and it's now time to collect the many patent royalties and hardware design innovations justly due the winner or winners. High technology and competitive spirit still continues as an American tradition . . . may it never falter.

Your author, throughout, has been a member of three of the working parties and an expert observer of the HDTV systems during ATTC laboratory testing and the many formative meetings preceding and following this intense, fruitful activity. Transmitters, studios, program material, and receivers must now follow.

1
HDTV retrospect and outlook

Originally, there were 20, now there are four, but with a world of difference. In the beginning, straightforward analog signal processing was the concept, along with improved definition, rather than pure HDTV. Today, digital TV has 16:9 wide-screen aspect ratios, low-ratio interference factors, compressed/expanded (companded) information content for both audio and video, a $5 million Advanced Television Test Center facility, qualified expert and consumer observers, and a promise by the Federal Communications Commission of a winner-take-all decision sometime during the latter part of 1994.

The long road of meetings, tests, analysis, explanations, major engineering proposals, and emerging hardware has now moved into the "put-up or shut-up stage," where, we hope, quality (not unqualified politics) reigns supreme. The beginnings of a new consumer-oriented multi-billion industry has great potential for America to once again become preeminent in serving its own viewing public. Patent royalties alone can amount to an extremely wealthy income; after 1996, sales should be astronomical as we move toward the 21st century. The international information data, fax, cellular telephony, local-area and wide-area networks, as well as extremely important video and satellite communications have finally arrived and all have a major opportunity to prosper.

In the meantime, the U.S. and other parts of the world continue to suffer the slings and arrows of inexpensive narrow-band television receivers, poorly designed indoor and outdoor TV antennas, cheap and dirty installations, and inadequate satellite systems, burdensome and expensive signal enciphering (scrambling), restrictive community development covenants coupled together with false pride, and a host of other real or borderline impairments. These problems might even slow the development of high-definition television and will certainly retard the spread of extremely important wireless cable. The latter two, of course, require rooftop antennas for adequate reception. Sorry folks, but the "I don't want that ugly thing on my roof" attitude is overdue for change.

But let's get on with the fascinating HDTV story as it has developed in the 1980s and 1990s, especially the transitions from analog to digital and the cogent reasons therefore. It is, indeed, an electronic treat!

In the beginning

For openers, let's return to a 1989 chart of initial offerors (proponents) that were developed by Systems Subcommittee Working Party 1 (SSWP1) of all those who had visions of finding a gold mine exactly in the center of the HDTV sun, or at least one or more creditable satellites (Fig. 1-1).

WP1 proponent listings
(As of 1989).

AVALEX	AVALEX-HDTV
BTA (Japan)	EDTV-1,-2
Faroudja	SuperNTSC
Hi Res Sci	Hrs-CCF
Iredale	HD-NTSC
MIT	RC,CC
NHK (Japan)	Muse
	Muse-9, Muse-6
	Narrow Muse
NYIT (Glenn)	VISTA
Osborne	OCS
N.A. Philips	(Netherlands)
	HDMAC-60
	HDNTSC 6 + 3
	HDNTSC 6 + 6
PSI	GENESYS
QUANTICON	QuanTV
Sarnoff	ACTV-E
	ACTV-1
	ACTV-11
Sci. Atlanta	HDB-MAC
Zenith	SC-HDTV

1-1 WP1 Proponent Listings (1989).

In addition to audio proponents (Dolby and Digidek) and video specialists (Fukinuki/Hitachi), others have various improvements, but not complete systems.

MUSE

Japan's frequency-modulated *MUSE*, which stands for multiple sub-nyquist encoding, recorded its beginning in 1970 as a wide-band frequency-modulated 1125-line, 60-field system with a signal transmitting bandwidth of 8.1 MHz, and a sampling clock rate of 16.2 MHz. FM modulation was designed to overcome much of the chroma triangular noise that is common to ordinary television, as well as other effects that have always plagued amplitude modulation, establishing compatibility with satellite transmissions for which it was designed. Now further developed in Japan, MUSE transmissions are received there with some regularity and have made possible very adequate recorders and receivers, which are already marketed in North America and Europe. Because our terrestrial broadcasts are limited to a passband of only 6 MHz and AM video modulation, the Federal Communications Commission was quick to announce original MUSE would not be permitted on U.S. airways. There are, however, as many as six versions of original MUSE, which the Japanese still submit as an alternate to the digital systems that were offered among the final six. There is no similar limitation, however, to satellite program distribution, provided you have special Japanese FM decoders and a wide-bandwidth monitor. A satellite signal passband of 72 MHz is possible in Ku band, and always 36 MHz at C band, so the original MUSE system can easily be accommodated either at C or Ku.

After a number of modifications, Japan's NHK (Japan Broadcasting Corp.) developed multiple versions of MUSE (Fig. 1-2)—especially Narrow MUSE that will fit within the 6-MHz NTSC passband and does not need a separate 3-MHz augmentation channel for added motion resolution. However, Narrow MUSE does possess identical encoding and decoding processes as original MUSE, but not the same line scanning conversion. This is described in detail where the final systems are reviewed. Japan's BTA (Broadcast Technology Association) was also initially apparent in early HDTV, but we've heard little or nothing of its recent activities, except that it has been involved in ongoing system evaluations.

HDMAC-60

HDMAC-60 identifies another satellite delivery system that was developed by North American Philips (the Netherlands), which can be configured also for terrestrial broadcast under the name *HDS-NA*, both of which will produce 16:9 raster ratios and a line structure of over 400,000 picture elements, but the terrestrial format does need an extra 3-MHz augmentation channel for maximum picture quality and digital sound. For satellite transmissions, HDMAC-60 requires an RF passband of 24 MHz to accommodate its FM sidebands. But the *High Definition System—for North America (HDS-NA* (Fig. 1-3)) featured the usual 6 MHz with AM video and vestigial sideband, the augmented channel developed as either digital or analog, along with progressive scanning of 525 lines or 1050 lines, interlaced and contemporary field rate of 59.94 Hz. Picture resolution amounted to 480 lines vertical and 495 lines horizontal—approximately 6 MHz plus at baseband. *Progressive scanning*, I might add, means doubling the scan rate and displaying the entire picture sequentially, rather than 262.5 lines twice in conventional interlace. During this period, both *sidepanel* (Fig. 1-4) and *letterbox formats* were under consideration. Eventually, the sidepanel format was universally adopted since it can accommodate both NTSC's 4:3 aspect ratio as well as HDTV's 16:9 expanded rasters.

Block diagrams of the encoder and receiver are illustrated in Fig. 1-3 as (A) encoder and (B) decoder, respectively. Notice that both channels are eventually combined into wideband with time and frequency division multiplexing to avoid inevitable crosstalk between quadrature-modulated signals. The input matrix changes RGB reception into Y (luminance) and IQ chroma, with a line difference (LD) generator proceeding from Y into the expanders, which also receive various signal splitting information from the vertical preamplifier and second bandstop. In the lower portion of A, there is also a line difference input, as well as a Yh high frequency input, which is the +3-MHz augmentation portion, including a main signal output, both of which are subject to pan and scan.

System description   Identified as either *HDNTSC* possibly, or more specifically as *HDS-NA*, the encoder channel offers an input RGB matrix, which translates into luminance Y and color signals I and Q. At this juncture, Y splits into a 2D-bandstop filter and an LD line-stop generator, thence on to the expander and output. Luminance also frequency-splits for both high and low information, with high continuing directly to the expander and low into the center panel time split.

Color of course derives, too, from RGB inputs and then is matrix-converted as I and Q into the vertical prefilter and from there to the center panel time split. The fourth input into the center panel time split comes from the pan and scan control, which controls panels and line difference signals plus higher frequency luminance from the frequency split block.

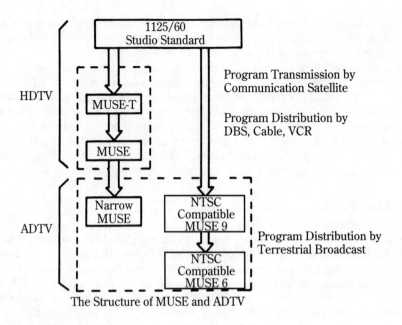

The Structure of MUSE and ADTV

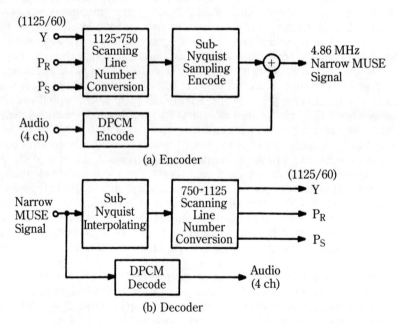

(a) Encoder

(b) Decoder

01-2   Japan's original HDTV proposals for the U.S. NHK Japan.

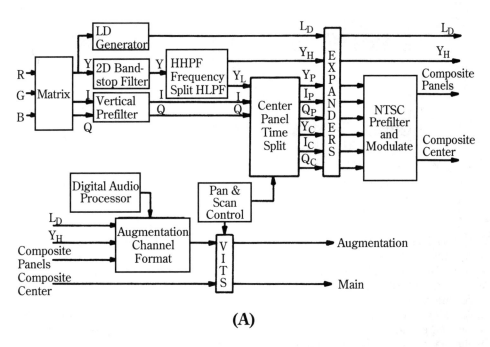

(A)

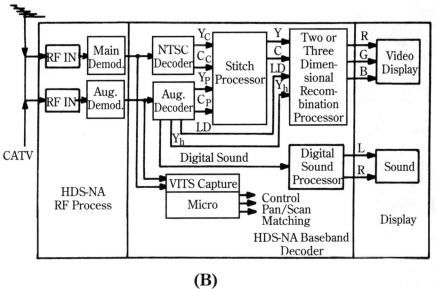

(B)

1-3 The HDS-NA proposal by the Netherlands' North American Philips. <small>North American Philips.</small>

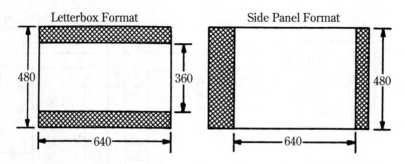

1-4 Letterbox and sidepanel formats used in picture size and augmentation resolutions in several proposed HDTV systems.

Also, line stop generator, high frequency luminance, and composite panels are injected into the augmentation channel format, in addition to digital audio from a fourth source. Then, audio, line difference, luminance, and the composite panels progress to VITS (the vertical interval test blanking period) together with a composite center voltage. With pan and scan also controlling VITS, as well as the center panel time split, upper outputs enter the Y and I, Q expander, and augmentation, plus main exit from VITS. From the expander, line difference, and high-frequency luminance proceed directly, while the remainder are NTSC-prefiltered and modulated for the various composite center panels.

In the receiver are dual pairs of RF inputs, one for the main demodulator and another for the augmentation demodulator; both outputs are directed to VITS capture as well as the NTSC and augmentation decoders. However, the augmentation decoder also supplies an extra digital sound signal for the sound processor serving its L and R outputs. In the block below VITS capture you see a MICRO block included for control, pan/scan and matching.

The stitch processor then converts various Yc and Cc inputs into plain Y,C for the two or three dimensional recombination processor, resolving all inputs into baseband RGB video display. Bandsplitting for high and low frequencies permits greater power for the lower frequencies and reduced power for the higher ones. The extra augmentation channel delivers high-frequency video, side-panel expansion, and even audio, while standard NTSC does the rest.

NYIT VISTA

Developed by Dr. William Glenn, the New York Institute of Technology system offered a single wideband or two NTSC channels (Fig. 1-5) that could either have been two 6-MHz time-shared station signals, or one 6 MHz plus 3 MHz in an additional augmented channel. Dr. Glenn suggested that the augmented channel carrying extra luminance would produce 8 MHz of baseband when subsequently detected from a 30-MHz tape or camera input. In this way, maximum *spatial and temporal resolution* was anticipated. Spatial resolution defines picture detail without motion, while temporal resolution involves a 0.7 Kell factor, plus the static/dynamic vertical interlace factor and the usual horizontal sweeps are the active line durations times compressed video bandwidth, as well as the inverse of the aspect ratio—all related to motion and fields for both horizontal and vertical resolution. NYIT VISTA would then expand to a 16:9 aspect ratio and also adopt progressive scanning requiring a full 525 lines in each field, but doubling the bandwidth.

Thereafter, standard NTSC is scan-converted and line-doubled so that both system signals are available as Y and R-Y/B-Y luma-chroma information. In Fig. 1-5, high Y and

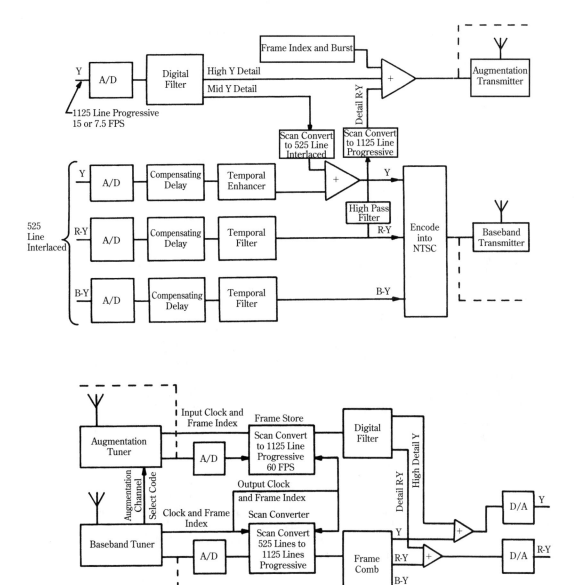

1-5 Basic block diagrams of the VISTA transmitter and receiver. NYIT.

mid Y are digitally filtered following A/D conversion, with mid Y scan-converted to 525 lines interlaced, while high Y combines with frame index and burst and sum-amplified with R-Y detail before reaching the augmentation transmitter. Below, Y,RB-Y are also A/D converted at 525 lines interlaced, compensated, temporally enhanced or filtered, and directed to the NTSC encoder for the baseband transmitter.

The receiver, of course, possesses both augmentation and baseband tuners, clock and frame index circuits, frame store, as well as scan converters, and D/A analog outputs for Y and RB-Y, as illustrated.

MIT-RC/MIT-CC

MIT's William F. Schreiber and A. S. Lippman proposed MIT-RC/MIT-CC, both of which are related, one being an extension of the other. This proposal (on paper) advocated a total transmit/receive (Tx/Rx) concept from camera to final display at a bandwidth between 30 and 50 MHz. Eliminated would be a separate carrier, retrace intervals, and vestigial sideband (transmissions). However, a pair of 3-MHz information basebanders are quadrature modulated on a single carrier with other components time multiplexed, allowing ½₂ of the remainder for FM/digital or audio/data. Broadcast and receivers would be designed to operate with separate scanning rates in addition to appropriate frame stores, with high line rates for best vertical resolution without interline flicker. But Schreiber and Lippman rejected a 60-Hz field rate, opting instead for the 24 fps motion picture rate and improved film interlace, plus motion compensation for smooth displays down to 12 fps. Admittedly, there was some picture blurring at slow, unvarying speeds, but a *smart receiver* would choose adequate frame rates for all motion scenes. Chroma, they say, would appear about half the bandwidth of luminance.

Weakest link in the scheme appears to be broadcast or cable transmissions and a "mixed highs" system with adaptive modulation that would raise signals in visible blank areas and reduce noise. This would need little additional channel capacity, according to Dr. Schreiber.

The smart receiver promoted by MIT could handle MITV-CC cable, as well as MITV-RC 6-MHz broadcast systems with open architecture and good programmability, could aid an extended definition (EDT) picture and act as a bridge for ultimate high definition. A general illustration of such a proposal appears in Fig. 1-6, which, it is said, could readily provide decoding for various TV transmissions, as well as motion-compensated temporal interpolation, echo cancelling, and noise reduction.

Inputs for this receiver are tuner and RF amplifiers, a detector, sync processor, A/D converter, and first framestore. Digital information containing the original frame transmitted passes the input's center, as well as accompanying modules and the programmable interpolator. Input framestore intelligence is received, and the processor rearranges such intelligence, making it available for display memory under control of manual or external data commands. Such a programmable receiver, MIT declares, might easily adapt decoding parameters to various television transmissions, as well as NTSC, and could accommodate other extras, such as motion-compensated temporal interpolation, echo cancelling, and noise reduction—all subjects of intense analysis and electronic design, especially because digital systems are already mandated as the ultimate objective.

ACTV-1 and ACTV-II

These are initial products of the David Sarnoff Research Center of Princeton, NJ, which has now become an HDTV consortium, consisting of the Netherlands' North American Philips, France's Thomson, the National Broadcast Company, collectively concentrating on an all-digital/NTSC-compatible system demonstrated in a number of exhibits throughout the U.S. Former RCA manufacturing Indiana acquisition of Thomson has already announced 16:9 aspect ratio receivers for Europe and the U.S., although not necessarily

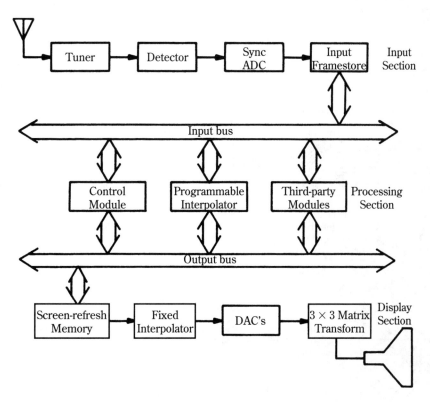

1-6 General block of MIT's "smart" receiver for all systems. MIT R and D Laboratory.

built in respective factories because the electronics here and there are considerably different, especially the 50/60-Hz power source requirements and subsequent scan and line rates.

ACTV-1 is interesting because four separate signals are actually generated, all of which are in the NTSC 6-MHz RF envelope, while three are said to occupy selected "subchannels" (Fig. 1-7). And although ACTV-1 and II are both designed for 1050 scanning lines and 2:1 interlace, ACTV-1 can easily be converted to a 525/1:1 progressively scanned system for other than conventional transmissions. Such flexibility (for both units) would encompass standard NTSC sync and signal functions and, with further changes, permit enhanced video/audio performance.

In ACTV-1, a pair of horizontal frequency bands are generated. One microsecond interval at the end of each active line accepts time-compressed low frequencies; at the same time, 700 kHz to 5 MHz non-compressed in overscan and chroma between 83 and 600 kHz is prefiltered in 3-D horizontal, vertical and temporal prefilters, with chroma quadrature-modulated on luminance at 3.58 MHz. Sidepanel pairs are now time-expanded to fill the center line panel. For further horizontal resolution, frequencies between 5 and 6 MHz are shifted 0.1 to 1.1 MHz by amplitude modulation and the 4.9-MHz suppressed carrier low-pass filtered to remove the upper sideband. Extra luminance is compressed for the center panel, establishing as much as 1.1 MHz of high-frequency detail across the total image.

The ACTV-1 receiver then downconverts the 1050/2:1 image to 525/1:1 progressively scanned format, adding a "helper" signal with additional vertical temporal lumi-

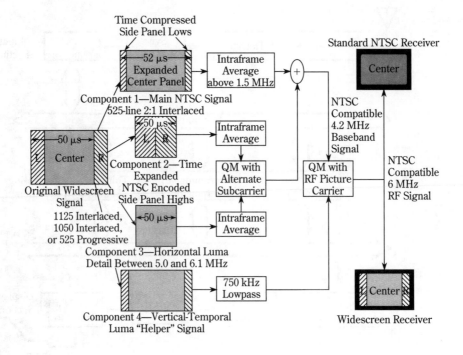

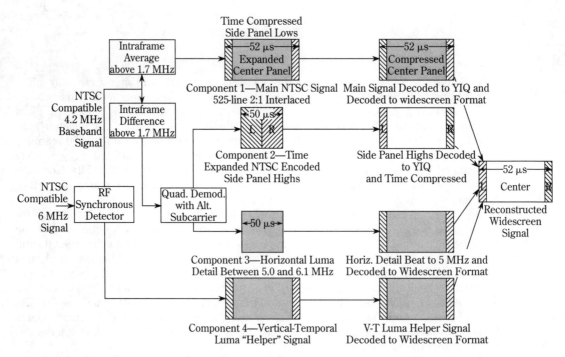

1-7 The initial ACTV-1 offered by David Sarnoff Princeton Research Laboratories. David Sarnoff Princeton Research Laboratories.

nance for improved vertical motion detail with low average energy. The 750-kHz "helper" is spatially correlated in the center picture panel and removed in the receivers with synchronous detectors or "hidden" on sets with envelope detectors.

Subchannel components are recovered by interframe averaging, identified as a linear, time-varying digital filter that separates modulated and baseband information from vertical-temporal crosstalk, whether in stills or motion.

When all four encoded signals have been recovered and converted to Y and I-Q intelligence, sidescreen decoding takes place. Sidepanels are expanded, the center picture panel is compressed to $\frac{4}{5}$ of an active line, and the high-frequency sidepanel detail is compressed into its original time slot. Now in widescreen format, horizontal luminance shifts to its original frequency range by 4.9-MHz carrier amplitude modulation and is then added to existing luma intelligence for a bandspread of 6 MHz. Interlace converts to progressive scan and Y,I,Q signals re-convert to analog and matrixed for an RGB output.

ACTV-II is actually a 2-channel system, but one that accommodates ACTV-1 transmissions for processing and expansion. While the ACTV-II contained ACTV-1 encoder for NTSC and the compatible channel, the proposal also possessed an ACTV-1 decoder to recover widescreen Y-I,Q and the 525-line progressive scan information. Here, 12-MHz and 1.2-MHz intelligence are subtracted from "original" HDTV to deliver 20 MHz of Y and 10 MHz each of I and Q, while progressive scan detail subtracts from interlace, leaving augmentation signals containing all spatial-temporal information that is not transmitted by ACTV-1, along with any necessary artifact corrections (extraneous "garbage") in the decoded ACTV-1.

Broadband Y now separates into bands of 0 to 6 MHz, 6 to 11 MHz, and 12 to 18 MHz, with the remainder suppressed. Middle and upper bands shift to dc by the 6- and 12-MHz carriers, with the low band identified as Y_L. Low-pass filtering then takes place at $\frac{1}{2}$ Nyquist vertically within each field and the product becomes line multiplexed as Y_H for a 6-MHz output. During scene movements, only Y_L transmits, while in still scenes Y_L and Y_H are frame multiplexed. Switching between the two occurs via a binary motion portion in the helper signal or from luminance frame differences in ACTV-1. Thereafter, 6-MHz compressed luminance encompasses 754 picture elements (pixels) at eight times the color subcarrier frequency and continues to the luma/chroma/data multiplexer, producing 910 samples/line. Of the 1050 lines, 960 carry video, with the remainder reserved for digital sound and data. The 10-MHz I,Q information is horizontally low-pass filtered to 2.4 MHz of $\frac{1}{2}$ Nyquist within a field and then line-multiplexed into a single block. Compressed five times horizontally, it emerges as 12 MHz, divided into the 0- to 6- and 6- to 12-MHz bands, the lower valued band now identified as C_L and the high band (shifted to dc by a 6-MHz carrier and upper sideband rejected by a 6-MHz low-pass filter) is called C_H. Only C_L transmits during moving scenes, while the rest are C_L and C_H frame multiplexed. The 6-MHz chroma now occupies 151 pixels at eight times the color subcarrier, then is routed to the luma/chroma/data multiplexer.

The 6-MHz augmentation information (at baseband) is divided into even/odd line data with time expansions by a factor of two, resulting in two 3-MHz transmissions, which are analog-converted and quadrature-modulated on the center of the RF channel.

ACTV-II receiver

The ACTV-II receiver, tuned to a selected ACTV-I subchannel, triggers on the first pixel in each field as the augmented channel equalizes to match the main channel. Odd and even lines are then multiplexed into a single frame. Y-I,Q are expanded for the extended passband after separate processing.

During motion, Y_L adds directly to ACTV-1 luma, but Y_L and Y_H are frame demultiplexed and repeated in forward time for Y_L and reversed for Y_H, which is vertically demultiplexed and vertically interpolated by line averaging for the 6- and 12-MHz original frequency carriers. All three bands further combine for an augmented signal allowing 18 MHz of horizontal resolution at low frequencies and 960 lines of vertical resolution.

I,Q chroma are processed similarly, with only C_L active during movements and added to ACTV-1 decoded information following expansion and I,Q demultiplexing. During still picture times, C_L and C_H are frame demultiplexed and frame repeated in forward time for C_L and backwards for C_H. Afterwards, C_H "beats down" to 6 MHz and adds to C_L for ACTV-1 decoded intelligence. Consequently, 2.4 MHz can be resolved at low frequencies and 240 lines of vertical resolution with full temporal display. Whether either of these systems are destined to see commercial application depends on the Federal Communications Commission selecting an analog or digital HDTV system for terrestrial and satellite broadcasts. At the moment, the trend is decidedly toward digital for any number of substantial reasons that are discussed candidly in a succeeding chapter. The paramount problems of interference with NTSC and HDTV signal dispersal have already been overcome in digital transmissions. And with the application of successful ghost cancellation, analog could or will have more of a difficult time remaining competitive, especially because 30-MHz luminance bandwidths are already common in digital HDTV. ACTV-II was never tested by the ATTC.

Zenith's 3XNTSC system

The 3XNTSC system (Fig. 1-8) could really be named the mother of subsequent digital systems, but beginning as part analog and part digital before progressing. Developed initially for cable TV, it is also transcodable for FM satellite up/downlinks and improves S/N ratios. Zenith also says that with reduced average and peak power requirements, a 6-MHz cable transmission HDTV signal is possible without the necessity of rebuilding CATV facilities or reducing available channels.

Based on a scanning rate of 3X, the 15,734-Hz NTSC line frequency, the system produces a 1575-line, 2:1 interlaced picture that is convertible to other formats and is able to also "carry 1125/60-Hz line information in a 16:9 wide-aspect ratio." Zenith compares its figures with an HDTV system offering only 725 lines of picture height and 1288 lines (width), assuming a nominal Kell factor of 0.7. Transcoding to NTSC involves only interpolation filters for converting the 787.5 progressive line format for either NTSC or Y/C. Magnetic tape or satellite transmissions in FM would involve a time-multiplexed format, such as MAC. Further, Zenith states its system would require only 0.2% power, compared to today's average transmitter, resulting in a number of hardware and signal savings.

The Zenith system operates within 6-MHz NTSC and its high-frequency portions use less than 1% of the total energy, with most real power needs stemming from low-frequency video, sync, and average or dc values. Consequently, with such power-hungry elements removed, high-frequency information requires little carrier power, improved S/N values, and virtually no other channel interference. Therefore, video above 200 kHz is transmitted standard analog, while video information below that frequency is digitized, along with sync and dc components. Together with two channels of digital CD-quality audio, such power-hungry remnants are A/D converted and placed among the 22 lines of the vertical blanking interval (VBI). In effect, 30 MHz of composite audio and video are compressed into the usual 6-MHz TV channel, with average transmitting power reduced by more than 90% for the same service area as NTSC. Further, because NTSC is redundant, average values and sync do not require continuous transmissions and respond effi-

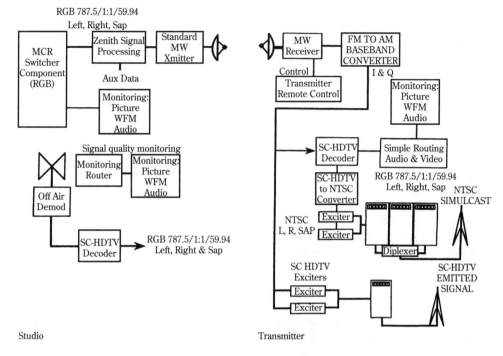

Terrestrial Block Diagram. Zenith DRAFT

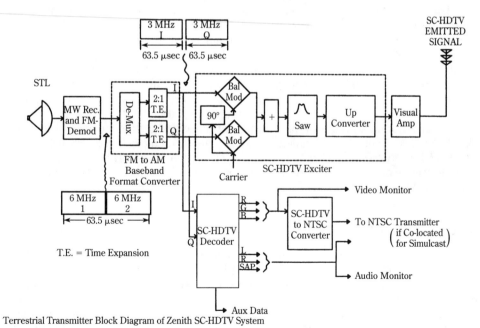

Terrestrial Transmitter Block Diagram of Zenith SC-HDTV System

1-8 The Zenith 3XNTSC compression system—a forerunner of the all-digital HDTV systems of today. Zenith Electronics Corp..

ciently to low-frequency sampling, video can now be transmitted as suppressed carrier modulation at the center channel without subcarriers, but with related NTSC timing for the interleaving of NTSC spectral.

HDTV, meanwhile, transmits as suppressed carrier modulation at channel's center, sans subcarriers, and converts into 480 analog components per 1/59.94 seconds, with each component occupying 63.5 µsec at a nominal bandwidth of 2.675 MHz. They are then paired and sequentially transmitted as 240 pairs on two quadrature carriers in the RF-channel's center, along with data and sync in the VBI, requiring 22 to 23 scan lines on successive frames. Encoding allows 59.94 fps for low-frequency scenes and 11.988 fps rate for high-frequency components. RGB information then separates into Y luminance and R-Y, B-Y color-difference signals, which are analyzed individually.

Luminance divides into components at different frequencies in 2-dimensional spectrum. The first, a 0 to 9.6 MHz, represents full 720-line vertical resolution. Between 9.63 and 19.27 MHz is the middle group and 480 lines of vertical resolution identified LL-LD, MH, HH, and C1, C2 for color, while a third group operates between 19.27 and 28.9 MHz for 240 lines of vertical resolution. Those at lowest vertical resolution are encoded at 59.94 fps, with the rest time-multiplexed and encoded at 11.988 fps. Filtering and re-sampling occurs prior to transmission, with most motion information dispersed between 0 and 9.6 MHz.

To conserve bandwidth, active video-only transmits with no intervals between lines, while higher speed-generated lines are time expanded 3.6:1, which reduces passbands to 2.675 MHz with duration expansion to the usual 63.5 µs. Temporal pre-emphasis then reduces interference and all low frequencies below 200 kHz are digitized and transmitted as data during VBI with no dc component.

Color encoding, sound, and sync are the final transmit segments, with color difference bandlimited to 9.63 MHz, filtered, resampled, divided into two components, and paired into 240 resolution lines each. They are then multiplexed down to 1 in 5, with active portions time expanded 3.6:1, much like luminance. Consequently, 96 color-difference components are transmitted in pairs each 1.59.94 second, occupying segments equal to 48 lines of NTSC. Color resolution, however, is only 33% of luminance.

So, 480 lines of 63.56-µs duration and 2.675-MHz luma/chroma components needing transmissions every 1/59.94 seconds in pairs, leaving some 22 to 23 lines available for data. This comprises two channels of compressed digital audio, low-frequency video, sync signals, captioning and error protection, all transmitted in 16-state quadrature amplitude modulation on video-modulated carriers. I and Q data clock rates are pegged at 5.34965 MHz and essentially flat to the Nyquist slope. Two lines carry sync signals with error protection and allow other VBI lines to carry 20,910 bits every 1/59.94 second, permitting 8334 bits for digital audio.

The 3XNTSC receiver

Here, the pairs of 240-line analog video and data are detected, producing a 787.5-line progressively scanned HDTV picture. The 6-MHz tuner converts RF into IF, where it is gain-controlled and frequency phase-locked for the resulting quadrature carrier regeneration, I and Q.

Analog I and Q is then detected, digitized, and time multiplexed into the four original luminance and two color difference components, effectively delivering 720 lines of progressively scanned luma/chroma for RGB.

Thereafter, detection and repositioning of picture, sound, and sync takes place much the reverse of their originating transmissions. *Digitized low frequencies* are initially reinserted and then line-averaged, with other information only line-averaged so that with the aid of an identical low-pass filter to the one in the transmitter, exact image restoration occurs without artifacts. All frequencies from LL to HH are then temporally de-emphasized, memory-line is added, and they experience some frequency shifting, plus interpolation filtering for the 9.6- to 19.3- and 19.3- and 28.9-MHz groups.

The several frequency groups now are interpolated back to 720 active lines, along with combining components at 11.988 fps following motion compensation and before recombining with active lines. There's additional motion compensation in the vertical blanking interval. These same techniques are involved in color decoding, as well as for automatic gain cancellation (AGE) to automatically adjust for zero carrier offset and gain changes.

The four Genesys technologies

The Genesys technologies was an interesting proposal that, unfortunately, was hampered by apparent inability to be both fully verbally and mathematically described and, therefore, failed to survive HDTV acceptance. However, it did introduce the idea of altering a carrier's shape, then being able to extract its intelligence by either sidebands or harmonics because these are produced by continuously modifying the carrier so that such "inflections" appear as V-shaped blips on waveform slopes. Such "blips" are said not to excite AM/FM or PM (phase) detectors, requiring sampling rates of 2X the carrier frequency and eight analog levels to demodulate each inflection. In transmission, modulations can be executed mechanically, by diodes or switches, in addition to summing fundamentals with specially-phased third harmonic sine waves. Here, sidebands about the fundamental and a dominant third harmonic appear in spectrum plots.

In changing analog to digital processing for the system, A/D quantizing produced 3 binary bits, with foreseeable prospects of 4 to 5 bits as further engineering effort progressed. Additional bits, of course, do double or quadruple resolution and are obviously desirable. The Genesys technologies, however, were said to rely on special Delta modulation, which actually had no quantizing values and offered infinite resolution when returned to analog output. Reportedly, digital bit compression (Bitcom) could accomplish this in real time without memory.

In receive, an "AllMod" detector was conceived to subtract the carrier from a pure phase-locked sine wave that was generated by an LC tuned circuit and a variable resistor establishing Q. The subtraction becomes the shape difference because of waveform modulation. There's more to this system, but considering the circumstances, you should already possess sufficient information to assess the general process.

BTA JAPAN

Broadcasting Technology Association (BTA) is composed of 43 Japanese companies and corporations involved in manufacturing and broadcasting with headquarters in Tokyo. Established in 1985 to study extended definition systems (EDTV) for terrestrial television, a total of 25 systems were proposed, 10 survived, and 8 could be demonstrated and tested.

During Phase 1, 18 still pictures were sourced from digital standing charts and interlaced cameras in three tests, six were scan converted from a progressive scanning camera, and nine were from a downconverted Hi-Vision camera. Interference tests for compatibility with TV receivers and videocassette recorders completed this phase. Picture quality was improved with combinations of 3-dimensional luma/chroma separation, 3-dimensional receiver scan conversion, and higher resolution transmissions.

Phase II involved precompensation of saturated colors in quasi-constant luma signal processing, as well as adaptive high-frequency component emphasis in luminance, which proved to be helpful. These tests extended laboratory examinations to ascertain picture quality, noise effects, and secondary images, plus signal degradation. However, tapes were also made for a dozen TV manufacturer's examinations. Reported results were OK in normal reception areas, but somewhat better performance compared to NTSC in fringe areas.

There was also a report of a ghost-cancelling reference signal from the transmitter, dark picture detail correction, and color pre-compensation. At the receiver, progressive scanning, Y/C separation, and ghost cancellation were similarly specified.

As indicated, this BTA effort was based on primary testing, rather than any attempt to introduce a new system (such as MUSE or any U.S.-type system) and is included to suggest that the Japanese have made considerable efforts toward establishing a more advanced baseband pattern for resolution/definition improvement over standard NTSC.

Today's update

Trite or not, what's past is but prologue (but certainly not an introduction to pentameter verse or lines), just a combination of history and fact, foreshortened in exact detail, but general enough to present a reasonable picture of events leading up to the first real advance in television and its transmission modes since the advent of NTSC color codified by the Federal Communications Commission in 1953. If you require either extended or extensive information about these early systems, *HDTV: High Definition Television, First Edition* should or will supply all that's necessary.

2
Ghost cancellation

A ghost-cancelling program was established by the Advanced Television Systems Committee upon request by the National Association of Broadcasters' V.P. Michael Rau, May 24, 1989 to ATSC Chairman James McKinney. At the July 25, 1989 meeting of ATSC/T3, a specialist group was formed and designated ATSC/T3S5 with 13 members. The objective was: "to recommend a new special reference signal and associated guard space . . . that can be used as a training waveform by specially equipped receivers or processing devices to aid in cancelling ghosts in the received images." Respective chairman of T3 and T3S5 were Dan Wells and Tony Uyttendaele.

Groups in the U.S. and Japan were immediately contacted and, eventually, five "serious" proposals were forthcoming from BTA of Japan (Dec. 1989), AT&T Bell Laboratories (Mar. 1990), North American Philips (March 1991), DSRC/Thomson, and Samsung (May 1991). In the interim, Hiroshi Miyazawa of NHK and Shinichi Makino of Toshiba provided considerable aid by lecturing on recently completed ghost-cancelling work in Japan that resulted from surveys in several Japanese cities, showing that secondary images existed at 75% of all locations surveyed.

BTA then promulgated a working set of values for ghost corrections (Fig. 2-1).

- Image rating, after ghost cancellation should be 4 on the CCIR 5-point impairment scale.
- Correction range should fall between –1 and 24 μs.
- Frequency range should extend to 4 MHz.
- Cancelling time 5 seconds or less (128 frames) when S/N is 35 dB or more.
- Should operate as an equalizer to eliminate close-in ghosts.

Between July and December of 1988 two separate field and laboratory tests occurred, resulting in the adoption of the sinx/x wide-bar waveform in an 8-field sequence as the recommended standard. This was adopted over the sinx/x pulse because the wide-bar version reduced dc fluctuations "associated" with APL changes in the video signal, reducing dc offset errors.

The sinx/x wide-bar (an integrated sinx/x pulse) actually consists of two signals: one a bar of 44.7 μs duration and an amplitude of 70 IRE, with a sinx/x pulse on the leading edge and a $2T$ pulse on the trailing edge. Signal No. 2 is the 0 IRE pedestal. In the vertical interval test signal (VITS), it is inserted on line 18 of field 1, paired with a 0 pedestal in line 18 of field 5. In reverse order, a second paired bar and pedestal are produced on field 2 and field 6. The same process repeats for fields 3 and 7 and fields 4 and 8.

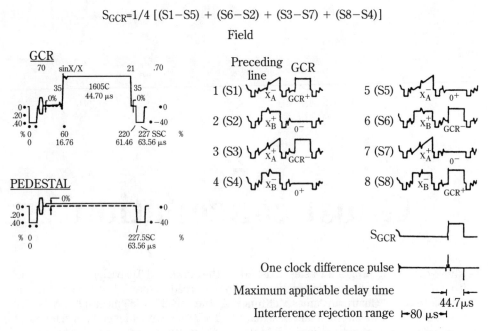

2-1 The 8-field BTA GCR sequence upon which much of the study was based.

GCR origins and evaluations

Consequently, by subtracting signals separated by four fields, line sync pulses, color burst, and their generated secondary images are cancelled, leaving only the bar waveform at somewhat reduced amplitude. So to recover ghost-cancelled signals, "pair-wise" constant signals must be carried on the line preceding the GCR signal in all paired fields. According to BTA, such a method delivers an 80-μs zero IRE pedestal before the beginning of GCR, resulting in a total pre- and post-ghost detection range of 44.7 μs, with GCR cancellation in the range from –2 to 44.7 μs. GCR signal level here sets at 70 IRE, which is the traditional Institute of Radio Engineers 1-volt video-scale reference of 0 to 100 plus –40 units of sync, or a total measurement of 140 IRE (see Figs. 2-2 and 2-3).

Ghost-Cancelling Committee T3S5, however, was concerned with excessive time needed to capture channels during "moderate-to-weak" signal receive conditions. Pioneering work on high-energy GCR signals by AT&T Laboratories established that GCR transmissions that were based on a pseudo-random noise sequence could contain some 20 dB additional energy over the BTA signal (Fig. 2-4). Therefore, in response to a NAB RFP, responders AT&T, Philips, and Sarnoff/Thomson proposed their own versions of high-energy GCR signals, followed by Samsung three months later with its offering.

Testing was conducted over-the-air, on cable, computer simulations, and in the laboratory, respectively, under management by NAB, Cable Labs, and the Canadian Research Centre, which provided both computer simulations and lab examinations. Philips and Sarnoff/Thomson were found to be the leaders.

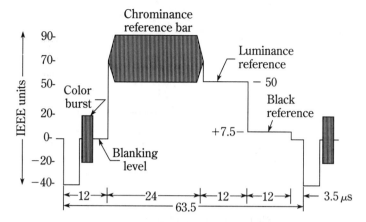

2-2 The Vertical Interval (color) Reference (VIR), which will probably be replaced by GCR on line 19 of the vertical blanking interval (VBI).

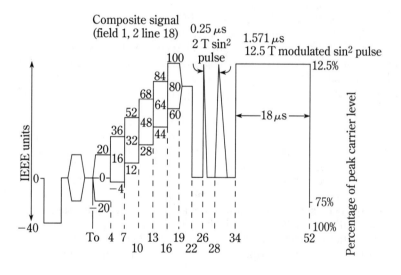

2-3 Former VITS composite signal seen on both fields of line 18 in the past, usually followed by VIR on line 19.

Details

The ghost-cancelling system evolved into two major digital signal processes: the channel identification portion and the ghost cancelling filter. The channel ID portion calculates GCR distortions for impulse response and/or impaired channel characteristics, while signal-to-noise channel response determines deghosting filter tap coefficients "as high as possible," which depends largely on GCR signal energy content.

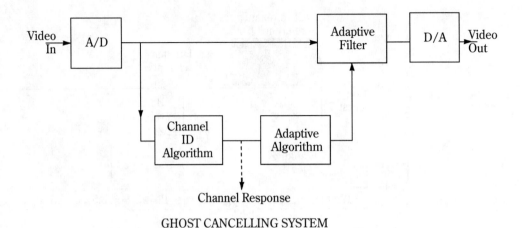

GHOST CANCELLING SYSTEM

2-4 A very simplified diagram illustrating the principles of GCR.

The AT&T (joined by Zenith) proposal uses a discrete and modified pseudo-random noise (PN) sequence of length $N = 255$ (symbols) of 53.43 microseconds. The correlated PN sequence produces an autocorrelation response of 0 everywhere, but in precise alignment resulting in a value of $+N$. According to AT&T, this sequence delivers a gain advantage of 20 dB over a single pulse and some 36 dB over the BTA GCR signal. It's said that this permits rapid and accurate channel portrayal, especially during low S/N conditions, as well as faster convergence times to calculate deghosting filter coefficients.

Sarnoff/Thomson would also use PN sequences, but in a series of four related one-line waveforms sequentially inserted "on the same line" in the VBI vertical blanking interval. Three repetitive PN sequences of length 255 go to color field 1; color field 4 receives the same signal, but it is inverted; one PN sequence reaches color field 2 and its inversion occupies color field 3. These latter single PN sequences estimate position, magnitude, and phase of received ghosts between –12 and +45 µs, and the three PN representative sequences determine accurate equalization. Ghosts are said to be "handled" with a maximum delay of 46.13 µs and with no constraints on adjacent line contents.

Samsung offered a complementary sequence GCR signal within an 8-field sequence with pair-wise constant signal processing. This, Samsung said, would prevent inherent limits on leading or trailing ghost limitations. Fields 1 and 3 would each carry half of the complementary pair with fields 2 and 4 supporting a 26-IRE unit pedestal.

Philips' tender had neither a single pulse nor a PN sequence. Its GCR proposal would consist of two signals of opposite polarity arranged in an 8-field sequence like BTA. Signal shape derives from continuous mathematical equations and produces, according to N.V. Philips, the greatest energy for any given length of time of all GCR signals under committee consideration. Each of the two signals appears as a frequency sweep superimposed on a 30 IRE pedestal.

Claims were that Philips system responds to secondary images within a range of from –3 to +45 µs and supports the following specifications:

- Adjustable to any length and amplitude.
- Energy level is proportional to signal duration.
- Essentially flat amplitude/frequency spectrum.

- Permits detection of both leading and trailing ghosts with no fundamental restriction on total detection range.
- Insensitive to constant offset sampling errors caused by sampling pulse location shifts.

Test objectives

The following information is reflectively taken verbatim from T3S5 Report, Doc. T3/188 dated 20 March 1992 and is largely unaltered because we feel that arbitrarily rewriting its contents would be nonproductive for technical personnel following such engineering concepts. So, the next several pages are substantially that of the T3S5 report. The "rationale" for nominating the two outstanding systems, however, is that of the proponent and not necessarily that of the Committee, but such writeups do add further information that could be useful now and in the future. Further, a little salesmanship won't blindside the engineering fraternity in the least, and liberal arts types are not technical readers.

GCR evaluations based on four inputs

This first part of the T3S5 report is Philips submission for evaluating GCR signals.

1. Analysis of performance specifications claimed by proponents and analysis of answers to questions prepared by T3S5.
2. Testing by computer simulation of the proponent GCR signals.
3. Laboratory testing of complete systems.
4. Field testing of complete system.

Analysis of performance specifications: An RFP issued by the NAB called for complete system descriptions and performance specifications.

Computer simulations The computer simulations were sponsored and conducted at the Communications Research Centre (CRC) of the Canadian Department of Communications. These simulations were intended to compare the effectiveness of each proposed training signal in estimating the channel response. This step was necessary to isolate the ability of the proposed training signal to estimate the channel response from the performance of the complete system and from the limitations of the current prototype hardware.

The agreed upon procedure was as follows:

1. The proponents send digital files of their GCR signals to CRC.
2. CRC subjects the GCR signals to 10 different combinations of complex multipath situations and returns the corrupted versions of the GCR signals to the proponents.
3. Proponents analyze the impaired signals and return their best estimate of the channel response that could cause such impairments to CRC.
4. CRC analyzes the results and issues a report.

The results of the report are summarized later. Only 3 of the 5 proponents completed the computer simulations: Philips, Sarnoff/Thomson, and Samsung.

CRC laboratory tests Laboratory tests were also sponsored and conducted at CRC. The purpose of these tests was to establish the objective and subjective performance of each prototype ghost canceller under controlled conditions of artificially generated ghosts and noise.

The objective measurements included measuring the unweighted S/N, pulse-to-bar ratio, 2T-K factor, luminance non-linearity, and amplitude/frequency response and group delay/frequency response of the sinx/x signal.

For the subjective evaluations, seven video sequences were used. These were selected by CRC from a CCIR tape that was originally prepared for the evaluation of video codecs. The video signals were impaired by different combinations of ghosts and noise. Up to 7 ghosts, with a relative delay time of up to ±64 μ and ranging in amplitude between 0 and –55 dB, could be generated. The phase of each ghost could also be changed from 0 to 359 degrees.

The corrected output of each prototype ghost canceller was monitored and compared with the reference signal on side-by-side monitors. Recordings were made for many of the tests for future reference. Observers were asked to restrict their evaluations to ghost ratings and not take into account some of the impairments associated with hardware problems.

NAB field tests NAB field tests were initiated by NAB's Advanced Television Task Force and managed by NAB. The EIA, MSTV, and CableLabs contributed to the direct funding of the project and PBS contributed equipment and technical support.

The field tests took place in the Washington D.C. area between September 27 and November 8, 1991. Three local television stations participated in these tests; one VHF station (WRC-TV, Channel 4), one low UHF station (WDCA-TV, Channel 20), and one high UHF station (WFTY, Channel 50).

Exactly 106 locations, where a variety of ghosting conditions could be found, were selected for measurement sites. Testing consisted principally of visual evaluation of the received television picture by two expert observers rating the overall picture quality and level of ghost impairment before and after insertion of the ghost cancellers. The visual evaluation was based on the subjective quality and impairment scales specified by the CCIR.

Cable tests The purpose of the cable lab and field tests was to compare the effectiveness of the proposed ghost-cancelling reference (GCR) signals in the cable environment at headends and cable plant. The tests were also designed to determine if any cable-related compatibility problems are associated with the proposed GCR signals. The field tests also investigated the ghost-cancelling equalizer performance on cable systems.

The cable laboratory tests were conducted from November 18, 1991 through November 22, 1991. CableLabs' ghost-cancelling laboratory tests were conducted on the CableLabs tests bed, at the Advanced Television Testing Laboratory in Alexandria, Virginia. The purpose of the laboratory tests was to measure the performance of the ghost-cancelling systems under controlled cable conditions.

The field tests were conducted on four cable systems in the Washington, D.C. area. The cable field tests started on November 25, 1991 and ran through December 17, 1991. The cable field tests were intended to measure the GCR performance at the headends' off-air receive point and at the set-top converter's output in the home. The cable field test plan called for measurements to be conducted at the headend, AML or fiber hubs, taps, and in subscribers' homes. Measurements were made at three headends, one AML hub, one fiber hub, 12 taps, 12 homes and at two off-air sites.

VBI requirements Based on surveys, broadcasters believe that ghost cancelling and correction of linear distortion is so important that space in the VBI can be made available for the GCR training signal. Broadcasters have been studying the replacement of the VIR signal on line 19 (Fig. 2-2) with the selected GCR signal and on the use of line 19 for this purpose.

Rationale for selection of Sarnoff/Thomson GCR signal as a standard

The collaboration of Sarnoff and Thomson for their version of a standard for the GCR signal is given here, as it appeared in the T3S5 report.

The Sarnoff/Thomson ghost-cancelling reference (STGCR) offers:

- High energy for robust operation.
- A true one-line system. Broadcasters and cable operators do not need to restrict signals on adjacent lines.
- A variety of deghosting methods, including fast tracking of time varying ghosts for cable head-ends.
- Economical and high performance deghosting and equalization for home receivers.
- A waveform that is proven in simulation, laboratory, and field tests.
- A waveform that is appropriate for NTSC television use.

Appropriate The STGCR has been designed to deghost NTSC television signals. GCR signals can be designed that are detectable with a zero dB carrier to noise ratio, but the hardware will be unnecessarily complex. Signals can be designed that will work with very simple hardware, but they won't work with anything but the cleanest video. And a signal can be designed that works with noise and simple hardware, but the algorithm will be so slow that the viewer will "tune out" before the calculation is complete. In designing the STGCR, we struck a balance between energy, speed, and hardware complexity. The result can work down to 20 dB SNR, converge quickly, and use simple hardware with a "digital signal processor" type microcomputer. Trade-offs have been made between signal power and computation simplicity, and ghost-canceller designers can choose between convergence time and microprocessor power. The signal is appropriate for both consumer and professional use.

Energy The STGCR waveform is based on a stretched PN sequence. This high-energy waveform provides maximum energy per IRE dynamic range over all frequencies from 0 to 4.2 MHz. We generate two waveforms from this PN sequence, a single repetition signal and a triple repetition signal. Each waveform has been optimized for a particular task. For example, a flat spectrum is useful for equalization. When used properly, the STGCR's triple repetition signal has a perfectly flat spectrum and was designed for use in a particularly simple equalization algorithm.

Ghost range without interference The range over which a GCR can cancel ghosts is theoretically unlimited, but there is a practical limit. We believe that the ghost canceller should only use the signal received within the GCR line. If the ghost of a GCR pulse extends into the following VBI line, that ghost information can be either lost or corrupted by the following line's signal. The single-repetition STGCR waveform is designed to have a 46-μsec post-ghost range without information loss or corruption. Pre-ghosts of up to 10 μsec can also be detected without loss. These limits exceed all commonly accepted ghost ranges.

Rapid [simple] calculations Equalization, which includes correction of pre- and post-ghosts within 8 μsec of the incident signal, represents the only ghost-cancelling task needed at most receiving locations. The STGCR triple repetition signal can be used with a 256-point FFT to provide rapid and accurate equalization and ghost elimination over this range. Our simple, fixed-point DSP could recalculate the equalization coefficients within a single frame. In the CableLabs tests, our prototype hardware corrected these ghosts down to a carrier-to-noise ratio of 25 dB. Any residual ghosts were consistently masked by the noise. Removal of the noise for evaluating the ghost level was not possible because the prototype "immediately began its rather fast calculation to a new solution [no ghosts were observed]." The prototype hardware proves that the STGCR has been designed for appropriate received signal to noise ratio and speed of operation.

Answers to questions about the STGCR When Sarnoff and Thomson engineers first proposed inverting alternate fields of a GCR, everyone wondered why. The answer is simple; inversion offers a 6-dB advantage over the older BTA approach, which used blank lines on alternate fields. The alternate line system is used to allow dc offset to be subtracted out when field pairs are differenced. Sync and burst, and their ghosts are also removed in this process. This provides a waveform of the GCR alone. The alternate field inversion provides a further advantage: the effects of differential phase and gain (common in cable systems) are reduced by the averaging of positive and negative waveforms. This innovation was later adopted by AT&T/Zenith and Philips for their systems.

Why are there two dissimilar waveforms? The use of a short and long waveform has many advantages. For low-cost home receivers, each of the waveforms is optimized to a particular task. This specialization reduces computation by more than a factor of two (a savings of over 1000 complex multiplies per iteration) over non-specialized systems, where one waveform must do double duty. We can, of course, use either waveform type for ghost cancelling or equalization, but each has been optimized for a particular task.

The two waveforms also provide a highly noise-immune DC gain reference, which is superior in many ways to VIRS. When the two short waveforms are subtracted from the sum of the long waveforms, the result is a known amplitude, 35-μs pulse without sync, co-channel or clamp-related interference. This can be effectively used as a final stage of AGC, and to eliminate "brightness shifts" in the deghosted output.

How fast can I deghost with the STGCR? The STGCR can provide updates to a deghoster as often as the signal is sent, 60 times per second. We do not know if this is fast enough for airplane flutter, but it is fast enough for wind-related equalization problems and the effects of "rabbit ears" reception. The simplified calculation method used with the triple repetition signal can help make this a reality in consumer receivers.

The prototype ghost canceller used in the field tests did not exploit the full capabilities of the STGCR to track ghosts. This is understandable because the hardware was a first hardware prototype. Despite this, the hardware provided the fastest close-ghost elimination, and a respectable rate of far-ghost elimination.

Note: because of a flaw in the generation of simulation signals, the CRC warns readers not to use the simulation tests to provide a comparison of GCR tracking speeds.

Why did you use I and Q demodulation in the hardware tests? The NAB hardware tests began less than a month after the ACTV tests were done at ATTC. For ACTV, I and Q demodulation was critical. For NTSC it is not. In their design of ACTV systems, Thomson Consumer Electronics has found that I/Q video demodulation is not significantly more expensive than I-only demodulation—including the cost of the additional A/D. I/Q demodulation simplifies ghost modeling, and Thomson intends to use I/Q demodulation, regardless of the GCR chosen.

This does not mean that the STGCR is designed to use a complex demodulator. We have presented data to T3S5 that shows no discernible difference between channel models made with real-only and complex demodulators. The complex demod enjoys a 0.4-dB signal-to-noise advantage, which is not a significant factor.

Why did you choose a waveform with special properties at 14.3 MHz? Digital consumer television receivers for the NTSC system use the 14.32-MHz sampling rate. This allows for relaxed tolerances on A/D converters, simplified chroma demodulation, and vertical filtering. Unlike Europe, where sample rates vary between manufacturers, the NTSC sample rate is the only logical choice. The STGCR's PN sequence has exactly one cycle in 256 samples at 14.32 MHz. This makes correlation and filter calculations simple. Digital cable headends are not yet common. When they are, they will probably be based on 14.32 for the decoding of NTSC at least. Algorithms exist for changing sample rates, and a cable headend box at another sample rate could use these algorithms to take advantage of the simple calculation method.

Philips comments on CRC laboratory tests

CRC (Canadian) laboratory tests were intended to evaluate the five ghost-canceller options under carefully controlled laboratory conditions. However, the applicability of these results to real-life situations is limited for the following reasons:

- The qualitative evaluation of ghost-cancellation efficacy was made by the proponent representatives themselves, each person being given one vote. Despite an attempt by CRC to minimize the problems that this method introduced, this tended to produce an inadvertent bias in favor of the proponent who happened to have most representatives on site at any given time. It turned out that Philips usually had only one person there.
- The Philips equipment was held and damaged by Canadian customs. Therefore, most of the early lab results were not representative of the capabilities of the canceller.

The CRC results were presented by B. Caron at the Feb. 20, 1992 meeting of the ATSC T3/S5 Specialist Group. At that meeting, he presented a chart of summary data, which is reproduced here as Fig. 2-5. The graph shows on a 5-point CCIR subjective scale, how effective the ghost cancellation was. Despite the disadvantages to Philips that were described above, even the CRC showed in their summary data that the Philips system was the best.

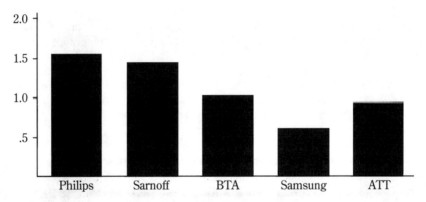

2-5 A 5-point CCIR subjective scale.

This final CRC table (Table 2-1), on which the above graph is based, is reproduced below. It compares the NAB lab tests for Channels 4, 20, and 50, with the finally reduced CRC lab test results. The superiority of Philips is clear.

Table 2-1. A comparison of NAB and CRC lab tests.

System	CH. 4 NAB	Ch. 20 NAB	Ch. 50 NAB	CRC Lab test
BTA	1.2	1.21	1	1.08
Samsung	0.23	0.34	0.13	0.67
AT&T/Zen.	0.06	0.32	0.2	1.03
Philips	1.54	1.49	1.52	1.57
Sarnoff/Thom.	0.91	0.85	0.88	1.47

Rationale for selecting Philips' GCR signal as a standard *The following section contains Philips reasons that their GCR standard is the optimum for the industry.*

It should be noted at the onset that three independent organizations, the NAB, the CRC, and CableLabs considered the competitive merits of the five proposed GCR signals. The NAB final report was as unequivocal as it could be in stating that the Philips approach was clearly the best. In fact, the Philips GCR was the only signal to demonstrate better performance than the BTA GCR. The CRC results, especially as interpreted by B. Caron of CRC when he presented his results at the Feb. 20, 1992 meeting of the T3/S5 Specialist Group of ATSC, also showed good quantitative agreement with the NAB results. The CableLabs tests evaluated parameters irrelevant to ghost cancellation in broadcasting, did not test realistic ghost conditions; and was not conclusive. Thus, the "vote" of impartial expert organizations was that Philips has the best GCR. Philips is convinced that its GCR is the optimum choice as the standard.

The Philips approach is clearly proven to work best by NAB tests The United States can only choose to adopt a standard that has been proven under actual operating field conditions to work robustly. The NAB field tests were performed by impartial experts. They covered the whole gamut of real-life operational situations. The field exercise covered 106 test sites, 318 different ghosting combinations, a total of 3600 individual tests. These included strong- and weak-signal areas, VHF and UHF frequencies. The results were presented in 17 tables. In each and every table, the Philips system was shown to have the best performance. The NAB's table summarizing this data is shown below. The three clusters of bars represent average results for the three channels involved in the tests, Channels 4, 20, and 50. The leftmost bar of each set is the Philips performance, expressed as deghosting improvement, measured on a 5-point subjective scale.

Philips GCR provides the most signal-to-noise ratio (SNR) Figure 2-6 shows that the Philips GCR is superior in three major areas. All numbers are in relative to the Philips GCR. Table 2-2 shows that over an 8-field sequence, the energy of the Philips GCR is higher. Higher energy can be used for greater noise immunity, more accurate ghost cancellation and/or the ability to cancel ghosts faster.

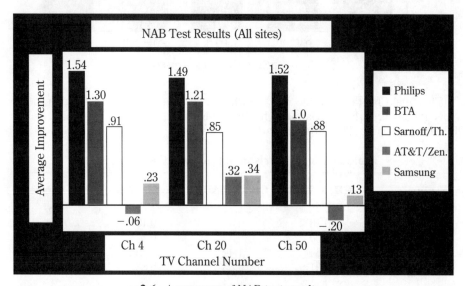

2-6 A summary of NAB test results.

Table 2-2. Finite impulse response (FIR)
filter characteristics assumed for the simulation.

Number of Taps:	640 (44.75 µsec)	Signal:	10 bits
Sample Frequency:	14.3 MHz	Coefficient:	10 bits

Philips GCR has a spectrum that is flat under all conditions This guarantees maximum SNR and most accurate channel characterization for ghost cancellation. The figure shows the flat Philips spectrum and the non-flat PN spectrum. Combining the SNR loss numbers with the energy numbers for an 8-field sequence results in the relative performances shown in Fig. 2-7. The table shows a processing gain advantage for Philips.

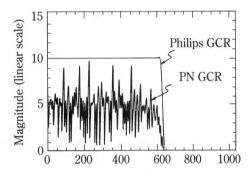

2-7 The spectrum of Philips GCR vs. PN GCR.

Philips GCR permits simpler system implementation Very importantly, the cost-effective implementation for the consumer was considered in the design of its GCR. Philips expects the production cost for a ghost-cancellation system based on the Philips GCR to follow that of picture-in-picture (PIP), which is now a widespread consumer feature. As shown by estimates of cost and quality, systems based on any other GCR will prevent ghost cancellation from moving from the research labs to the consumer.

Summary of the Philips GCR
Theoretical

- Flattest spectrum.
- Highest total energy.
- Highest energy to time duration ratio.
- Linear group delay.
- Flat time-domain envelope.
- Noncyclic. No problems in determining ghost locations.
- GCR properties independent of sampling rates.
- No theoretical limit on ghost-cancellation range.
- Uniform noise suppression.
- Insensitive to impulse noise.
- No noise enhancement in processing.
- Capable of 1-field ghost cancellation.
- Properly characterizes sharp ghosts, as well as smeared ghosts.
- Only two different signals in 8-field sequence. GCR plus/minus on a pedestal.
- All transmitted energy is used in algorithms.

Algorithm

- Maximum flexibility in algorithm selection.
- Single algorithm for ghost cancellation and equalization.
- Single algorithm for all ghost delay ranges.
- Requires only inphase processing.
- Correlation algorithms can be used for channel characterization.
- Can be used with open loop or closed loop algorithms.
- Compatible with simple, well known, and proven algorithms.
- Not biased towards any algorithm.
- No time aliasing introduced in processing.

Microprocessor

- Capable of being processed with inexpensive fixed-point microprocessor.
- Low memory requirements in microprocessors.
- Allows implementation in both low-end and high-end microprocessors.

Filter

- Filter architecture independent of GCR and algorithm.
- Requires only inphase filter. ¼ of complexity of inphase and quadrature filters.
- Compatible with simple, well-known, and proven filter architectures.
- Allows implementation of both low-end and high-end filters.

Demodulator

- Requires only inphase output. No need for quadrature component.
- Requires no modification to existing professional or consumer demodulators.

Analog-to-Digital Converter

- Usable as synchronization signal.
- Qualitative indicator of ghost presence and strength.
- Qualitative indicator channel frequency characteristics.

Broadcasters VBI working group: report on the VBI

The Broadcasters VBI Working Group produced the following report regarding the GCR signal, as it applies to the VBI.

Based on recent surveys, broadcasters believe that ghost cancelling and correction is so important that space in the VBI can be made available for the GCR training signal. Indeed, in various locations in the United States, proponents' GCR signals have been tested over the air.

Broadcasters have been studying the replacement of the line 19 VIR (Vertical Interval Reference) color-reference pulse with the GCR training signal. Also suggested was the combination or multiplexing the GCR with the current VITS signal for more efficient use of the VBI. Lines 10 or 11 were also suggested if they would not adversely affect home reception.

Lines 10 through 13 are not currently used. If we decide to use 10 through 13, compatibility with older receivers must be considered along with other technical issues. All other VBI lines are used by one or more networks for various purposes. However, many of these uses are network applications only and serve only the network-to-affiliate communications. Many of these signals could be reshuffled or moved, or the GCR signal could be inserted at the transmitter.

Only two lines have been allocated by the FCC for broadcast-related signals in the VBI: line 19 for the VIR signal and line 21, field 1 and up to one half of line 21, field 2. Other VBI lines are available for test, signaling, and data signals. Line 19 and 21 have VBI signal receivers. There are currently a limited number of receivers in the United States, which use the VIR color-reference signal. In most cases, the reception of the VIR signal on a VIR-equipped receiver implies illumination of the VIR detection light only. Preliminary experiments with deletion of the VIR signal indicate that aside from a noticeable elimination of the VIR indicator light, there was no effect on picture or audio quality.

Line 20, field 2 is an unchanging, static test signal. It may be composed of the line bar, $2T$ and modulated steps. Line 20 field 1, is used for the Source Identification or SID signal. It is also known as the *AMOL* or *Automated Measurement of Lineup signal*. The first 10 to 15 microseconds of the SID contains addressing information; phase reference, start of message and frame address. This portion of the signal does not vary with information content.

Begging to differ

David Koo and Stephen Herman of Philips Laboratories, Briarcliff Manor, NY immediately attacked the CableLabs report of March 10, 1992, even though a public document conducted "in association" with ATSC's T3/S5 Ghost-cancelling Specialist Group is copyrighted and "all rights reserved." Therefore, we shall not attempt to either print or extract excerpts, other than to supply general comment because there might well be two systems of ghost-cancelling adopted: one for broadcast and the other for cable. CATV has its own priorities and problems, despite the hope that only a "winner take all" would become the single U.S. standard.

CableLabs used a specially equipped test van for both field and laboratory tests that included a Rohde & Schwarz demodulator, a Scientific synchronous demodulator, A Tektronix VM700A measuring tester, a Sony D-2 digital videotape recorder, a spectrum analyzer, a plotter, a tunable bandpass filter, a video processing amplifier, a Sony color video monitor, a vectorscope, and video distribution amplifiers. Power for van field checks required a separate power generator mounted on a truck, and the five GCR recorders were mounted in the van. Cable system headends were also energized by a portable test rack containing a Rohde & Schwarz test pattern generator and a Tektronix 1910 test signal generator that would generate the various proponents' ghost-cancelling signals.

Phase noise and residual FM seemed to give at least one tester sync-lock problems, while another detector did not possess wideband I and Q, excluding some proponents from the tests. In addition, the AT&T GCR was often out of service, as was Samsung.

Included in field tests were individual head-end originations, as well as off-the-air pickups from DC broadcast stations channels 4 and 20. Cable channel 10 was the originating head-end test source, located in the Jones office building in Alexandria, VA for all signals other than those broadcast, while the latter were cabled to Jones office via 12 amplifiers.

As you might conclude, the various systems performed differently, according to whether they did or did not do average deghosting, if low signal energy caused slow deghosting, if there was some luma bounce, and if wideband quadrature and phase-lock problems reduced some proponents' test spreads.

The Philips rejoinder

Koo and Herman took strong exception to CableLabs statement that Sarnoff/Thomson "consistently outperformed all other proposed systems in the laboratory and in the field."

The reply is directly quoted in part as a substantial disagreement apparent among both testers and proponents. This is why we could well have more than one ghost-cancelling system between broadcasters and CATV.

CableLabs conclusions inconsistent with CableLabs own data *Here are excerpted quotes from Philips to back up their protestations of CableLabs findings regarding GCR standards test results.*

On page 45 of the T3S5 report, CableLabs writes, "The Sarnoff/Thomson ghost-cancelling system tested by CableLabs consistently outperformed all other proposed systems in the laboratory and in the field.

"In fact, we have reanalyzed the tabular data presented by CableLabs in their detailed final report. We averaged all results for the $2T$ Pulse K factor. We included in this average, all tables where the three proponents, Philips, Sarnoff/Thomson, and BTA were represented. We found that according to CableLabs' own results in the field tests Philips was the best, whereas in the lab tests BTA was the best. In neither case did Sarnoff/Thomson score best!

"We do not consider CableLabs' results of the frequency response ripple to be significant. This considered only the amplitude of the frequency response, totally ignoring the phase response. Thus, it has no conceivable relevance to ghost cancellation. This was shown by the Philips Laboratories paper 'Technical Comments on the CableLabs tests for Television Ghost Cancellers,' that was mailed out to T3 during the week of 23 Mar 92.

"We totally disagree with the test results from the following tests reported on in the full CableLabs report: L3.3.4, L3.3.5, L3.4, L3.8, L3.9, and L3.10. In our own tests, we never experienced waveforms such as those reported by CableLabs . . . We duplicated completely the ghost setups that were reported to be used by CableLabs (300 ns, 600 ns, 1250 ns, −15 dB). Our test showed that after ghost cancellation, the frequency ripple was only 0.6 dB, not the CableLabs report of 2.5 dB. In addition, the $2T$-K factor in our tests was only 0.6%. This is not even close to the CableLabs published 1.7%. We have difficulty explaining the CableLabs results, in view of our earlier experience and the experiments mentioned here."

Canadian computer simulations and lab tests Computer simulations and lab tests were conducted by the Communications Research Centre, Broadcast Technologies Research Branch, Department of Communications Ottawa, Ontario. This was Canada's "contribution towards the standardization of a GCR signal for NTSC broadcasting in North America." We'll quote verbatim from the report in text, but not include all of the illustrations, but certainly Tables 2-3 through 2-7, which are highly informative.

Prototype descriptions The results presented were obtained using the ghost cancellers that were provided by each proponent. These ghost cancellers were at different levels of development and it has not been possible for the proponents to use in their prototype the same devices for analog-to-digital conversion, synchronization, and clock generation.

The AT&T/Zenith prototype was built using low-cost analog components. This was intended to demonstrate their GCR signal's and algorithm's capability to compensate for a low-cost implementation. In the tests, their synchronization and phase-lock loop circuits were not able to always perform correctly. A proprietary algorithm was then used to correct for resulting defects as much as possible. However, even in the no-ghost condition, their prototype degraded the picture quality more than the others. Its cancellation range was also limited by filter hardware to −1.8 to 29 microseconds. AT&T/Zenith was also not able to participate in all the laboratory tests because of the delay in the shipping of their equipment to CRC.

The prototype from Samsung could not operate correctly for some of the ghost combinations. When a ghost was outside its 35 microseconds cancellation range, it went into a bypass mode. It also sometimes produced an improper dc shift and gain adjustment, which made the picture unviewable.

The prototype from Philips was damaged during customs inspection. As a result of damage, the synchronization made frequent errors, resulting in visible artifacts. Some test results were obtained before the prototype was repaired. This problem disappeared once the unit was repaired.

The Sarnoff's prototype was the only one processing a complex signal (I&Q). Sarnoff claimed, however, that this is not a requirement of their proposed GCR, which can also be used with the in-phase component only. This prototype sometimes displayed white flashing lines near the top of the picture, probably caused by an improper timing of the loading of the digital filter coefficients. It also displayed some "low-frequency noise" because of misalignment of the synchronization circuit. This "noise" was judged to be minor and it was decided not to risk realignment of the circuit at CRC.

Broadcasters Broadcasters have been looking for a long time for a device or a system that could reduce or eliminate video ghosts. These ghosts are created when television signals are reflected one or more times from obstacles, such as hills or buildings. A television picture received under these conditions will be degraded and might be annoying to watch. Viewers are particularly sensitive to this kind of degradation because they have access to ghost-free sources of video, such as video cassette recordings.

Video ghosts were accepted as a fact of life until the Broadcasting Technology Association (BTA) in Japan developed a video ghost-cancelling system. This system was evaluated in the Atlanta area in the United States [1] and found generally effective in nearly all test locations. However, also some weaknesses were identified and several organizations made proposals for an improved system. A formal request for proposals was issued by the NAB in July 1990. Five different proposals were received. They are listed in Table 2-3. Each system requires a different Ghost-Cancelling Reference (GCR) signal to be included in the Vertical Blanking Interval (VBI) for television transmissions. For obvious practical reasons, a single one has to be selected as a standard.

To do so, it was planned to evaluate the proposals in three different ways, namely through computer simulations, laboratory tests, and field tests. This paper will present the results of the computer simulations and laboratory tests that were performed at the Communications Research Centre (CRC) in Ottawa, Canada. These tests were done in collaboration with the proponents and were part of the evaluation process of the Advanced Television Systems Committee's (ATSC) Specialist Group on Ghost Cancelling (T3/S5).

The specialist group on ghost cancelling (T3/S5), is eventually to recommend one of these reference signals for use as a training waveform in specially equipped NTSC receivers for cancelling ghosts in the received signals.

The ATSC Specialist Group on cancelling will select the best Ghost-Cancellation Reference (GCR) signal based on criteria, such as:

- Cancellation Range (Target: −2 to 45 μsec)
- Convergence time
- Ultimate correction
- Robustness
- Complexity (cost)
- VBI requirements

Table 2-3. List of GCR signal proponents.

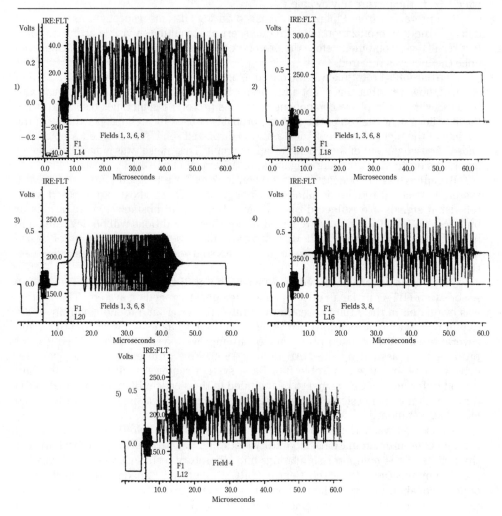

Proponents	Type of GCR
1) AT&T/Zenith	Pseudo-Random Binary Sequence (PRBS)
2) Broadcast Technology Association (BTA)	Integrated Pulse
3) Philips Laboratories	Deterministic Sequence
4) Samsung Electronics	Complementary Binary Sequence
5) Sarnoff/Thomson	Pseudo-Random Binary Sequence (PRBS)

The information required to select a ghost-cancelling system was to be obtained from the following sources:

1. Specifications provided by each proponent.
2. Computer simulations to evaluate the performance of each proposed GCR.
3. Laboratory tests of ghost cancellation systems.
4. Field tests.

This report presents the results obtained by computer simulations and laboratory tests. And Ghost-Reference Signals: (1) AT&T/Zenith, (2) BTA, (3) Philips, (4) Samsung, (5) Sarnoff/Thomson.

Computer simulations This section covers the results that were obtained from computer simulations completed at CRC in Canada for 3 of the 5 proponents with the help of the proponents. The 3 GCR signals evaluated by simulation were the ones proposed by Philips, Samsung, and Sarnoff/Thompson. BTA (Japan) could not participate because the software for ghost cancellation had been developed many years ago and was no longer available. AT&T/Zenith participated in the simulations at the beginning, but could not complete them.

Description of the computer simulations Computer simulations were carried out to compare the proposed GCR signals, with respect to their effectiveness to characterize a video channel. The objective was to isolate the channel-characterization performance of the proposed GCR signal from the performance of a complete Ghost Cancellation system and the limitations of any hardware implementation. For the purpose of these simulations and to allow comparisons under the same conditions, the proponents were asked to assume that the following Finite Impulse Response (FIR) filter, described in Table 2-2 was used.

In order to carry out the simulations the proponents provided CRC with a digitized version of their proposed GCR signal in an agreed upon computer file format. These digitized GCR files were used by CRC to create 10 different impaired versions for each GCR signal. For this purpose, after consultation with all proponents, a computer program was used which had been developed by the David Sarnoff Research Center. Each proponent received 10 files containing their GCR, impaired by the filters of an NTSC transmission and the multipath and noise combinations listed in Table 2-4. The details of these combinations were known only to CRC. Each file contained 304 lines of the digitized impaired GCR signal. It was assumed that a black burst was on the lines preceding and following the GCR signal. Except for one ghost in the first combination, all simulated ghosts were static. The first combination included one ghost that varied over time to reproduce dynamic ghosts sometimes observed in the field.

Table 2-4. Combinations of ghosts used for the computer simulations.

Combination	#	Delay	Amplitude	Phase	SNR
F(Dynamic)	1	0.80 μs	−18.4 dB	0	40 dB
		1.50 μs	−21.9 dB	0	
		4.25 μs	−30.5 dB	−80	
A(Typical)	2	0.45 μs	−21.9 dB	30	40 dB
		2.30 μs	−28.0 dB	−80	
	3	0.40 μs	−19.2 dB	30	35 dB
		2.80 μs	−24.4 dB	−80	
	4	0.45 μs	−19.2 dB	30	25 dB
		2.30 μs	−24.4 dB	−80	
B(Typical)	5	0.20 μs	−14.0 dB	−40	50 dB
		1.60 μs	−16.5 dB	0	
		3.40 μs	−23.1 dB	30	
		8.70 μs	−18.4 dB	−60	
	6	0.20 μs	−14.0 dB	−40	40 dB

Table 2-4. Continued.

Combination	#	Delay	Amplitude	Phase	SNR
		1.90 µs	−18.4 dB	0	
		3.40 µs	−23.7 dB	30	
		8.20 µs	−21.9 dB	−60	
	7	0.30 µs	−16.5 dB	−40	35 dB
		1.90 µs	−18.4 dB	0	
		3.90 µs	−23.1 dB	30	
		8.20 µs	−21.9 dB	−60	
	8	0.20 µs	−16.5 dB	−40	25 dB
		1.90 µs	−18.4 dB	0	
		3.90 µs	−23.1 dB	30	
		8.70 µs	−19.2 dB	−60	
C(Micro-reflections)	9	−0.70 µs	−26.0 dB	−40	35 dB
		0.10 µs	−26.0 dB	−70	
		0.15 µs	−30.5 dB	0	
		0.25 µs	−28.0 dB	30	
		0.40 µs	−28.0 dB	−50	
D(Long Delay)	10	−1.80 µs	−23.1 dB	−50	35 dB
		2.20 µs	−10.5 dB	−20	
		38.90 µs	−20.0 dB	70	

The combinations 2, 3, and 4 are representative of average over-the-air reception (A) for 3 different levels of noise. The combinations 5, 6, 7, and 8 represent more severe conditions, (B) where 4 ghosts are received. Each combination has a different signal-to-noise ratio. Combination 9 represent microreflections, (C) similar to those that could be observed on a cable network. Finally, the last combinations include a very long ghost (D) to evaluate the range covered by the GCR signal. Similar combinations of ghosts were used for the laboratory tests to allow some comparison between the two experiments.

Each proponent used a computer simulation of their channel characterization scheme to produce an in-phase (real) impulse-channel response for each of the 10 combinations of ghosts. The proponents then provided CRC with the channel responses obtained: (a) after the minimum number of iterations to get an acceptable approximation; and (b) after the number of iterations required to converge, up to 304 iterations.

The evaluation was then carried out by comparing the channel responses calculated by the proponents with the one directly obtained from the computer simulation of the multipaths. The channel response of combination 5 was provided to the proponents as a benchmark to confirm the correct operation of their software.

Results of the computer simulations The results of the computer simulations (Table 2-4) have shown that the 3 GCR signals evaluated could provide very good, if not excellent, channel characterization. An example is shown where the reference and the channel impulse responses calculated by the 3 proponents for combination 8 are superimposed and no difference can be seen.

The few discrepancies found were for ghosts with either very short or very long delays. The differences between the reference and the channel responses estimated by the 3 proponents are however very small. They might have been caused by differences in the techniques used to process the calculated channel response.

Differences were also noticed for the long delay ghost of combination #10. The ghost with the long delay was correctly located by each proponent, but its amplitude was property estimated only by Sarnoff. Samsung and Philips could not complete the channel characterization as accurately because the data required for this case should have extended to 38.9 μs after the end of the GCR signal. It was found after the completion of the simulations that the files created by CRC provided only 9.43 μs of data after the end of the GCR line.

Description of subjective measurements The observers were proponents' representatives or members of T3/S5. At least 1 representative of 3 of the proponents was present for all the tests. The observers were asked to make an effort to restrict their ratings to the ghost and not to take into consideration some visible hardware problems or the presence of noise.

For most of the tests a rating was given by each expert observer for each video sequence. An average was estimated and announced to all the experts. This average rating was recorded only if it was agreed to by all the observers. If no agreement was reached, the video sequences were replayed and rated again. The final result was obtained by averaging the rating given to the seven video sequences. The observers were not normally informed of which prototype was under test. They could, however, guess by identifying the particular artifacts created by each prototype.

The observers were first shown the picture produced by the prototype under test once it had eliminated ghosts for one particular ghost combination. Then, the ghost generator was switched to a no ghost combination. Once the prototype had "corrected" this new condition, the signal was again impaired by the ghosts. Simultaneously, a tape recorder was switched to play. The recorder was stopped once the observers judged that the ghost canceller had eliminated the ghost as best as possible. The picture used for this test was a white circle on a flat grey field, which made the ghost very visible. Table 2-5 presents the results for these tests.

The evaluation of each signal was also done subjectively. The subjective evaluation was done by at least 5 expert observers using the CCIR impairment scale shown.

Table 2-5. Time required (seconds) to complete ghost cancellation.

Test conditions	AT&T	BTA	Corrected by: Philips	Samsung	Sarnoff
B					
48 dB	4(A)	46	6.5(B)	31	12(A)
25 dB	9(C)	46	6(B)	28	11(A)
D					
49 dB	2(D)	45(E)	5(B)	(F)	19(A)
25 dB	(G)	45(E)	5(B)	(F)	19(A)

Notes: A – Close ghosts eliminated after 2 seconds

B – Including about 1.5 seconds to synchronize

C – Close ghosts eliminated after 4 seconds

D – Long ghost was not cancelled

E – Short ghost was not cancelled

F – Could not synchronize because 1 ghost was outside the delay range of the prototype

G – Could not synchronize

The AT&T prototype was fast. For combination B, it seems to cancel ghosts in two steps: first, the close ghosts then, in a second step, the longer delayed ghosts were cancelled. For combination D, it cancelled the close ghosts in 2 seconds. It could not cancel, however, the longest delayed ghosts as it was outside its delay range. It also could not operate with this combination when it was impaired by a high level of noise. The BTA-NEC prototype always took about 45 seconds to complete ghost cancellation. It could not cancel the long delay pre-ghost of combination D.

The Philips prototype was performing well for all the tests. The short time required to complete ghost cancellation included, about 1.5 seconds to acquire synchronization.

The Samsung prototype was initialized manually and was controlled by a personal computer. It could not operate correctly for combination D because it included one ghost outside its delay cancellation range.

Finally, the Sarnoff's prototype was performing correctly for all the tests. Like the AT&T's prototype, it cancelled ghosts in 2 steps: the short delay ghosts were cancelled in about 2 seconds.

In conclusion, some of the prototypes can already cancel ghosts in a few seconds. Some of the proponents, however, are claiming that their GCR will eliminate ghosts within 1 second once more powerful prototypes are built.

Effect of the amplitude of the ghosts Some subjective rating was conducted to test the effect of the ghost's amplitude on the performance of the ghost canceller. To perform this test, the amplitude of all the ghosts in combination B were set to the same attenuation. The test was repeated for 5 different values of attenuation from –6 dB to –14 dB. The results are presented in Table 2-6.

Table 2-6. Impairment rating (1–5) of ghost amplitudes.

Ghosts amplitude	No correction	Corrected by:				
		AT&T	BTA	Philips	Samsung	Sarnoff
–6 dB	1	N.A.	2	2.7	(A)	1.6(B)
–8 dB	1.2	N.A.	2.6	3.2	(A)	1.8
–10 dB	1.5	N.A.	3.3	3.7	(A)	2.2
–12 dB	1.6	N.A.	3.5	3.9	3.1(B)	3.0
–14 dB	2	N.A.	4.1	4.2	4.5(B)	4.0

Notes: A – Ghost canceller could not synchronize: By-Pass mode.

B – Streaking visible but not included in the rating.

As shown in the first column, the rating of the picture before correction was quite low. Despite these bad conditions, all ghost cancellers, when operating, could provide some improvement. The improvement is significant for all prototypes when the ghosts had an attenuation of more than 14 dB. The prototypes from BTA-NEC and Philips were particularly good in cancelling high-amplitude ghosts.

Effect of the ghost delay Some tests were conducted to evaluate the subjective performance of the prototype over a range of delays for one of the ghosts. To perform this test, the delay of the 3.9-µsec ghost in combination B was changed. The results are presented in Table 2-7.

Four tests were done for a long delay post-ghost. No significant improvement was obtained for ghost delays of more than 40 µsecs, as this was probably outside the range of all the prototypes. The prototypes from Philips and Sarnoff both improved the signal with a 40-µsec ghost. The improvement for the two other prototypes was significant for ghosts with delays of 35 µsec or less.

Table 2-7. Subjective impairment rating for long delay and pre-ghost.

Ghost delay (μsec)	No correction	AT&T	BTA	Corrected by: Philips	Samsung	Sarnoff
50	2.8	N.A.	3	3	3	3
45	2.8	N.A.	3	3	3	3
40	2.8	N.A.	3	4.7	1(A)	4.7
35	2.7	N.A.	4.8	4.8	4.3(B)	4.7
−1	3.3	N.A.	4.6	5	4.9	5
−2	3.3	N.A.	3.9	4.9	4.5	5
−3	3	N.A.	3.6(C)	4.9	3.7(C)	5
−4	3	N.A.	3.4(C)	4.7	3.9(C)	4.9
−5	3	N.A.	3.8(C)	4.7	3.5(C)	3.7(C)
−10	3	N.A.	3.4(C)	3.5(C)	3.5(C)	3.5(C)

Notes: A – The ghost canceller is not operating properly as the ghost is just outside its range of correction.

B – Streaking visible.

C – Does not cancel the pre-ghost because it is out of the range of the ghost canceller.

Six tests were also carried out for pre-ghosts. None of the prototypes could significantly improve pictures with a pre-ghost of 10 μsecs. The prototype from Philips could significantly improve a picture with a pre-ghost of 5 μsec. The performance of the Sarnoff prototype was similar for a 4 μsec pre-ghost. Samsung's prototype offered the same performance for a 2 μsec pre-ghost and BTA's for a 1 μsec pre-ghost.

Background   The obvious need for deghosting of television signals has been known for years, but we have never had a cost effective method of eliminating them. The traditional method of ghost elimination involved a variable length RF delay line and summing amplifier. This was only practical for cable headends or other fixed, high-cost receiving locations. It lacked two important properties: it was not very effective and it was not automatic.

Television reception also suffers from other assaults on signal fidelity—cable roll-off, mistermination, channel traps, and response variations of the receiving and transmitting antennas all degrade the equalization of the received signal. Early color sets suffered from widely varying chroma saturation because of the lack of chroma/luma gain equalization. Automatic color control was the first automatic "equalizer" in home receivers.

As television screen sizes get larger, manufacturers try to use more of the bandwidth of the NTSC signal. The effects of ghosts and mis-equalization become more obvious. Automatic color control is no longer enough. Edges have excess rings, or are smeared out. Sharpness on UHF stations varies from minute to minute, sometimes second to second. Multiple-image "ghosts" makes text hard to read or ruin the quality that video engineers try so hard to produce.

The realities of today's television environment make cable head-end signal processing an integral part in delivering quality broadcast video to the home. Head-end receivers must include ghost cancellers that will deliver the highest quality signal to the cable system. These must be able to track ghosts, which vary in time.

Broadcasters are, of course, the greatest potential beneficiary of ghost cancelling. A ghost-cancelled television signal is an advanced television signal. But broadcasters must invest in this improvement by inserting a signal in the Vertical Blanking Interval. The investment of VBI space must be justified by a benefit. Broadcasters agree that two lines of restricted signal in their VBI is too much. Thomson Consumer Electronics understands this, and even the lowest cost STGCR ghost canceller will have no interference effects from signals on the line preceding or following the GCR.

The introduction of ghost cancelling will be like that of color television. An extra cost feature in today's high-end sets will eventually be introduced in the main line. We have designed the STGCR to have what is needed for today's high-end set and for the cost-reduced set in the future. We take special advantage of the 14.32-MHz sample rate, which is and will remain the standard in NTSC home receivers. This allows us to provide increased speed of deghosting and equalization using this year's generation of digital signal processors, and to take advantage of the lower-cost number-crunching microcontrollers of the future.

Before the tests, proponents were also asked to use a few lines to characterize each channel response to show how fast channel characterization could be completed using their proposed GCR signal.

Philips identified all the ghost combinations using 8 lines and 304 lines. The responses calculated with only 8 lines were almost all identical to the ones calculated using 304 lines. In particular, noise was very well eliminated from the calculated channel responses after processing only 8 lines.

Sarnoff could identify all the ghost combinations (except combination 4) after using only 4 lines. But for some ghost combinations, it required more lines to eliminate the noise from the channel response: 16 lines for combination 9 and 60 lines for combinations 4, 8, and 10.

Samsung could identify all the ghost combinations with only 8 lines. Elimination of the noise on some combinations required more lines, however: 24 lines for combination 10 and 80 lines for combinations 4 and 8.

These results are difficult to compare because each proponent might not have used the same criteria to determine the number of iterations (lines) after which the channel was correctly identified or the noise was eliminated. It is therefore difficult with the results to determine which GCR signal provides the quickest channel response capabilities.

The simulations with the moving ghost could not be completed as planned because the files sent to Philips and Samsung were different than the ones sent to Sarnoff. The analysis of the results was made even more difficult because proponents used a different number of fields to characterize the dynamic channel responses.

The file sent to Sarnoff contained the 3 ghosts of combination #1. Every 4 fields, the delay of the second ghost increased by 135 nanoseconds in field 1, decreased by 50 nanoseconds in field 2 and by 67 nanoseconds in field 4. The phase and the amplitude of this ghost also changed in 3 of every 4 fields. Sarnoff decided to use the file to estimate a channel response every 4 fields. One of the impulse responses calculated by Sarnoff every 4 fields is compared in Fig. 2-5 with the superposition of the reference impulse responses of the 4 fields used in the calculation.

The files sent to Philips and Samsung also contained the 3 ghosts of combination #1. The delay and the phase of the first ghost were increased in this case by 100 nanoseconds and by 45° every field. Its amplitude changed within every 4 fields.

Philips decided to calculate an impulse response for each field. This calculated impulse response is compared with the reference. The two responses are very similar.

Finally, Samsung calculated an impulse response every 8 fields. The result is compared with the superposition of the reference impulse responses of the 8 fields used in the calculation.

It is difficult to compare the potential of each GCR signal to characterize moving ghosts based on the above results. More thought may be required to design computer simulations which would enable a fair comparison. Among other things, it may be interesting to repeat a similar test for a lower signal-to-noise ratio than the one used in the simulations (i.e., 40 dB). However the results of the simulations demonstrated the possibility of characterizing a channel in one field.

In conclusion, it appears that all 3 proposed GCR signals can be used for precise channel characterization. Additional computer simulations may however be required to determine the limits of each GCR signal and to precisely determine how fast each one can accomplish a channel characterization.

Executive summary

Listed here is the executive summary of the Canadian computer simulations and lab tests found by the Communications Research Center, Broadcast Technologies Research Branch, Department of Communications, Ottawa, Ontario.

The laboratory tests were completed on prototypes from AT&T/Zenith, BTA/NEC (Japan), Philips Laboratories, Samsung Electronics and Sarnoff/Thomson. The prototypes were at different levels of development. Therefore in most of the cases the results from the laboratory tests did not show the ultimate capabilities of a GCR signal but the limitations of the hardware available for the tests.

All the ghost-cancellation systems tested improved the subjective quality of the picture, sometimes very significantly. The impairment rating could go from as low as 2 (on a scale of 5) before correction to as high as 4.8 after correction. Ghosts with a delay as long as 40 microseconds could be eliminated. Pre-ghosts with a delay of –5 microseconds were also cancelled. The time required for the cancellation of ghosts could be as short as 2 seconds. Prototypes from AT&T/Zenith and Philips Laboratories required less time than the other ones to complete ghost cancellation. BTA/NEC was the slowest unit at 45 seconds. A test also demonstrated the potential of ghost cancellation to greatly improve teletext reception.

The prototypes from BTA/NEC, Philips Laboratories and Sarnoff/Thomson operated well under almost all the test conditions. The ones from AT&T/Zenith and from Samsung were at an earlier stage of development and did not operate well for all of the tests. When the ghost cancellers were tested within their range of operation, the difference in performance between them was relatively small.

But more tests could be required if the selection of the best GCR signal is to be based on differences in the potential of each GCR signal. Tests are required to establish the limits of each GCR signal for ghosts with very long delay, high amplitude or time variation. To complete these tests the proponents may have to develop appropriate versions of their ghost cancelling systems.

However, before using the laboratory results to evaluate a GCR, it must be clear that some deficiencies of the tested prototypes are not related to the proposed GCR signal. It is then very important to remember that the results presented here show the capabilities of presently available hardware. In most of the cases they will not show the limit of the performance of a particular GCR signal. Many observed deficiencies of a tested prototype are not related to the GCR signal for which this prototype was designed. This factor must be considered before using the laboratory tests results to evaluate a GCR signal.

The GC result

After much conversation and not inconsiderable effort, the responsible T3 Technology Group on Distribution decided that hybrid systems from Sarnoff and Philips weren't as effective as Philips' original, and the committee voted 25–0 for Philips' with two abstentions. So, the NAP system for secondary image (ghost) cancellations was and is adopted for high-definition television. Voting date was June 25, 1992. Both cable and terrestrial are now in agreement and system testing will continue as planned.

3

There were five, now less

As 1992 grew out of rompers, the analog HDTV picture changed radically from analog to all digital, system offerors (proponents) declined markedly from many to basically a "chosen few," and laboratory, expert viewers and Canadian "public" viewers all had their day in the sun, their nights in quizzical reflection. By the end of 1992, field tests of the final system selection(s) were made ready by the ATTC and Public Radio on TV channels 6 and 53 near Charlotte, NC.

Although Sarnoff's ACTV-1 was ATTC Laboratory tested between July 12 and September 15, 1991, it was withdrawn from competition on March 4, 1992. Japan's Narrow Muse (the same analog system offered many months ago) progressed through the laboratory ATTC process (September 20 through November 13, 1991), digital systems received prime attention and their exhaustive examinations continued into September 1992 before cutoff. Biggest surprise of 1992, however, came with an announcement from AT&T/Zenith and General Instruments/MIT and DigiCipher/G.I. that these entities will continue to promote their own systems pending ATSC and FCC decisions later in 1993, but will share royalties if they are included in the system-win in addition to possibly collaborating on any selected technology. According to G.I., this "ties up" 90% of the market because only the Sarnoff/NBC/Thomson/Philips consortium remains as a major digital competitor. The significance of this move means that winners will collect as much as billions of dollars from U.S., Canadian, Japanese, European, and other world-wide royalties because no other all-digital systems have been through the American selection process and approved for terrestrial HDTV telecasting. Minimum/test payment by these proponents is estimated at $300,000, and Zenith's (and others) additional days following other ATTC examinations will add considerably more. Consequently, this is one specific means of recouping such costly outlays through collective cooperation and fewer proponents. We were told that "the FCC is pleased" by this May 1992 action because it simplifies their selection procedure and combines engineering talents for maximum technical applications. A few threatened or anticipated law suits could be avoided also, which is a salutary blessing for taxpayers.

For the record, the final five survivors before the end of ATTC tests were:

- AD-HDTV (digital) by N.A. Philips, Sarnoff, Thomson, NBC, and CLI
- CC-DigiCipher (digital) by MIT and G.I.
- DigiCipher (digital) G.I. and Compression Labs.

- Narrow Muse (analog) NHK (Japanese)
- DSC-HDTV (digital) Zenith, AT&T, and Scientific Atlanta

By the end of ATTC testing, you could guestimate 4, 3, 2, or 1, as it suits your interpretation. Was this a desirable condition? Probably, because an apparent choice between few groups can certainly make the FCC's selection easier and bring HDTV terrestrial or transmissions from our satellite Clarke belt to the airwaves considerably sooner with coordinated U.S. and/or auxiliary effort. Sony already has a digital HDTV recorder, Thomson and the Japanese can produce 16:9 aspect-ratio TV receivers immediately, and Zenith is probably not far behind. So KISS (keep it simple stupid) could be the rallying cry for HDTV in late 1994 or early 1995, provided that broadcasting equipment is in place for second-channel operation. Program material isn't an outstanding problem because multiple sources are usually available. Hughes Communications' high-powered, wide-band Direct Broadcast Service (DBS) satellite(s) is/are ready for action around 1994 (nominally pay service, of course). They'll be circularly polarized, have 16 transponders, and operate on the downlink between 12.2 and 12.7 GHz. France's Arianespace will do the launching from Kourou, French Guiana. Less powerful satellites in the Fixed Satellite Service, according to estimates by Hughes, will make available 224 K-band and 336 C-band transponders by 1995, with C-band decreasing and Ku increasing, both by better than 20%. However, C-band capacity is expected to reach 99% and Ku 74% use by the same year. The 1994/1995 years should be outstanding for visual/audio/data communications and put a resounding cap on the recent electronic recession!

Space loss between Ku and DBS is only ½ dB, according to our calculations, but multiwatts of power and probable digital downlinks could permit some rather small antennas (at subscription prices, naturally!) Whether public support will underwrite all these pay-per-view or annual spot beam deliveries remains open to question and operating proof. But at $100,000,000 per satellite design and launch, computer predictions must be offering encouraging answers, whether engendered by more leisure time, accumulated masses of couch potatoes, or specious algorithms. Our crystal ball says "we simply don't know." Their DOS and special spreadsheets probably hold most of the answers. They had better!

HDTV operating overview

Thanks to Dr. Robert Hopkins, Executive Director, Advanced Television Systems Committee (ATSC), we'll try and give you an idea of how the five 1992 surviving systems worked without actually describing electrical and mechanical characteristics as a way of introducing their complex specifics, which will be outlined and discussed in succeeding individual chapters. Dr. Hopkins presented much of this material during a 1992 spring meeting of the National Association of Broadcasters in Las Vegas, Nevada. The illustrations belong to Dr. Hopkins, all text is paraphrased and/or expanded by your author.

Narrow MUSE

Narrow MUSE transmits alternate picture elements on alternate fields, with 373 luminance samples transmitted during each line and four fields needed to transmit a complete sample (Fig. 3-1) in dot interlaced format. For moving images, a line offset subsampling is used, while for stationary portions a frame and field subsampling offset system operates and scanning lines are reduced from 1125 standard MUSE to 750 Narrow MUSE. Sampling times for luminance are 40.095 MHz and 13.365 MHz for the two chroma signals. The 6-MHz signal is non-NTSC compatible.

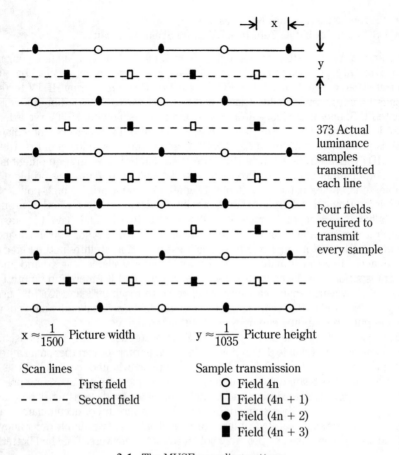

x ≈ $\frac{1}{1500}$ Picture width   y ≈ $\frac{1}{1035}$ Picture height

373 Actual luminance samples transmitted each line

Four fields required to transmit every sample

Scan lines
──────── First field
- - - - - Second field

Sample transmission
○ Field 4n
□ Field (4n + 1)
● Field (4n + 2)
■ Field (4n + 3)

3-1 The MUSE sampling pattern.

Dr. Hopkins' tutorial now launches directly into digital HDTV because Narrow MUSE is the only analog system that remained to be considered by the ATSC and the Federal Communications Commission in picking a winner.

Pure Digital

Here, resolution becomes a function of motion, and the more bits available, the merrier because picture elements (pixels) produce the image. Therefore, look at a given studio standard and consider the results:

- 1080 vertical picture elements
- 1920 horizontal picture elements
- 30 pix/second
- 8 bits/pix element in R,G,B

Then, multiply all these factors together and you'll arrive at 1500 megabits per second, while standard NTSC occupies approximately 80 megabits per second, or 80 lines/MHz in a luma/chroma passband of just over 4 MHz for a 6-MHz RF transmission.

As Dr. Hopkins states, typical digital rates amount to 1 bit/Hertz; therefore, you're faced with compressing 1500 bits into a 6-MHz channel, and this is a load of 1500/6 = 250X.

So, to squeeze all this into a standard broadcast channel and avoid serious bit rate reduction, digital techniques, as well as companding (compression and expansion) are decidedly required.

Consequently, a very different broadcast system is needed to accommodate these special elements, which include considerably more than A/D analog to logic transfers. For, in addition to companding, there's motion estimation and compensation, memory (Fig. 3-2), quantizing, coding, prediction, audio, control, and sync, all multiplexed together, then error corrected and modulated for a suitable output.

Key elements in much of this are motion prediction and compensation, as well as removal of spatial redundancy, efficient pictures and modulation, effective coding and accurate error detection, and correction. Because there often are few changes between adjacent pictures, motion information inside the frame(s) can be transmitted retaining its former background, or new intelligence about the block substituted or relocated for further passage. Major scene changes, however, must be recognized and dealt with accordingly.

In blocks, there are some 8-x-8 picture elements, which means that 64 picture elements are required to transmit this small block. But an entire scene can require 10,000 to 20,000 blocks per picture—a far different condition from dealing with only a few minor changes.

Spatial redundancy is the next compression requirement, which necessitates application of discrete cosine transforms (DCT). First, says Dr. Hopkins, transmit the *average value* of all 64 picture elements in the block and then recognize how individual elements "vary from the average."

However, should a "busy" program result in multiple changes between or among pictures, even a very fast system can't cope, and picture blocks and elements will be lost because they won't possibly contain within a narrow 6-MHz permitted channel (identical passband to NTSC). In this event, "transmitted values" must be *rounded off*—even though full information and resolution are curtailed.

There are, fortunately, additional techniques that "help save the day" when expanding problems arise, such as run length coding and shorter codes for frequently reoccurring values or sequences of the same value. A number substituted for a string of 1s or 0s, for instance, rather than the entire group, can help. And when a television channel approaches its limits, there must be error detection and correction, either discovering these discrepancies and correcting them or masking (hiding) the problem.

This would be where the buffer capacity feedback into the adaptive quantizer results in inverse and summing operations for motion vectors and compensation. Following this, the final encoded coefficients that reach the multiplexer and formatter (Fig. 3-2) are forward error corrected and then modulated along with control, audio, and sync.

Modulation methods vary somewhat among the surviving proponents, but the final schemes are either 4 or 5 levels, depending on the manufacturer. General Instrument, for instance, can or will use either 16 or 32 quadrature amplitude modulation (16 or 32 QUAM) for 4 or 5 levels, while Zenith and its 4-VSB system sticks to 4 levels. Compared with the usual digital 2-level output, such modulation is considerably more intensive and obviously produces far better results. *VSB*, of course, stands for *vestigial side band*, thus, the symbolic 4-VSB nomenclature with carrier suppressed. Both QUAM and 4 VSB are covered at length where individual systems are investigated in detail.

Decoding begins, naturally, with a demodulator and FEC decoder before entering a demultiplexer for its various outputs for audio, control, and sync, as well as motion vectors for compensation, and the encoded coefficients, which are sorted out by the entropy decoder and inverse quantizer and transformed. All these are summed, along with the predicted picture information (based on picture memory) and reproduced as digital video in the output (Fig. 3-3).

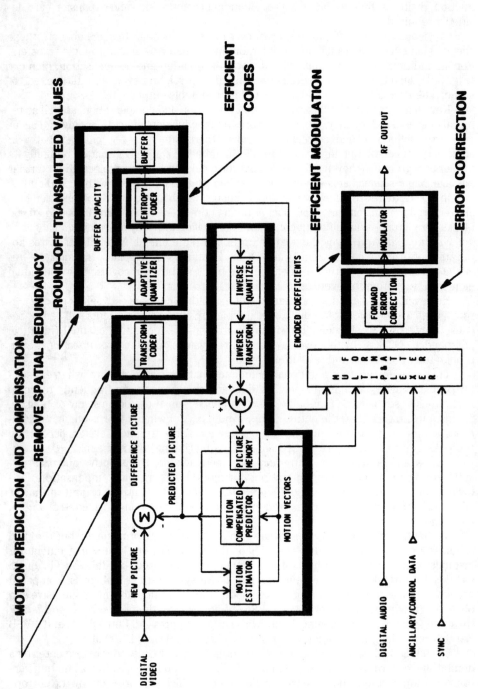

3-2 A typical HDTV broadcast encoder.

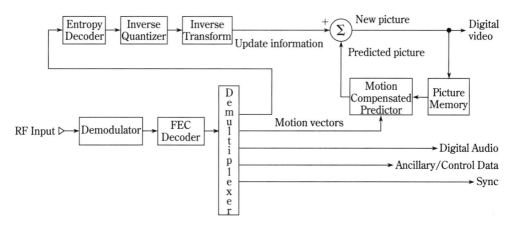

3-3 Digital HDTV broadcast decoder.

A useful table of system values (Table 3-1) has also been included by Dr. Hopkins, and remains at least symbolic of the surviving digital systems as they were. Some changes have undoubtedly been made since this painstaking origination, but most or all principles remain as set forth. Any further revisions should be caught during the system descriptions that follow . . . at least we'll do our best, trusting that all's well and substantially remains so through ATTC testing when individual system(s) undergo final evaluation and certification to the ATSC and FCC. We might add that changes were originally not permitted during system tests, but Zenith/AT&T was allowed to substitute a couple of ICs because of faulty programming, although an additional week was needed to complete that system's evaluation—a costly enterprise for those two because they had to pay liberally for each additional day.

At any rate, with preliminaries behind us, we're now ready to launch into specific descriptions of those fairly durable (if not tenacious) HDTV hardware and software collections of advanced engineering, at least one of which should be serving us into the 21st century. Field tests are the final hurdle for the fortunate system and these won't be completed until sometime in 1994. Thereafter, major events should occur at almost warp speed (perhaps slightly slower, but you'll know a great deal more in 1994 and 1995).

NHK's Narrow Muse

The only analog system contending for America's terrestrial HDTV, Japan's Narrow Muse, is a spinoff of wideband 8.1-MHz Muse originally that was designed for satellite delivery. To reduce bandwidth for insertion into the U.S.'s 6-MHz standard broadcast channel delivery, the original number of scanning lines were converted to 750 by multiple sub-Nyquist sampling, but vertical resolution was affected only slightly.

This sub-sampling for non-moving picture images combines field and frame offset operations, while for active pictures only line offset sampling functions. For interference reduction with standard NTSC, the Narrow Muse signal is divided into two parts: low- and high-frequency components, with an accompanying shift upward of the latter, then multiplexed back toward the low-frequency component, opening an actual window between the two, reducing any anticipated interference.

Figure 3-4 illustrates the luminance signal, with first and second fields identified as small open and filled circles, respectively, patterned orthogonally originally at 48.6 MHz. Afterwards, during stationary scenes, it is interfield offset sub-sampled at 24.3 MHz so

Table 3-1. Table of attributes, characteristics, and processes of digital HDTV terrestrial broadcasting systems.

	DigiCipher	DSC-HDTV	AD-HDTV	CC-DigiCipher
Lines per Frame	1050	787/788	1050	787/788
Frames per Second	29.97	59.94	29.97	59.94
Interlace	2:1	1:1	2:1	1:1
Horizontal Scan Rate	31.469 kHz	47.203 kHz	31.469 kHz	47.203 kHz
Aspect Ratio	16:9	16:9	16:9	16:9
Active Video Pixels	1408(H) × 960(V) (luma) 350(H) × 480(V) (chroma)	1280(H) × 720(V) (luma) 640(H) × 360(V) (chroma)	1440(H) × 960(V) (luma) 720(H) × 480(V) (chroma)	1280(H) × 720(V)
Pixel Aspect Ratio	33:40	1:1	27:32	1:1
Bandwidth	21.5 MHz (luma) 5.4 MHz (chroma)	34 MHz (luma) 17 MHz (chroma)	24.5 MHz (luma) 12.25 MHz (chroma)	34 MHz (luma) 34 MHz (chroma)
Colorimetry	SMPTE 240M	SMPTE 240M	SMPTE 240M	SMPTE 240M
Video Compression Algorithm	Motion-compensated DCT coding	Motion-compensated transform coding (DCT & VQ)	Motion-compensated DCT coding (MPEG-based)	Motion-compensated transform/subband coding
Block Size	8 × 8	8 × 8	8 × 8	8 × 8
Sampling Frequency	53.65 MHz	75.3 MHz	54 MHz	75.3 MHz
Audio Bandwidth	20 kHz	20 kHz	23 kHz	20 kHz
Audio Sampling Frequency	48 kHz	47.203 kHz	48 kHz	48 kHz
Dynamic Range	85 dB	96 dB	96 dB	
Number of Audio Channels	4	4	4	4
Video Data Rate	12.59 Mbits/s (16 QAM) 17.49 Mbits/s (32 QAM)	Automatically varies from 8.6 to 17.1 Mbits/s	17.73 Mbits/s (can be shared with additional audio and/or data)	15.636 Mbits/s
Audio Data Rate	0.503 Mbits/s	0.5 Mbits/s	0.512 Mbits/s (nominal)	0.5 Mbits/s
Control Data	126 kbits/s	40 kbits/s (spare)	146 kbits/s (headers)	126 kbits/s (access control)
Ancillary Data	126 kbits/s	413 kbits/s	256 kbits/s (nominal)	126 kbits/s
Sync	N/A	292 to 544 kbits/s	146 kbits/s	N/A
Total Data	19.51 Mbits/s (16 QAM) 24.39 Mbits/s (32 QAM)	11.1 to 21.0 Mbits/s	24.0 Mbits/s	19.43 Mbits/s
Error Correction Overhead	6.17 Mbits/s	1.3 to 2.4 Mbits/s	5.21 Mbits/s	3.042 Mbits/s
RF Modulation (Terrestrial)	16 QAM or 32 QAM	2-level and 4-level VSB	Spectrally shaped QAM (2 carriers)	16 QAM
3 dB Bandwidth (Terrestrial)	4.88 MHz	5.38 MHz	5.2 MHz	4.86 MHz
C/N Threshold (Terrestrial)	12.5 dB (16 QAM) 16.5 dB (32 QAM)	16 dB (4-level data) 10 dB (2-level data)	16 dB (SP carrier) 11 dB (BP carrier)	19 dB
Channel Equalization (Ghost Cancelling)	−2 to +24 μs (multiple ghosts)	−2 to +20 μs (multiple ghosts)	17 μs (may be extended to 40 μs)	2 μs (complex multipath) 32 μs (single long multipath)
RF Modulation (Satellite)	QPSK	MSK	QPSK	
Bandwidth (Satellite)	24 MHz /2 channels	20 MHz / channel	24 MHz / 2 channels	
C/N Threshold (Satellite)	7.5 dB	8 dB	8 dB	

Note: Data subject to change; data provided by the proponents; methods of measurement may vary by system.

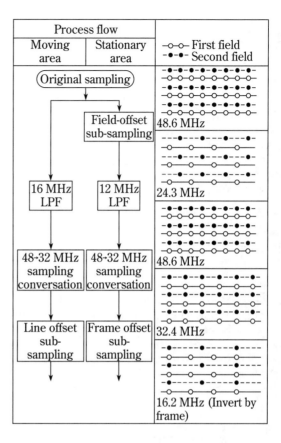

3-4 Sampling procedures for the MUSE luminance signal.

that the pattern alternates by field. With low-pass filtering at 12 MHz, sampling converts to 32.4 MHz and interpolates back to 48.6 MHz, then inter-frame offset sub-sampled, and finally phase alternated by frame. Where scenes are in motion, the original 48.6 MHz is band-limited to 16.2 MHz, line offset, inverted by frame, and sub-sampled with similar stationary patterns.

In reception, stationary information interpolates with interfield action and moving scenes are interpolated by intrafield processing. Where camera tilt and panning occurs in active images, dynamic resolution is affected and a motion vector transmits to compensate for this problem. Block diagrams of the transmit and receive decoders for Narrow Muse are illustrated in Fig. 3-5. Notice that Narrow Muse uses the full-band original Muse codec, and therefore contains the same coding process.

With direct sampling of 40.095 MHz for luma and 13.365 MHz chroma, the information is line-number converted, and the extraction of 750 lines from interpolation. The motion vector operates horizontally from –8 to +7 clock/frame, and the vertical vector from –4 to +3 line/field. The full (original) Muse encoder/decoder blocks are shown in Fig. 3-6. Thereafter, video Narrow Muse is extracted at a bandwidth of 4.86 MHz, with audio multiplexed during the vertical blanking interval (VBI) in ternary format at a baud rate of 12.15 MBaud. The downconverted format (Fig. 3-7) is an interlaced signal of 750 lines with 1188 picture elements in each line at 60 Hz. Chrominance information is reduced to ⅙ luminance bandwidth before Muse encoding. The signal format, line-by-line, is illustrated. When received, the 750-line signal is reconverted to the 1125 format and displayed.

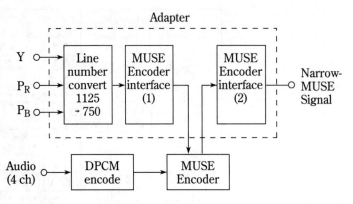

(a) Narrow-MUSE Encoder

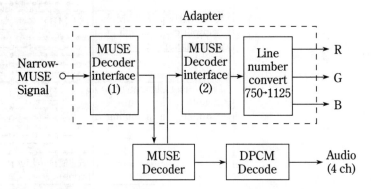

(b) Narrow-MUSE Decoder

3-5 NHK's Narrow MUSE encoder/decoder block diagrams.

Audio is delivered digitally as either 4-channel or 2-channel at respective bandwidths of 15 kHz or 20 kHz with a dynamic range of 90 dB. The coding scheme is DPCM, virtually instantaneous companding, with 8 ranges for 4 channels and 6 ranges for 2-channels. The encoded information becomes multiplexed in the vertical blanking interval. System synchronizing appears under 0.75 MHz and is transmitted below the NTSC picture carrier. Sync drops out at approximately 18 dB C/N.

Narrow Muse also possesses a limited ghost-cancelling ability and is said to handle delay times up to ±13.3 μsec. Present hardware accommodates delay times of ±6.6 μsec with a ghost-canceller convergence time of about 30 seconds. Parts of this explanation are not totally complete, but, together with better-than-average diagrams, most of the pertinent information should satisfy.

Advanced Compatible Television (ACTV)

A product of the Advanced Television Research Consortium, ACTV required an additional week of testing (June 20, 1991 to September 15, 1991) because of NTSC-compatible elements, test material changes, two days additional for re-runs, and one further

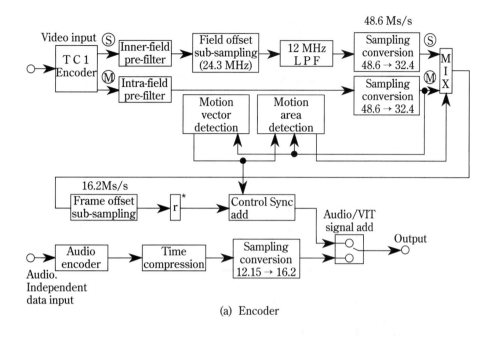

(a) Encoder

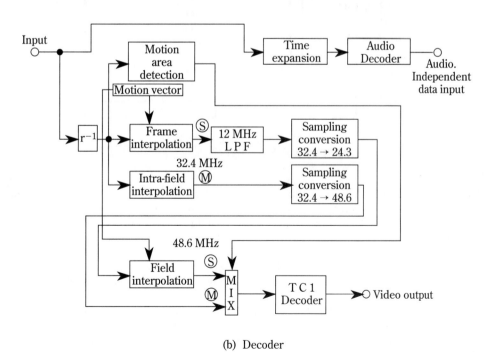

(b) Decoder

3-6 The original MUSE encoder/decoder differs from narrow MUSE.

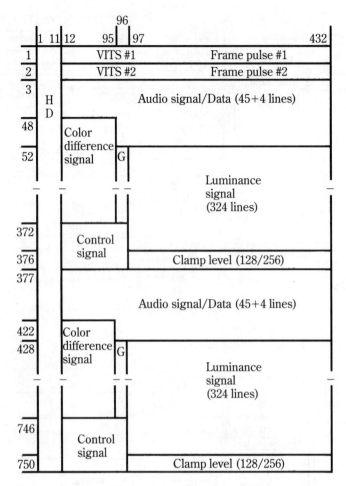

3-7 The narrow MUSE signal format of 750 lines is expanded to 1125/60 by the MUSE receiver.

system-specific test day. After further consideration and proponent examination, this system was withdrawn from competition by ACTV on March 4, 1992. However, because this was a major step forward in attempting to improve existing NTSC by adding new techniques and additional engineering, a fundamental description of most of its attributes is in order.

Because ACTV-1 is essentially the same as originally conceived and submitted to ATSC and the Federal Communications Commission during September/November of 1988, we'll use some of this material to illustrate the system and explain its operation.

Sarnoff Research Laboratories claims ACTV-1 offers wider, sharper, compatible pictures, doesn't obsolete present NTSC receivers, delivers widescreen EDTV and can be put on the air immediately. A dual-channel augmented system was also proposed, but appeared to be largely computer-simulated and was never offered for ATTC testing. In the meantime, ACTV-1 was said to be an intermediate approach between NTSC and ACTV-II, the latter described as offering "full HDTV performance."

A 1050-line, 2:1 interlaced signal was first converted to 525/1:1 line progressively scanned information with four separate signal components all added to NTSC for both wider aspect ratios and improved definition. Of the four, three are contained in subchannels within the conventional 6-MHz spectrum (Fig. 3-8).

After widescreen camera scanning in 525-line, 2:1 interlace, Y (luma) and I,Q (chroma), intelligence is converted to an NTSC 4:3 aspect ratio with line times remaining the same, increasing signal bandwidth because the widescreen camera has scanned the usual 63.5 µs in faster than NTSC time.

The middle of each line is now time-expanded to consume all but 2 µs of the entire NTSC active line time. This results in bandwidth reduction, allowing widescreen luma and chroma information to occupy ordinary signal areas.

One microsecond on each end of the active line time-compressed side panel contains low frequencies, which also carry the video's dc component, and are obscured by conventional horizontal overscan in home receivers. "Cutoff frequencies" in these 6X-compression side panels are 700 kHz for luminance and 83 kHz for chroma.

Therefore, the Y and I,Q information contained in the center of the picture has standard 4.2-MHz luma and 500-kHz chroma bandwidths and is NTSC encoded with horizontal, vertical, and temporal prefilters, plus being luminance bandstop filtered in 3-D for special spectral separation of chroma modulation at 3.58 MHz (the usual NTSC chroma subcarrier frequency). Any seam visibility between side and center panels is limited by transmitting low-frequency information as a portion of the main signal, matching dc levels automatically, and sending also-transmitting redundant intelligence, where some 10 video samples are "effectively" radiated twice. Overlaps permit mixing center and side-panel information, allowing a "feathered" seam, rather than distinct separation.

Characterizing the main signal as Component 1, sidepanel frequencies as Component 2, Components 3 and 4 are now ready for explanation. The first two components carry 5 MHz of luma in the 525-line, 2:1 interlaced transmission, augmented by additional passband information between 5 and 6 MHz. This occurs by shifting these frequencies 0.1 to 1.1 MHz by amplitude modulation with a 4.9-MHz suppressed carrier and low-pass filter, which eliminates the upper sideband. Thereafter, the additional luminance is compressed to time-fit the center panel, and this allows addition of an extra 1.1 MHz of high frequency information throughout the complete image.

Recall that ACTV-1 derives from a 1050/2:1 interlace with conversion to 525/1:1 progressive scan. In transmit, the 525-line scan conversion is interlaced and so the 525 progressive scan signal permits a "helper" source to add vertical-temporal luminance detail for receiver use in reconstructing the 525/1:1 display (Fig. 3-9).

The helper signal restores certain vertical detail originally in the 525/1:1 transmission before interlace and is described as vertical-temporal to contain the difference between the average value that a receiver can calculate among corresponding pixels separated by two fields and the real value existing at the encoder. Only known errors are sent by the helper, according to the receiver's predicted algorithm. This is low average energy and the helper is horizontally filtered to 750 kHz.

Sarnoff Laboratories also considered a digital signal to contain the helper signal, but much depended on "other information to be sent" and available "subchannels."

Modulation techniques (Fig. 3-10) are the next points for discussion, especially uniting the four ACTV-1 signals and how they are combined and transmitted over the usual 6-MHz broadcast channel with compatibility and adequate reception. Additionally inserted components have to be physically or perceptually hidden in the "main signal" when appearing on NTSC receivers. These same components need to be separated without crosstalk in any ACTV receiver.

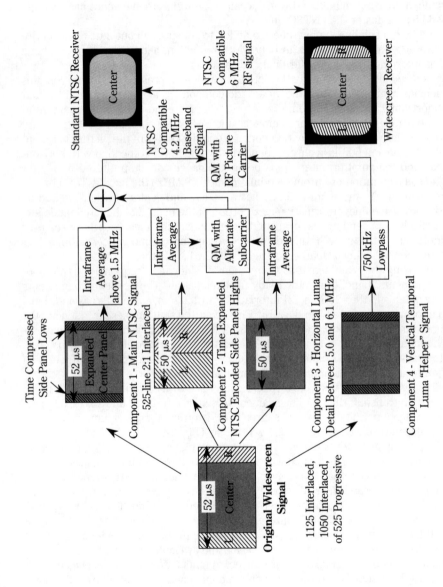

3-8 ACTV-1. A single-channel NTSC compatible widescreen EDTV system by Sarnoff Laboratories.

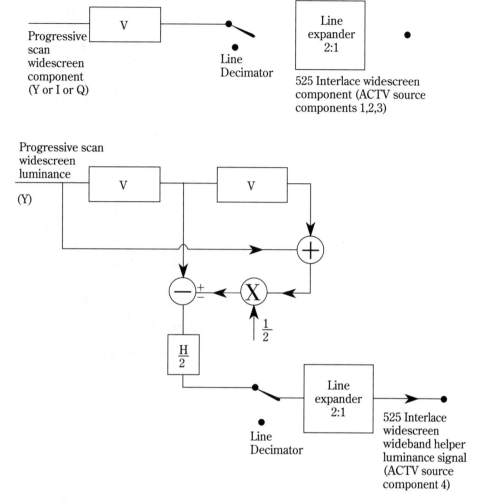

3-9 Line scan conversions in ACTV-1.

According to Sarnoff, here's how it's done: side-panel low frequencies are "hidden" in normal receiver overscans. Low-energy components 2 and 3 are amplitude compressed and quadrature modulated on a new 3.1-MHz subcarrier, which is line interleaved with phase inversion on alternate fields. Complementary color flicker at 30 Hz hides the modulation because this is something the eye doesn't see.

As for Component 4, the 750-kHz helper signal is spatially correlated in the center of the main picture and quadrature-modulated on the RF picture carrier. NTSC receivers with ancient envelope detectors hide this factor, and synchronous detectors remove it completely.

Now, so that Components 1, 2, and 3 are fully recoverable, intraframe averaging (Fig. 3-11) has been originated as a linear, time-varying digital filter operation to separate modulated and baseband signals free from vertical-temporal crosstalk, regardless of motion. Horizontal crosstalk responds well to guardbands between pre- and post-filtering.

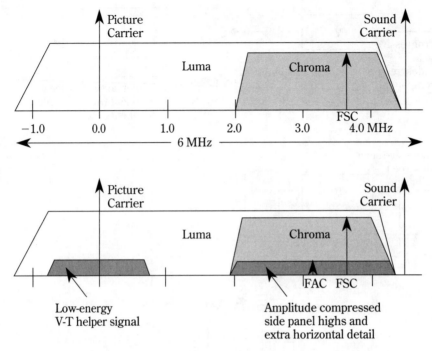

3-10 Standard NTSC RF spectrum (top) and ACTV RF spectrum (bottom), showing location of extra modulated components.

The averaging process averages pairs of pixels one field separated within a frame, but does not cross frame boundaries. In Component 1, this takes place only on frequencies over 1.5 MHz and no averaging on the compressed side panels. So when Components 2 and 3 are quadrature-modulated and added to component they form an M+A or M–A. The latter, when M is a sample of the main composite information above 1.5 MHz, and A represents a sample of the auxiliary modulated signal.

The receiver averages and recognizes pixel differences one field apart and above 1.7 MHz, and completely separates main samples from auxiliary samples. Therefore, with intraframe averaging, vertical-temporal crosstalk is eliminated with a single-frame store. Figure 3-10 illustrates the developed spectrum with extra components and the 750-kHz helper vertical-temporal helper situated on right and left sides of the main picture carrier.

ACTV-1 decoder processing

ACTV-1 decoder processing involves wide-screen decoding, memory, and recovery of all four transmitted components, as illustrated by Sarnoff in Fig. 3-12. Main signal paths follow the heavy black lines, while subsystems, such as intraframe differences, quadrature demodulation, side panel compression, NTSC decoding, and interface operations support postfiltering and 5-MHz luminance highpass operations. Finally, Y,I,Q once again becomes RGB for the 525-line progressive scan display.

Once all components are shaped and expanded to design time-shared allocations, extended luminance detail is amplitude modulated and shifted to its original frequency range and added to existing luma for 6 MHz of horizontal resolution. Interlaced luma is

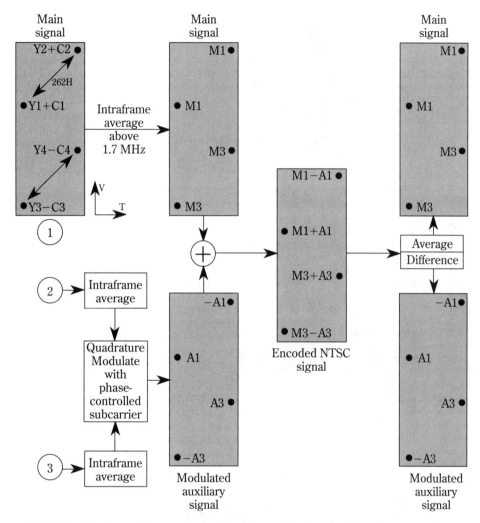

3-11 Combination and recovery of main and aux. signals using interframe averaging.

then converted to progressive scan with temporal interpolation and the helper signal. Chroma information also converts to progressive scan, but without aid from the helper. Lastly, the Y,I,Q information converts to progressive scan analog and matrixed to RGB for display.

In the receiver's memory portion, three major functions operate to produce the image. They are the intraframe averager/differencer, NTSC decoding for components 1 and 2, and interlace/progressive scanning for Y,I,Q. But only active video information is really stored for signal processing so that reduced bandwidth information needs proportionally less memory. Thereafter, temporal filtering recovers most or all signal components, while a frame store of about 0.4 Mbytes is used to aid the intraframe averaging and the different functions. The audio portion of the system was not decided upon when the Sarnoff description was initially written; consequently, it is not included. However, there was talk

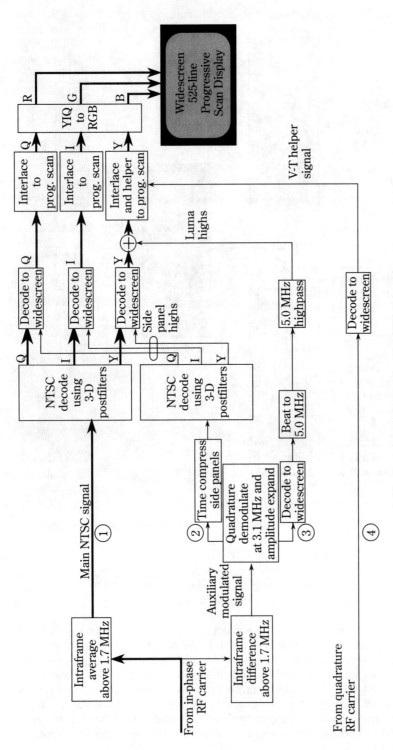

3-12 System block diagram of ACTV-1 decoder.

of digital stereo, a helper signal, Teletext, and quadrature modulation. As for sync, Sarnoff suggested some new signals to train an adaptive receiver on a transmitted line that is not visible.

Digital to the rescue

Although several analog systems suggested apparent potential, various interference factors, noise, power requirements, area-coverage equivalent to NTSC, and wideband delivery all combined to generally eliminate any HDTV transmissions and reception other than digital, following preliminary investigations by major proponents and the obvious stimulation supplied by Zenith Electronics. To quote Jerry Pearlman, Chairman and President of Zenith, "people are buying performance . . . consumers always rank picture quality first in their TV purchase decision . . . and the third factor driving early (HDTV) adoption is immediate utility. HDTV sets will be dual mode receivers . . . better displays, more scanning lines and lots of digital signal processing . . ." And we might add that such receivers should be available by late 1995, if present test and FCC schedules hold. If not, delays of 6 months to a year are probable, with some additional dependence on the complexity of the system or collective systems selected. At the moment, the ball game narrows further to principals Sarnoff, General Instrument and Zenith—a topic worth expanding somewhat later because all remaining system offerors (proponents) are busy talking among themselves and to one another prior to ATSC and FCC system selections.

In early HDTV examinations, Zenith in its 3XNTSC proposal discovered that video high-frequency components need only 1% or less of the total projected energy and most power requirements are necessary for low-frequency video, sync, and average or dc values. That meant high-frequency video could be transmitted with little carrier power, improved S/N, and virtually no nearby channel interference. So, video above 200 kHz was an improvement already over NTSC and the other heavy power users could be digitized—all at an overall passband of some 30 MHz for video and audio, and using the vertical blanking interval (VBI) for sync and dc. 30 MHz versus 4.2 to 4.5 MHz, even though companded (compressed and expanded), constituted a huge advance in resolution and definition. NTSC, of course, remained as originally constituted and approved in 1953 by the FCC.

Although all this could be compressed into a standard VHF or UHF 6-MHz broadcast channel, only part of the system was digital and the remainder continued to be analog. Industry-wide digital designers began working feverishly to develop all-digital systems that would not only complement NTSC, but would avoid HDTV (digital) undesirable interaction.

The American Television Alliance

The American Television Alliance consisted of a pair of all-digital HDTV systems, both of which were products of General Instrument Corp., allied with 1) DigiCipher and 2) the Massachusetts Institute of Technology. These groups were selected first because G.I. and DigiCipher was the first all-digital system proponent, followed shortly by G.I. and MIT. G.I. also was the first to broadcast an HDTV signal over the air at the National Association of Broadcasters Convention in April of 1992. DigiCipher portion has now been renamed *Alliance Interlace* and features 1050 scanning lines, 2:1 interlace, and 29.97 frames or 59.94 fields per second. Interlace proceeded nicely through the Advanced Television Test Center's Laboratory tests, which began on Dec. 10, 1991 and ended February 5, 1992.

The first actual terrestrial broadcast picture transmitted over the air was generated by G.I./DigiCipher at the National Association of Broadcaster's convention in Las Vegas on April 12, 1992. Using low-power transmission over channel 15 from the southern portion of the Las Vegas Convention center to the Las Vegas Hilton Center (about ¼ mile) encoded data in digital format was delivered by microwave to the channel 15 transmitter and then transmitted to the Hilton (Fig. 3-13). The undertaking was an evident success, with due credit going to executive engineers Robert Rast and Dr. Woo H. Paik, Ph.D. Received images were taped and shown throughout the convention between April 12 and April 16. Simultaneously, General Instrument and Toshiba America jointly announced a working prototype of a consumer digital high-definition Video Cassette Recorder based on DigiCipher technology, an 8-mm platform that both records and plays compressed DigiCipher HD information. Metal evaporated tape allows high-density recording during two-hour record and playback times. Should the FCC select DigiCipher as America's HDTV standard, Toshiba America plans to manufacture such receivers at its plant in Lebanon, Tennessee.

The second member of the American Television Alliance is the Massachusetts Institute of Technology, involved in *Alliance Progressive,* which offers 787.5 scan lines, progressive scanning at 59.94 frames/second. Alliance Progressive actually replaces the channel-compatible hybrid system. Alliance Interlace and Alliance Progressive are individual systems, but will share the same transmission subsystem.

G.I.'s digital television was developed by its VideoCipher division, which, when owned by MA/COM was known as *Linkabit,* developed the original VideoCipher scrambling technology for cable and satellite operations. Today, the improved system is known as *VideoCipher 2 Plus.*

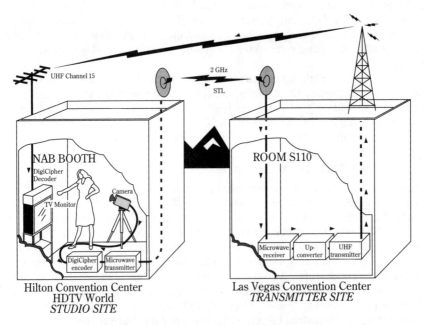

3-13 Drawing of the first over-the-air digitized HSTV transmit/receive generated by General Instrument/DigiCipher, and MIT.

DigiCipher™/General Instrument HD System's explanation was submitted to the Advanced Television Systems Committee (WP1) on August 22, 1991 as the "world's first all-digital system for compression and transmission of high-definition video and CD-quality sound over a single 6-MHz VHF or UHF television channel." It combines 1050 lines of interlaced video, four channels of digital audio, text, and control information within a "single data stream" and delivers "full HDTV performance" with little or no visible impairments that result from multipath, noise, or other varieties of interference, according to General Instrument Corp.

It's a digital simulcast system (Fig. 3-14) using a predictive/transform compression algorithm for video bit rate reduction in two transmission modes: 32 quadrature amplitude modulation (QUAM) and 16 QUAM, both with rates of 4.88 M symbols/sec. The video data rate of 17.47 Mb/sec has been selected for the 32 QUAM primary mode with a transmission rate of 24.39 Mb/sec. Broadcasters can select either mode and receivers are said to automatically decode either transmission. The 16-QUAM mode can be important to TV stations having co-channel spacing and power limitations. But, 16 QUAM, although having a lower system threshold of 12.5 dB, suffers from "a small sacrifice" in picture quality, and G.I. believes that most TV stations will prefer 32 QUAM because of its superior video. We will, therefore concentrate on the prime system, rather than on 16 QUAM.

Video with 32 QUAM is an analog RGB source, 2:1 interlaced, with frame rate of 29.97 Hz, and an aspect ratio of 16:9. RGB is sampled and converted to Y,U,V information after low-pass filtering and A/D conversion (Fig. 3-15) of 8 bits. Luminance sampling occurs at 53.65 MHz, while chroma is sub-sampled horizontally "by a factor of 4" and vertically by a

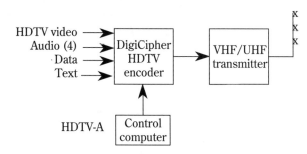

HDTV VHF/UHF Station

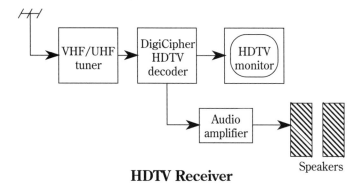

HDTV Receiver

3-14 The digital system block diagram.

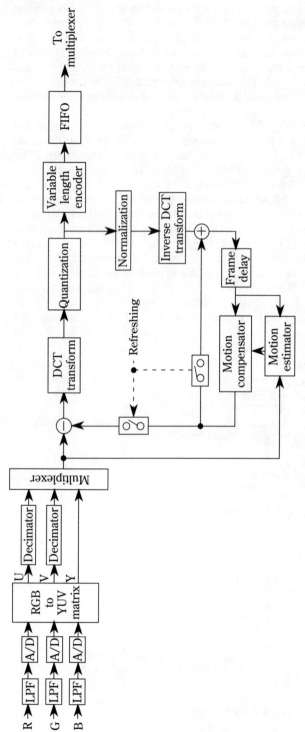

3-15 Digital video encoder block diagram.

factor of 2, discarding every second field. Data, audio, video inputs are multiplexed into a single data stream at 18.22 Mbps, and the FEC encoder adds error correction overhead bits and delivers 24.39 Mbps of information to the 32-QUAM modulator. Of the total, 126 kBits are "available" for captioning, program guides, Teletext, etc., and an additional 126 kBits is reserved for control data and any conditional access requirements.

Complete images in single frames consist of 960 lines of 1408 pixels, divided into 21,120 blocks (176 × 120) or 2640 superblocks (44 wide × 60 high) or even 240 macroblocks. Motion-compensated predictive coding (DPCM) manages temporal correlation, while a discrete cosine transform (DCT) handles spatial correlation. DPCM eliminates frame-to-frame redundancy at the superblock level. Where DPCM becomes less efficient than PCM, DigiCipher adaptively switches to PCM for intraframe coding. However, when PCM is present, motion vectors are not processed, but PCM will probably be used 85% of the time.

At times when significant high-frequency detail becomes insignificant to the viewer, images in the frequency domain are further bit-reduced by discrete cosine transform (DCT). Such processing occurs on images in blocks of pixels 8-×-8 (horizontal by vertical), yielding 8-×-8 sets of coefficients, in terms of frequency. They are then divided by weighting factors that emphasize dc and low frequencies with a slight favoring of vertical frequencies over horizontal. Chroma and luma blocks are processed together by DCT, but, because of decimation, 8 luma blocks continue on while only two chroma blocks accompany. Quantized DCT coefficients are then Huffman-coded for variable word-length coding, which results in a variable data rate. Compression occurs with short words representing frequently re-occurring values of run-length and quantized DCT coefficients, and long words infrequently. Rate control develops by adjusting the quantization level for macroblocks, based on buffer accuracy.

DigiCipher develops a high level of compression with a motion-compensated DPCM algorithm (Fig. 3-16). A motion-compensated prior frame estimates a current frame and the difference between the two is encoded with DCT that uses a full search block to generate one motion vector per superblock and continues as one vector per superblock at 10 bits resolution. If, during fast scene changes, the frame-difference image contains more energy than the original, video coder selects between PCM intraframe coding and interframe coding (DPCM) and whichever needs the lesser number of bits continues on.

Channel errors are protected by concatenated trellis coding and Reed-Solomon block coding. The inner code is a rate 4/5 trellis coder. A full-search Viterbi coder with 4-bit accuracy soft decisions and a constant length of 7, is described as the trellis decoder and a Reed-Solomon code that can correct transmission errors affecting 5 successive 8-bit Reed-Solomon blocks—a burst of as many as 40 bits.

Motion estimation utilizes a full search block matching algorithm, generating one motion vector per superblock (4 DCT blocks horizontally and 2 vertically), and the search area measures +31 to –32 pixels horizontally and +7 to –8 pixels vertically.

As for film sources originating at 24 frames/second, after conversion to video using the three-two pulldown technique, an inherent redundancy is apparent so that one in every five fields are affected. DigiCipher automatically detects this sequence and drops the redundant field. Normal video is not affected.

Multipath distortions are compensated by a 256-tap adaptive equalizer with a range of –2 to +24 microseconds and can be as high as –6 dB for close ghosts. Non-ideal frequency response or group delay distortions can also be compensated by this equalizer, and when there is an "interfacing" NTSC signal, the equalizer furnishes notch filtering at picture, color, and audio carrier transmissions.

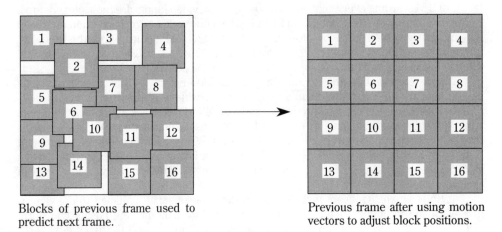

Blocks of previous frame used to predict next frame.

Previous frame after using motion vectors to adjust block positions.

3-16 Using motion compensation to predict succeeding frames.

Some of this latter information might change with the selection of the system ghost canceller for all proponents because terrestrial advocates and cable have now adopted a firm compromise.

Although compression by spatial processing by itself is limited, an inter-frame coder benefits from both temporal, as well as spatial correlation. Frame processing, says G.I., works better than field processing with little or no motion. But field processing needs a higher bit rate because frame processing offers better accuracy when frame and field rates are equal. Nonetheless, field processing operates the best in detailed images with movement.

DigiCipher, therefore, developed a novel means of combining the advantages of both subsystems in that it allows video information to be compressed and then reconstructed with minimum degradation during motion. The system simply adjusts to scenes both static and moving, with decisions extracted from encoded video. And where film rates are 24 frames/second, a 3:2 pulldown operation changes frame numbers from 24 to 30 without adding extra information to the signal. A similar 3:2 pulldown action restores the 60 Hz fields/second prior to TV display. A block diagram of the video decoder is illustrated in Fig. 3-17. Notice the first-in first-out (FIFO) input, the variable length decoder, inverse normalization and DCT transform, a switched refresher, a demultiplexer preceded by motion compensation and frame delay, then the feed-through Y luminance signal and the two interpolators for U,V chroma. Finally, notice the RGB matrix and the low-pass filter output.

Audio when decoded operates at 252 kBits/sec in a clocked signal serial data stream. Complementary processing recovers the two main audio signals, which continue on to high-quality 16-bit D/A converters and baseband.

The American Television Alliance II

After taking a slight liberty with the title of this section, we hasten to explain the II simply signifies the second American Television Alliance System—this one offered by the Massachusetts Institute of Technology and fathered primarily by Dr. J.S. Lim and G.I. It was submitted to the Advanced Television Systems Committee on May 14, 1992 and is the "progressive" scan portion of the two systems, in addition to other differences, which will be described further on.

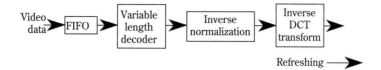

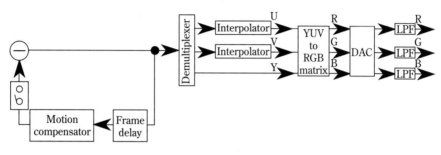

3-17 Digital video decoder block diagram. DigiCipher.

The ATVA-Progressive system produces a high-resolution video signal of 720-x-1280 picture elements at 60 frames/sec and a 16:9 raster aspect ratio with considerable noise and interference immunity, low transmit power, and possible use of UHF taboo channels. Source material is RGB 787.5 line, 59.94 fps progressive scan format with 1280 square picture elements. RGB translates (as in DigiCipher) to Y,U,V, is then source adaptive encoded, motion estimation and compensation, quantizing, entrophy encoding, and multiplexing/modulation. A system block diagram is illustrated in Fig. 3-18, which shows matrix conversion, transform/subband analysis, motion estimation and compensation, and multiplexing for auxiliary data and digital audio. The receiver de-multiplexes these different modulations, decodes, does transform/subband synthesis, adds motion compensation and vectors, then converts Y,U,V via matrix conversion to regular RGB. However, instead of converting 24 frames/sec film to 60 frames/sec and then transmitting, there's no conversion until the receiver institutes the 3:2 pull-down for 60-frame display, improving coding efficiently "significantly," according to MIT.

Motion estimation classifies into two groups (Fig. 3-19). You can either adopt region-matching methods or spatio-temporal constraints. The former method "sees" a small frame portion and searches for a "displacement" to detect the best match between the two. Spatio-temporal constraint depends on errors defined in the illustrated equation, which includes motion vectors of horizontal and vertical velocity and the video signal as a function of two spatial variables. Uniform motion within a small, local region, rather than broad areas produces "significant reduction in temporal correlation." This method works well for both noisy and noise-free video games, which can become significant problems.

Motion compensation occurs when a prediction difference between an already encoded frame and the next frame that requires encoding. Their difference is noted and a prediction generated, which is called the *motion-compensated residual.* This is done for the luma-chroma Y,U,V information, but when compensation develops considerable energy, motion compensation is disabled and the actual image frame is encoded—usually with a scene change.

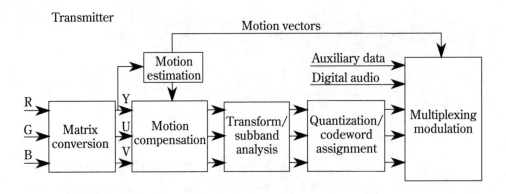

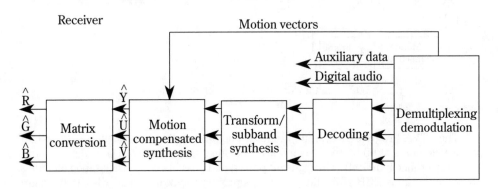

3-18 The ATVA progressive scan transmitter/receiver block diagram.

The Transform/Subband analyzes the Y,U,V luminance/chroma intelligence via a transform/subband filter. It's a 2-D separable filter that divides motion-compensated residuals into 8-x-8 bands. MIT declares that "unlike the Discrete Cosine Transform (DCT), our method reduces artifacts significantly." Transform/subband coefficients are weighted, according to frequencies and luma/chroma content for visual sensitivity variations, and then are selected according to energy. Coefficients with the greatest energy are processed until encoding bits are filled. This amounts to 14.99 Mbits/sec.

Quantization follows with Huffman encoding the location and amplitude of each selective transform/subband coefficient. Quantization steps and adaptive selections work together so that bits/frame number less than 0.24956 Mbits (Fig. 3-20). This results in a variable bit rate system within a fixed-rate channel situation. As its buffer fills, quantization becomes coarser, avoiding overflow; as the buffer empties, quantization tightens to increase the bit rate and fill the buffer. The buffer is locally adaptive; among busy details, it allocates additional bits. Enough storage is available for one complete frame (0.24956 Mbits) to fill the buffer, allowing the buffer to react "globally," rather than locally, "significantly improving system performance."

Decoding, as usual is the general inverse of encoding with demodulating and demultiplexing occurring first, then identification of the transform/subband coefficients. The motion-compensated residuals combine with prior frames to generate the present frame.

Motion estimation

• Translational motion

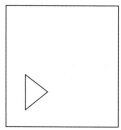

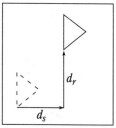

Past frame (time t_{-1})   Current frame (time t_0)

• Two approaches

   * Region matching methods

$$f(x,y,t_0) = f(x - d_x, y - d_y, t_{-1})$$

   * Spatio-temporal constraint equation methods

$$v_x \frac{\partial f(x,y,t)}{\partial x} + v_y \frac{\partial f(x,y,t)}{\partial y} + \frac{\partial f(x,y,t)}{\partial t} = 0.$$

3-19 Motion estimation divides into two approaches.

The receiver itself has an RF that downconverts to the standard 41- to 47-MHz intermediate-frequency spread and will receive VHF and UHF between 54 and 806 MHz. The demodulator (Fig. 3-21) consists of baseband filters, a symbol synchronizer, an adaptive equalizer with symbol error correction, a carrier tracking loop with phase error correction, a symbol decoder, forward error correction, a de-randomizer, digital demultiplexer, and video/audio decoder outputs, plus auxiliary data, and access control.

Zenith's all-digital HDTV system

No, we did not deliberately overlook powerful AT&T, nor are we discounting Scientific Atlanta, but the lion's share of this major endeavor belongs to Zenith and that's the primary emphasis. AT&T, however, deserves more than passing reference because of its digital video codec development since it can operate successfully over NTSC taboo channels at a compression ratio of some 50:1. Consequently, this contribution will be described in some detail as we proceed with the overall explanation.

Zenith, as you may recall, first introduced a hybrid HDTV proposal that was half analog, half digital, and showed other proponents how low-value video and dc could consume small, but primary power while signal remainder and sync could use considerably less. The successive step, of course, was development of an all-digital system that was even more efficient in avoiding noise, interference, and a surprising reduction of power with NTSC-equivalent coverage. But all this did not occur without a few lumps along the way.

Quantization and buffer control

- Adaptive selection of transform/subband coefficients

- Statistical encoding of location and amplitude of transform/subband coefficients

- Available bits/frame = 0.24956 Mbits (14.99 Mbits/sec)

- Global buffer control on a frame-by-frame basis

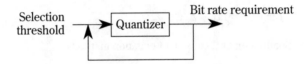

* Simple buffer control method

* Very good performance

3-20 Locations and amplitudes of transform/subband coefficients are Huffman encoded.

This explanation is essentially based on a paper originally delivered at a National Association of Broadcasters' convention and other data generated by Zenith over the past several years. Paper originators were R. Citta, C. Eilers, R. Lee, and J. Rypkema—all members of Advanced Television Systems Committee working parties and, of course, excellent engineers working with and for Zenith Electronics Corporation (Fig. 3-22).

HDTV Video signals are projected at 787.5 lines/frame, 59.94 frames/sec, progressively scanned at triple the NTSC rate of 15,734 Hz or 47.202 kHz, at a passband of 34 MHz. Because this is a progressive scan system, however, 1575 lines are scanned every 1/29.97 second delivering 1280-x-720 active square pixels/frame. Such scan rates make available simple conversion to the established NTSC format of 525 lines interlaced and 59.94 Hz. But instead of basic luma and chroma processing, linear red, blue, and green information is sourced, which also produces wideband color and genuine-value luminance signals.

If all pixels were encoded at 9 bits, the bit rate for luminance only would amount to 497 Mbts/sec. Add chroma and this would become 994 Mbts/sec. Compression reduces these rates to 17.2 Mbts/sec, although the total data rate does expand to 21.52 Mbts/sec because of additions of audio, captioning, text, forward-error correction, box address, cryptography, and other ancillary information.

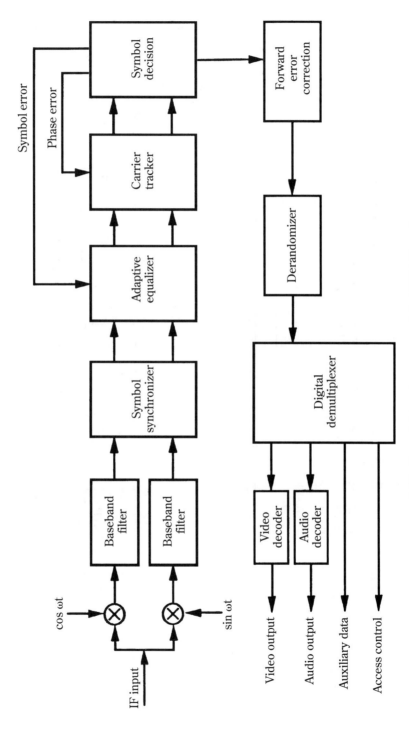

3-21 Demodulator components of the ATVA-II receiver.

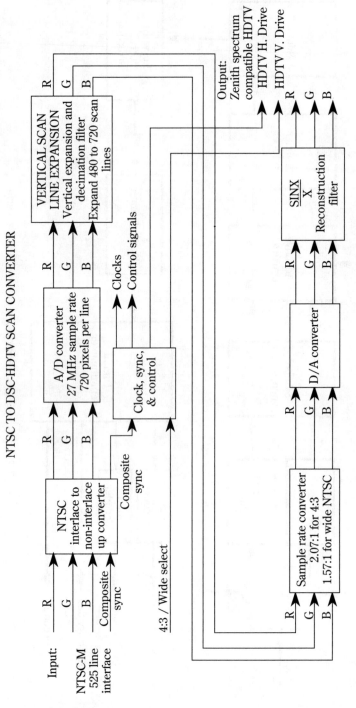

3-22 Digital HDTV programming by Zenith Electronics fairly easy and low cost.

Why digital? Digital transmission, according to Zenith, removes most or all thermal noise you see as picture snow. There's better bandwidth compression, noise-free tape recording in studio and at home, secondary-image (ghost) removal, and avoids problems of cascaded transmission segments. Additionally, picture impairments are avoided with Reed-Solomon codes; transmitters need less power, no aural transmitters, and no notch diplexers; rejection of NTSC co-channel interference; plus equal broadcast coverage with NTSC.

Formerly, video transmitted as analog by double sideband suppressed carrier amplitude modulation in quadrature was originally digitized before transmission and the final output stage actually consisted of a pulse amplitude modulated signal (PAM). Zenith's new system also uses PAM, but all possible amplitudes are reduced to four so that all remains within a 4-level digital delivery. This offers considerable thermal noise immunity and protection against other picture problems. And while square pixels at a 720 line rate and 1280 array were chosen, an additional pixel guard band at all four raster edges will mask transient processing, analog rise times, timing tolerances, and certain production edge effects, which might detract from the overall picture. Such square pixel numbers facilitate easy conversion from or to NTSC simulcast because 4:3 and 3:2 horizontal and vertical conversions do the job nicely and also aid the design of dual-purpose HDTV and NTSC receivers. The line and array rate format is also within the range of commercial high-definition tape-recording technology.

As an example of initial (although simplified) NTSC to digital HDTV conversion, Zenith suggests the following means of taking RGB analog, passing it through a 2:1 interlace to 1:1 scan converter, then analog-to-digital conversion, line expansion, sample rate change, back to analog, followed by a sinx/x RGB reconstruction filter and output, obviating the need for expensive equipment and allowing network pass-through programs at minimum expense. The million-dollar extravaganzas could come later as telecasts and receivers begin to proliferate. Transcoding from HDTV to NTSC also seems fairly simple, according to Zenith because of its established relationship between the two formats and upconverting to HDTV requires line tripling and video encoding "without loss of NTSC quality." Further, Zenith says its HDTV system will adapt to cable, satellite, VTR, VCR, video disc, and fiber without inventing or manufacturing new technology because it already exists.

Other factors, such as constant luminance and broadbanded color renditions, are further plus factors for either HDTV or NTSC conversions because luminance is "optimized in terms of quantization error and/or coding artifact visibility," and gamma correction in the receiver aids any particular display. Matrixing, therefore (of Y,U,V for either transmitter or receiver primaries and encoder hardware with additional A/D converter resolution) will soon, if not now, be able to accept linear RGB information directly. In the Zenith digital system, luminance, and chroma are band-limited to 34 and 17 MHz, respectively.

A new enhanced performance digital HDTV codec is also in the Zenith system, this one developed and supplied by Ma Bell's AT&T of Murray Hill, N.J. and originally explained by A. Netravali, E. Petajan, S. Knauer, K. Matthews, B. Safranek, and P. Westerink.

The codec operates through a video compression algorithm that was optimized for terrestrial broadcasting within very few VLSI ICs. The Y,U,V ratio amounts to 4:2:2 at 9 bits/sample, progressive scanning at 59.94 Hz and 720 active lines. Initially, the video bit rate is 994 Mbits/sec, but after removal of redundancies, it operates at 17 Mbits/sec with error correction.

During video compression, three fundamental redundancies are affected (Fig. 3-23): motion compensation removes temporal redundancy; spatial frequency transformation removes spatial redundancy; and perceptual weighting removes amplitude redundancy by placing quantizing noise in obscure areas.

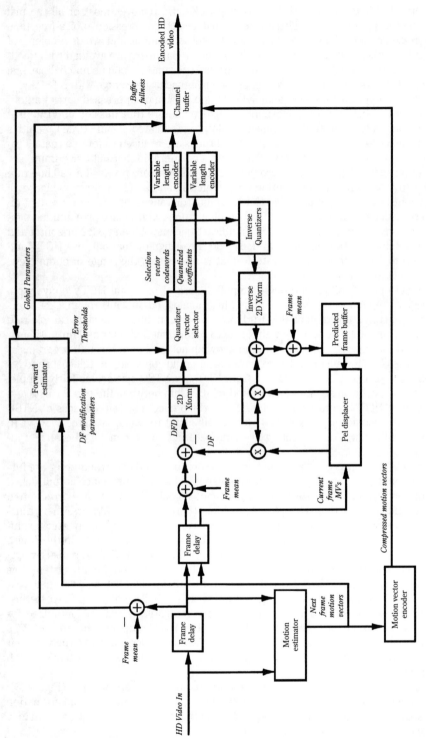

3-23 Video encoder block diagram. Zenith/AT&T.

Temporal redundancy removal results by estimating object motions from frame-to-frame with hierarchical block matching; motion vectors compute a displaced frame (DF) difference based on little information in the original frame, and the displaced frame difference is 2-dimensional transformed to alleviate spatial redundancy.

Each new frame of the displaced frame difference is analyzed before coding for rate determination versus perceptual distortion and the dynamic range of each coefficient. Quantization commences, based on perceived importance of the individual coefficients, their dynamic range, and rates compared to distortion. A human visual model regulates color sensitivity, brightness, spatial frequency, and spatial-temporal masking, and this minimizes any coding artifacts in the picture. Motion vectors then compress transform coefficients, and others are packed into a format quite immune to errors in transmission. When transmission errors occur, the decoder masks such errors, and in the event a channel is changed or there's loss of signal, the decoder switches to another mode, quickly returning the received picture to full quality.

Blocks of pixels containing the frame differences use a spatial transform that is derived from an algorithm minimizing the various multiplications. The number of bits are also reduced and controlled by recognizing that transform coefficients vary in importance according to visual limitations. Vector quantization then represents combinations of patterns of quantizers applied to any given block of coefficients. Coding efficiency, therefore, can compress and transmit the associated index, rather than the pattern itself.

Perceptual-based coding depends on matching the coding algorithm to human visual characteristics. Artifacts concentrate, unfortunately, in local image regions, where they are most visible. However, if coding distortions are uniformly distributed, these artifacts will tend to disappear with the application of perceptual thresholds. The perceptual threshold generator generates separate luma and chroma thresholds for coefficients in each frame, and although not transmitted, it maximizes transmitted information while re ducing artifacts.

Motion vectors, quantizer selection vectors, and quantized coefficients are then variable-length coded while other coding information is fixed length and placed in specific segments by the segment formatter.

Variable length coding assigns short code words to most frequent data values and expanded words to longer ones. All this passes through the slice formatter, compressed frame buffer, segment formatter, and on to the encoded video output.

Decoding for the receiver (Fig. 3-24) enters a complementary buffer to that of the compression video buffer, where it exits in four directions. First through the motion vector decoder, the DF (displaced frame) modification parameters, vector codewords, and coded coefficients, thence to a pair of variable length decoders, a vector decoder, inverse quantizers and join Pel displaced previous frame buffer and onward to the DFD, the mean frame, and a decoded HD video output. Processing and memory in the decoder are fairly short, consisting of one inverse spatial transform and a variable length decoder, and decoder memory consists of only one full frame and several compressed frames. Vector codewords look up a quantizer vector, which is really an entire group of quantizer selection codes. An inverse quantizer is applied to each quantized coefficient and quantized coefficients are received in an order that corresponds to vector selection codes. The coefficients are inversely transformed, resulting in the DFD, which is added to the DF so that a frame becomes displayed. The frame mean then adds before display and storage in the frame buffer, part of the frame is written into the buffer, and motion vectors then generate the next DF. As a reminder, *DFD* stands for *displaced frame difference* and *DF* represents the *displaced frame*.

VIDEO DECODER

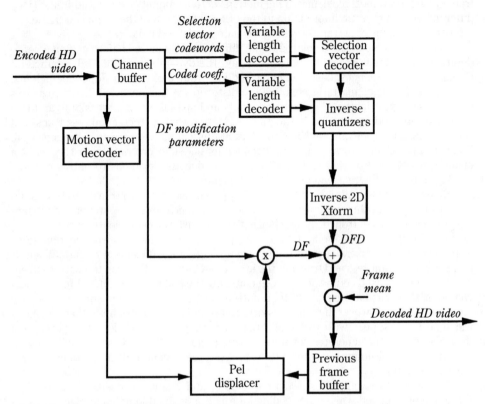

3-24 Video decoder block diagram. Zenith/AT&T.

Granted, some of the foregoing is, indeed, a difficult concept, but it's highly possible that many of the desirable portions of several of the individual systems will amalgamate in the final ATSC and FCC selections—at least that's the way the Federal Communications Commission has been leaning throughout the ATTC testing process. Therefore, more (rather than less) detail has been included so that all possible technical aspects are available for reference or theory of operation.

Zenith has also drawn a suggested block diagram of a studio and simulcast transmitter for those possible HDTV broadcasters, which might prove useful in assessing general aspects of HDTV/NTSC operations. We have no comment other than to say Fig. 3-25 is a starter, and serious TV owners and managers in the terrestrial business might want to study further possibilities.

Advanced Digital Television (ADTV)

The consortium of David Sarnoff Research Center, the National Broadcast Company, North American Philips, and Thomson Consumer Electronics submitted its initial system description to the FCC and others of its all-digital terrestrial broadcast HDTV system on February 27, 1991; and it's primarily from this detailed description that the information is derived.

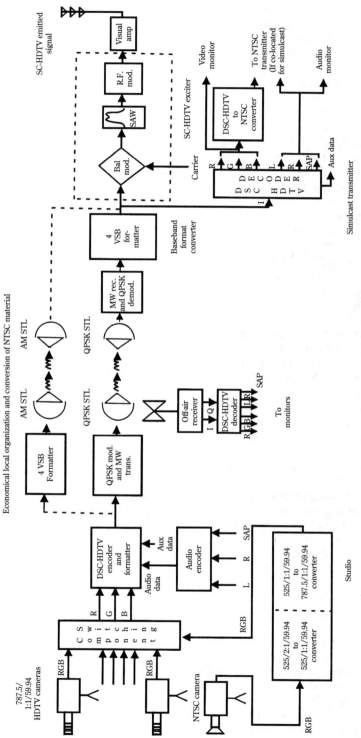

3-25 Zenith's example of suggested simulcast HDTV operations.

Compressed, as usual, within a 6-MHz channel (Fig. 3-26) ADTV claims "significant improvements to proven digital compression and transmission techniques . . ." within three key elements called *MPEG, Prioritized Data Transport (PDT)*, and *QUAM*, which we all have come to know as *Quadrature Amplitude Modulation.*

MPEG++ (Moving Pictures Expert Group) upgrades the standard HDTV approach, including a video data prioritization layer permitting significant video information transmissions with maximum reliability.

PDT is described as a cell relay-based data transport "layer," supporting prioritized video data for "graceful service degradation" under degrading signal conditions, as well as flexibility to carry mixtures of video, audio, auxiliary data, and also accommodate broadband integrated services digital network (ISDN) transmissions.

SS-QUAM furnishes spectral-shaping techniques to standard QUAM to minimize interference—either from or to any-co-channel NTSC broadcasts. ADTV is offered as a 1050 line, 59.94 Hz, and 2:1 interlace, plus the usual 16:9 aspect ratio that is associated with HDTV. It provides better than double NTSC resolution, but it can be adapted to other video formats in the future, according to the Consortium.

Active video has been allocated 1440 horizontal lines × 960 vertical, and chroma, 720 H lines × 480 V. Static and dynamic resolution is assigned 810 lines per picture height, with payload cell sizes of 253 bytes. Total data rate amounts to 21 Mbps, of which video absorbs 14.98, audio 1.02, maximum data 0.04 Mbps, and 23.6% of the total rate consists of overhead.

Area coverage, according to ADTV, is primarily limited by co-channel interference, plus other constraints, such as adjacent and taboo channels, out-of-band problems, ATV/ATV co-channel, as well as economic and other factors that affect ATV transmitted radiated power. FCC planning requires equivalent noise power in a 6-MHz channel as 28.5 dB below TV signal power at sync pulse peaks: a TASO definition. Here, the peak power of a 16-QUAM signal is theoretically 2.5 dB higher than average power, but the average ratio is approximately 4.5 dB, considering transients, according to ADTV engineers.

The study continues that digital interference into NTSC appears as random noise, and the receiving antenna's temperature increases adding dBs of noise. Obviously, any reduction aids ADTV coverage. Fortunately, ADTV is rarely limited by NTSC interference, and no ADTV signal can be received on co-channel NTSC grade-B contour. Otherwise, "the limitation is the ADTV C/N ratio, which depends on antenna pattern, noise figure, and carrier-level statistics," these engineers believe. The foregoing amounts to some of the interesting portions of the Sarnoff, et. al, group report. The remainder will paraphrase much of the system description.

The system description that follows is based completely on information supplied by the consortium and its members with an occasional interpretation for extra clarity. Otherwise, what's here is theirs.

An overall transmit/receive simplified block has been furnished by ADTV showing video/audio/data in and out with receiving simply the inverse (Fig. 3-26) of transmitting. We'll get into more detail of compression, prioritization, transport, and modem actions as the explanation unfolds because simple playback is not always identical or desirable. However, each entity will be explained in order for best understanding and technical outline.

Compression encoder/decoder is spelled out in detail in Fig. 3-27—a considerable difference from a simple block diagram. These are the video compression MPEG++ algorithm electronics, which include motion estimation, motion-compensated predictive coding, adaptive DCT quantization, and variable-length coding and decoding (VLC/VLD). Picture frames are generated as intra-frames (I), predicted (P) frames, and bidirectional B frames. I frames are independent, P frames result from motion-compensated predic-

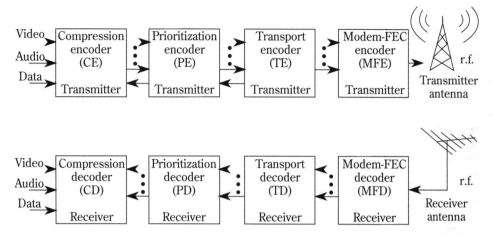

3-26 Overall 6 MHz ADTV system block diagram.

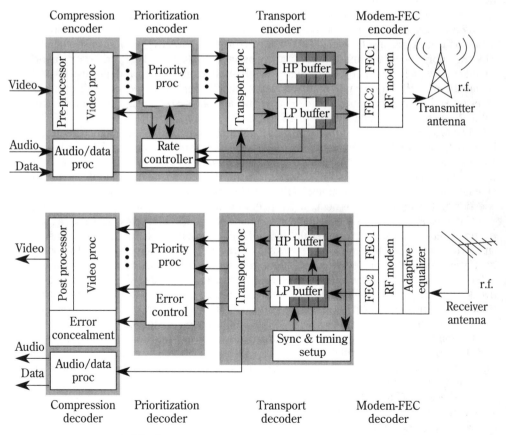

3-27 Typical blocks/modules of each layer in detail.

tive coding using either previous I or P frames, and B frames code by bidirectional motion-compensated predictive coder via adjacent I or P frames, often identified as *anchor frames*. Coded pixel values for I and residual error after prediction for P and B operate by Discrete Cosine Transform (DCT) and are then adaptively quantized. Subsequently, variable length coding (VLC) is applied to quantized DCT coefficients.

In the receiver, video decoding also must supply error recovery and could involve data manipulation during each "layer" of decoding. Next is the *prioritization encoder/decoder (PE/PD)*, which receives video from the compression encoder/decoder and is also governed by the rate controller. Prime function of the priority processor identifies channel error protection for each element of data or general information. Data elements are codewords and video data elements, for instance, include motion information, block size DCT coefficient, quantization parameters, and so forth. It assigns different priorities to each data element according to rule, with assignments executed dynamically so that any changes in channel loads are apparent. Channel loads vary with time because of variable output rates of video data compression.

The rate controller below monitors channel loads and tells an appropriate video encoder module to increase or decrease data channel flow. It will also regulate video compression, according to output data rates, in addition to communicating with rate buffers in the transport encoder for buffer loading checks. The rate controller primarily maintains and controls variable data rate flow into some fixed rate channel, and its rate regulation is termed *buffer feedback control* from the LP buffer to the rate controller.

The Transport Encoder/Decoder (TE/TD), according to the ATRC, has developed a "sophisticated transport format" for diverse error protection over a simulcast channel. The transport processor multiplexes priority-assigned data into "basic transport units" called *cells*, which contain cyclic redundancy error-checking codes, and also use special segmentation with little or no cell-to-cell error mix. The encoder/decoder delivers variable-to-fixed-bit-rate conversion, video data sync, and the system claims to produce a reliable delay, despite variable length encoding.

The Modem-FEC Encoder/Decoder (MFE/MFD) contains an "outer layer" consisting of both Reed-Solomon error-correction coding (FEC) and the modem. Forward error correction affects data bytes prior to carrier modulation. According to priority, different FEC coding operates on the data and data is also interleaved in the FEC module. Bursts of channel bit errors can then respond to Reed-Solomon correction, and during receive, inspection and error corrections occur in the peer modules within the Modem FEC Decoder.

The final stage of the encoder has been named *Spectrally-Shaped Quadrature Amplitude Modulation (SS-QAM)*. Usually, each of these two carriers has a 32-point "constellation" to encode five bits into whatever symbol transmits on the channel. Trellis coding improves QAM performance by reducing bit error rate at certain C/N ratios as it maps bits entering the QAM encoder with 32 constellation points, and each 32-QAM symbol can carry five bits of intelligence. Although the input has a rate of 4.5 bits/symbol, the extra half bit introduces redundancy, which permits a trellis decoder in the receiver to do error correction. A signal comparison between SS-QAM and NTSC is illustrated in Fig. 3-28.

Ordinarily, 32-QAM will offer satisfactory area coverage and picture quality. We're told that 16-QAM is also available for special conditions when C/N ratios at slower data rates are desirable. Other high/standard priority rate conditions, such as symbol rates and bandwidths, remain the same.

The receiver (Fig. 3-29) receives spectrally-shaped QAM at 6 MHz RF and maintains system integrity by substantially doing the inverse of the transmitter, working basically as an asynchronous codeword multiplexer with added operations for data element error tracing. Here, the priority Processor reconstructs priority ranks from incoming data information.

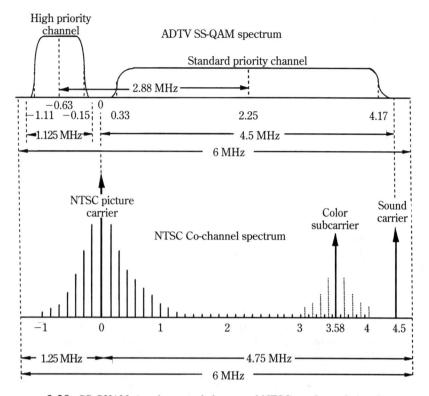

3-28 SS-QUAM signal spectral shape and NTSC co-channel signal.

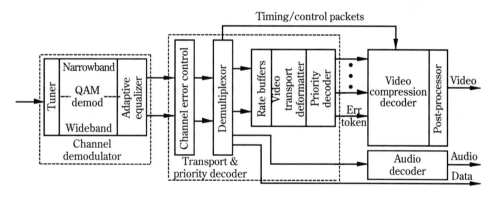

3-29 ADTV receiver block diagram.

Data that's missing or has error indicators passes to processors in the next layer, and the priority processor should flag such errors "to their respective compression Decoder processors," where actions vary according to different types of data elements. After this, channel rate regulation issues from the rate controller, which monitors rate buffer states in the transport encoder. Buffer occupancy determines compression needs for quantizing parameters and the video processor selects for slice or macroblock processing.

Thereafter, the HP/LP allocation is computed, which is actually a target HP:LP rate ratio. An algorithm, according to ADTV engineers, computes the ratio under maximum image-quality constraints, paying close attention to possible channel losses for any given target-rate ratio.

Admittedly, some of the preceding explanation is rather difficult and not given to ready simplification. Some engineers are somewhat more technical in their topic descriptions than others. It would be difficult to second guess good technical prose, where engineering and good descriptive writing (a somewhat rare combination) furnish both fact and excellent electrical insight into complex engineering. Here, we all benefit, although following some of the thought channels isn't always torrid tabloid reading.

Audio transmissions are designed for two stereo pairs, although the prototype under initial test carried only a single pair. A 16-bit digital encoder delivers this audio at a 48-kHz sampling rate using the MUSICAM masking pattern that is adapted for Universal Subband Integrated Coding and Multiplexing. Quantization subbands are varied so that noise is masked and performance is said to equal that of CD. Block companding and frame coding is used with adaptive bit allocation and Layer II coding for additional sophistication, including extra bit allocation. Incoming 1.54 Mbps serial data reduces via MUSICAM to 256 kbits, mapped and coded, with symbols framed and them moved to the output. Each audio frame consists of 1152 samples, mapped in 36 subsamples for 32 equally-spaced subbands, with the 48-kHz sampling frequency delivering 750 Hz of information. Thereafter, there's quantization and bit allocation to the various subbands.

The tuner, of course, receives the RF data stream and delivers it to the receiver by double downconversion, which, in the ADTV version, eliminates the necessity of FCC-imposed UHF taboo restrictions so that all 14 through 69 UHF channels can be used, the first IF being centered at 611 MHz, and the second at the standard 41- to 47-MHz passband. The VHF lower frequencies (beginning at approximately 50 MHz) are processed the same way.

4

The chairman's perspectives

Now that you're aware of most system mechanics, many of the ensuing problems and the endless hours of engineering preparations and their cumulative outcomes, several reports and testimony by former FCC Chairman Richard E. Wiley, who's now Chairman of the FCC Advisory Committee on Advanced Television Service for the entire HDTV program, should add further to this monumental endeavor by both foreign and domestic system offerors. Some of these declarations are necessarily dated, but all add to a general understanding of past, present, and future direction as developments have unfolded before America and the rest of the world. And if anyone still believes we are in the vanguard of HDTV and digital compression, every chapter of this second edition emphatically counters any and all such assumptions because the selected system and its backup are still the only accepted digital compression HDTV electronics in the world. Japan and Europe, especially, will simply have to play catch up, patent royalties and all.

Chairman Wiley's interim and HDTV testimony before Congress are especially pertinent in establishing background and projected efforts as the entire project somewhat painfully ramped up to speed with literally hundreds of working party meetings, intense engineering calculations and computer simulations, new technology introductions, and innumerable reports of individual and collective activities, not to mention the enormous cost to corporations sponsoring the various undertakings.

Was it all worth the prodigious effort? Only John Q. Public and time will tell. Fairly informative results might indicate the trend with some reliability by the year 2000, but probably not before. By then, a fair number of transmitters will be active and receiver/VCR manufacturers should have worked out most bugs for consumer comfort and confidence. The price? Your guess is as good as mine, but probably will double or triple that of the better NTSC comb filter sets of today. An HDTV cheapie is probably not in the cards for many years to come because someone has to pay for wide passband circuits, multi-channel audio, dual tuners, the considerably larger cathode ray tube, and ultra-reliable electronics. Silicon and glass are cheap, but engineering time and manufacturing robotics just doesn't grow on conventional trees. But HDTV might finally force the U.S. back into consumer electronics where it belongs. Amen!

Fortunately, there are already several notable signs: Zenith has its high-contrast, high-brightness, high-tension mask, flat-face tube, and a pair of major efforts by AT&T (a partner in HDTV with Zenith), and Motorola with In Focus Systems, Inc., are planning new flat-panel displays. Apparently not waiting for the Xerox joint program, AT&T, along with a Japanese partner will build active matrix liquid crystal flat plane displays (AMLCO) while Motorola will invest $20,200,000 as a 20% equity investment with In Focus of Tualatin, Oregon, forming a 50-50 partnership to produce passive matrix panels near Portland. Meanwhile, National Semiconductor and Motorola are nailing down an increasing number of patent rights, following the lead of Texas Instruments, all of which should produce some tidy incomes and more U.S.-originated products for commercial/consumer markets. Will flat panels arrive for consumers at the same time as HDTV? With some remarkable break-through anything's possible, but for now screens up to the size of 35 inches will remain glass and three guns during the foreseeable future, possibly for another five or more years.

Granted, some of this factual speculation isn't about to pay off immediately, so let's turn to the thoughts and reports of Mr. Wiley in planned HDTV direction for the U.S. and probably the rest of the world. The first is an Interim Report of the FCC Advisory Committee on Advanced Television Service, and one of which we'll quote directly:

Introduction

"On November 17, 1987, the FCC initiated an Advisory Committee on Advanced Television Service with the following objective: the Committee will advise the Federal Communications Commission on the facts and circumstances regarding advanced television systems for Commission consideration of the technical and public policy issues. In the event that the Commission decides that adoption of some form of advanced broadcast television is in the public interest, the Committee would also recommend policies, standards, and regulations that would facilitate the orderly and timely introduction of advanced television services in the United States.

The substantive work of the Advisory Committee was to be performed by three subcommittees for planning, systems, and implementation. An Interim Report, based primarily on the work of the Planning Subcommittee, was to be presented to the FCC on May 17, 1988. A brief delay, until early June, was required to complete this report.

In his opening address to the Advisory Committee, Chairman Patrick said:

Of pivotal importance to the FCC's efforts is the initial report which you are required to submit to the commission . . . six months from today. I recognize that it is not possible to resolve all, or even most, of the issues surrounding advanced television by that date. I do find it possible within six months, however, to develop recommendations on the fundamental parameters and spectrum requirements of advanced television systems that will facilitate the convergence of government and industry activity.

The work to date, summarized in this Interim Report, has made substantial progress toward the goal set by Chairman Patrick. Essentially, the Report responds to his urging that the Committee "develop recommendations on the fundamental parameters and spectrum requirements of ATV systems that will facilitate the convergence of government and industry activity," and that it "establish general technical parameters that will significantly narrow the scope, and direct the focus, of future research and development efforts . . ." Finally, this Interim Report outlines the work yet to be done, and highlights the most important issues to be considered.

Findings and conclusions

In establishing the Advisory Committee on Advanced Television Service (ATV), the Federal Communications Commission has set in motion an activity that seems certain to change the face of broadcasting in the United States. Indeed, it represents potentially the most significant development in the state of television art since the advent of color.

No one doubts that improvement in the existing NTSC television standard is possible. Proposals to implement such improvement range from simply enhancing the current standard all the way to what has been called *High-Definition Television (HDTV)*, an electronic image with a picture quality equivalent to 35-mm film. In between the existing NTSC standard and HDTV are various concepts of what generically may be referred to as *Enhanced Definition Television (EDTV)*.

This continuum is reflected in numerous proponent systems, from a host of different companies, that have been proposed to date. While nearly all of these systems would provide a wide screen display (with an aspect ratio of perhaps 5.3:3 in place of the current 4:3) and many also would offer digital stereo sound, they vary greatly in the amount of "information" that would be transmitted and in their spectrum requirements. In the VHF and UHF bands, the spectrum proposals fall into three categories: one channel, one and a half channels and two channels. These categories translate into spectrum needs of 6 MHz, 9 MHz, and 12 MHz, respectively. For spectrum above 1 GHz, no similar characterization exists.

Advocates of a 12-MHz approach suggest using two channels in one of two ways:

- an existing NTSC-compatible channel supplemented by a not necessarily contiguous augmentation channel, or
- an existing NTSC compatible channel, unchanged, and a not necessarily contiguous simulcast channel with an incompatible signal.

Both of these methods would be "compatible" in the sense that existing television receivers could continue to be serviced by an NTSC signal.

Based on current bandwidth compression techniques, it appears that full (analog) HDTV will require greater spectrum than 6 MHz. The Advisory Committee believes that efforts should be focused on establishing, at least ultimately, an HDTV standard for terrestrial broadcasting. It seems likely that viewers eventually will demand this level of reception quality and that non-broadcast media (with the capacity for broadband transmission) will offer it. Thus, to be competitive in the video world of tomorrow, terrestrial broadcasters will need the opportunity to deliver HDTV to their audiences. Indeed, the availability of such an opportunity may be essential if broadcasters are to continue to serve as a viable means of providing important local service benefits to the American people.

Some proponents have expressed the view that a 6-MHz EDTV system will suffice. Assuming that full HDTV on a terrestrial basis proves to be feasible, the Advisory Committee believes that EDTV systems could be considered as a temporary solution that might facilitate an orderly and effective transition to high-definition television. During such a transitional period, the Advisory Committee also believes that it is essential that compatibility with existing NTSC receivers be maintained. The nation's citizens have made a very substantial investment in television sets reflecting the current reception standard. While it could be argued that concerns in this area can be exaggerated given the reasonably rapid turnover in television receiver ownership, suffice it to say that no improvement in the state of the art should be permitted to obsolete such an investment overnight.

As previously indicated, compatibility may be achieved through one-channel systems or, in multichannel arrays, by either augmenting NTSC signals with high-definitional information or by simulcasting an NTSC channel with a non-compatible HDTV signal. One advantage to the latter, it should be noted, is that at some point in the future—after the NTSC standard and NTSC-equipped receivers are retired—part of the spectrum being utilized might be reemployed for other uses. However, such a transition from NTSC could be lengthy.

On the basis of preliminary engineering studies, the Advisory Committee believes that sufficient spectrum capacity in the current TV allocations might be available to allow all existing stations to provide ATV through either an augmentation or simulcast approach. However, this view is predicated on two assumptions: an elimination of the present UHF channel separation requirements ("taboos") and the establishment of power, co-channel and adjacent channel interference protection requirements that are substantially less than those demanded in the current NTSC system.

Without question, more detailed spectrum analysis (as described in the report of Working Party 3 of the Planning Subcommittee . . . and summarized herein) is required. Further investigations that affect the accuracy of the above two assumptions obviously also would impact the Advisory Committee's conclusions concerning spectrum availability. If the assumptions do not prove accurate, additional spectrum capacity outside of the existing television allocations may have to be considered.

For this reason, the Committee believes that a very high priority should be assigned to continuing spectrum analysis. During the pendency of this work, it is the Committee's view that the FCC should not reallocate UHF spectrum to other uses. Meanwhile, proponents should be able to develop their systems further so that they can be tested against the co-channel and adjacent-channel interference and spacing criteria that will emerge from the ongoing spectrum analysis efforts.

While such activity proceeds, hopefully as rapidly as possible, the Advisory Committee believes that no attempt should be made to retard the introduction of advanced television systems over non-broadcast media. Thus, although every video medium would be free to develop enhanced forms of delivery, the Committee believes that expeditious consideration should be given to the achievement of effective and inexpensive ATV interfaces between broadcast and non-broadcast media. The Committee notes that this objective may be achieved in ways other than requiring strict compatibility among various transmission media (e.g., the development of a so-called "open architecture" television receiver, which might be capable of accommodating different reception standards). The Advisory Committee is continuing to examine options and alternatives in this important area, including the costs and benefits thereof, as well as the appropriate roles of government and industry in implementing various compatibility proposals.

Advanced (including Enhanced and High-Definition) Television represents the potential to add greatly to the quality of television reception in this country and, thus, to consumer benefit and enjoyment. However, these advancements also represent an economic opportunity of almost unparalleled proportions. Given the importance of the economic stakes involved, it is appropriate for the Advisory Committee to consider the possibilities for U.S. involvement in this overall development. For this reason, two special advisory groups to the planning subcommittee were created: one involving "Creative Issues" (encompassing the important software market in which the United States is currently a world leader) and one involving "consumer/trade issues."

The Advisory Committee believes that the important work initiated by these groups should continue and be expanded. Specifically, the diverse opportunities available to

American industry in this area (ranging from creative activities, proponent system development, receiver manufacture, receiver assembly, component manufacture, etc.) all should be carefully considered by both the public and private sectors. The United States undoubtedly will be the world's largest market for future advancements in television reception. The Advisory Committee is strongly of the view that this nation also should play a significant role in the creative, industrial and employment elements of this entire scenario.

In all, the Advisory Committee believes that the Planning Subcommittee (under the able leadership of Chairman Joseph A. Flaherty and utilizing the earnest efforts of over 175 individuals from a host of different private sector organizations) has fulfilled its initial assignment to lay out a plan for the Committee's future work. Specifically, the Planning Subcommittee has examined the attributes of Advanced Television systems and begun consideration of the tests required to evaluate such systems, the spectrum that will be required to accommodate them, the interfaces that may be necessary between terrestrial broadcasting and other electronic media, the economic factors involved and, perhaps most importantly, the subjective analyses of how consumers may respond to various proposed ATV systems. In addition, as noted, the Subcommittee also has begun the exploration of other, highly significant issues attendant to this development (e.g., creative, consumer and trade matters, etc.).

The process involved has been directed not to making public policy determinations that belong properly to government officials, but, instead, to laying out a blueprint for the rest of this Advisory Committee's lifespan and, more importantly, for the overall analysis of advanced television systems which is ongoing in both the public and private sectors. In so doing, the Committee hopes that it has been responsive to FCC Chairman Patrick's challenge to define ATV system parameters, to note various trade-offs that may be involved, and to direct the focus of future research and development efforts.

With this Interim Report, the Advisory Committee now closes the initial planning phase of its activity and turns its attention primarily to systems and implementation issues. In making this transition, the Committee wishes to express appreciation to the FCC for all of the support, cooperation and encouragement that it has received. We look forward to the next year and a half with optimism and with the profound hope that the Committee can make a positive contribution to the introduction of Advanced Television Systems in this country.

Summary of activities of working parties and advisory groups

As indicated, substantive background work for this interim report was essentially the responsibility of the Planning Subcommittee. This subcommittee is charged with an overall objective of "plan[ning] the attributes of advanced television service in the United States." The scope of its activity includes:

(a) defining the desirable characteristics of advanced television service (e.g., picture quality, population served, costs to broadcasters, consumers, and manufacturers; and relationships to non-broadcast services) and

(b) reviewing the technical planning factors for the existing television service and recommending planning factors for advanced television service (e.g., consideration of factors, such as coverage area, quality of service, frequency reuse criteria, receiver quality, and spectrum allocations).

Working parties

To perform this work, the Planning Subcommittee organized six working parties and two advisory groups. These entities were instructed to gather members with appropriate expertise and interests, to formulate precise objectives and to prepare draft reports that would form the basis of the Advisory Committee's interim report to the FCC. Altogether, some 175 people have contributed to this effort.

The reports of each of the planning subcommittee's working parties and advisory groups are summarized below (together with comments, where appropriate, by the Advisory Committee). Readers are encouraged to review their complete reports for a fuller appreciation of the work that has been performed.

Working Party 1: ATV attributes

Working Party 1 (WP-1) was assigned the task of defining the attributes that characterize all ATV systems and that will permit a comparison of proposed systems.

The Working Party prepared a comprehensive list of 160 attributes. These were then organized into a matrix under the following categories: video, audio, ancillary signals, alternative distribution media, and consumer equipment. The important attributes, and their parameters for each proponent system, can be displayed in chart form (utilizing, as reference points, NTSC at the low end and the 1125/60 studio production standard at the high end); for example:

Table 4-1.

			Systems			HDTV Studio Stand.
Attribute	**NTSC**	**1**	**2**	**. . .**		**1125/60**
Compatibility with NTSC receiver						
Number of channels required						
Channel bandwidth						
Need for contiguous channels						
Display size						
Aspect ratio						
Vertical resolution						
Horizontal resolution						
Dynamic resolution						

Although members of WP-1 expressed reservations about including the 1125/60 studio production standard as a reference point, the Advisory Committee believes that this standard provides a useful yardstick for evaluating the picture quality that the various proponent systems promise. The Advisory Committee recommends that the matrix be filled out both with analytical estimations of the attributes for each proposed system and with measured results from the test programs. Because some of the attributes can only be evaluated by subjective assessment, the methodology developed by Working Party 6 should be used and a subjective rating included in the matrix.

Working Party 2: ATV testing and evaluation specifications

WP-2 was asked to establish specifications for the testing and evaluation of proposed ATV systems and to develop a draft schedule for the actual testing and evaluation to be performed by the Systems Subcommittee.

The Working Party determined that three types of testing are needed to provide a valid comparison of ATV systems:

(a) *Propagation testing* These tests should permit characterization of the transmission channel paths and should include a pair consisting of two non-contiguous 6-MHz UHF channels, two contiguous UHF channels, and a pair made up of one UHF channel, and one VHF channel. Propagation in the 2- and 12-GHz bands should also be investigated.

(b) *Laboratory testing* Tests in the laboratory would permit comparison of the performance of proponent systems under baseband and modulated RF conditions.

(c) *Over-the-air testing* Tests of proponent systems should be conducted in the following spectrum ranges: low- and high-band VHF, UHF, 2.5 GHz, and 12 GHz.

A list of appropriate tests has been prepared for proponent systems, based upon the attributes of ATV systems developed by WP-1. In addition, a start has been made in defining the methodology of such tests, although more work must be done in this area.

The Advanced Television Systems Committee (ATSC) has established a specialist group that has been engaged in planning and executing propagation tests with the same objectives as the FCC Advisory Committee. The Working Party reviewed a draft plan of this group. If the plan is adopted by ATSC, the Working Party would favor its acceptance by the Advisory Committee. The Working Party also reviewed the requirements for the laboratory and over-the-air tests and developed a test plan and a test procedure to permit completion of the attribute matrix for each candidate ATV system.

ATSC propagation tests are scheduled for completion by the end of 1988. The Working Party estimates that laboratory testing will require approximately one month for each candidate system. To meet the goals of the Advisory Committee, the laboratory testing should start by the fall of 1988. Moreover, the goals of the Advisory Committee require that the over-the-air tests start during the first quarter of 1989. Obviously, the completion of the test program will depend on the availability of systems to be tested, the number of systems submitted for testing, and the logistics of obtaining laboratory and field test sites.

While WP-2 has prepared a methodology and test plan for proponent ATV systems, it emphasizes that proponents must provide all the equipment to encode the high-definition input video and audio signals, to process the signal in a format that is suitable for transmission, to decode the received signal and to process it to interface with an HDTV display unit.

Working Party 3: spectrum utilization and alternatives

WP-3 was assigned the task of investigating the availability of spectrum for broadcast ATV. If Advanced Television is to live up to its promise in the broadcast field, it will be expected to provide over-the-air transmission of a much greater amount of information than is broadcast by today's television stations. It is axiomatic that the transmission of such a large amount of information will require either a higher density of packing of the information (data compression), or more spectrum, or both.

As its first step in dealing with this problem, WP-3 explored how much spectrum could be made available to ATV and the relative attractiveness of various spectrum alternatives. Thus, the Working Party examined existing UHF/VHF television allocations and also made an initial effort to identify other potentially available spectrum (giving due consideration to other services that might be affected by the introduction of ATV).

WP-3 made significant progress in developing a spectrum allocation structure that will permit the identification of ATV system possibilities that can work within the existing terrestrial system. With the help of FCC and NTIA staffs, a series of analytical tools were developed for determining the amount of additional UHF/VHF-TV spectrum that might be available under different conditions. Using a data base of existing TV assignments, a computer analysis estimated the number of stations that could be accommodated under the various scenarios. This evaluation assumed that television receiver-related interference taboos could be ignored, except for co-channel and adjacent channel constraints. The assumption is grounded on the presumption that the signal format of a new ATV transmission/reception system could be designed to avoid causing interference to (or receiving interference from) the existing NTSC system.

Although time limitations restricted the scope of the computer study, two conclusions were reached:

(a) the greatest likelihood of finding additional spectrum is when it is not necessarily contiguous to an existing station channel; and

(b) there are combinations of co-channel and adjacent-channel interference performance and protection criteria that might allow the utilization of additional spectrum for all existing stations to provide ATV systems.

The initial study of WP-3 is not yet in a condition to be used to develop final conclusions. The further work that needs to be done includes:

(a) extension of the software by NTIA/FCC;

(b) extension of the analysis to include the entire U.S., particularly major markets, where spectrum congestion problems are the worst, plus Canada and Mexico;

(c) analysis of adjacent-channel protection;

(d) examination of additional scenarios involving 3- and 6-MHz non-contiguous spectrum; and

(e) determination of the effect of reduced-coverage areas for all of the prior analyses;

(f) consideration of scenarios with appropriate protection ratios that provide for land mobile radio service;

(g) studies to provide technical support for the assumptions made in the spectrum scenarios, regarding taboos and interference protection.

WP-3 also studied preliminary spectrum allocations above 1 GHz. It appears that there is no large amount of spectrum that is "free and clear" in the range of 1 to 13 GHz. However, preliminary conclusions suggest that it may be feasible to accommodate an ATV system on a shared basis in certain parts of this frequency range. Finally, in looking at other services that might be affected by the implementation of a terrestrial ATV service, the group documented a catalog of possible areas of impact.

Working Party 4: alternative media technology and broadcast interface

WP-4 faced the task of developing a point of reference or baseline for designers of broadcast ATV systems so that a user-friendly interface would be achieved whenever broadcast signals interface with alternative distribution media. The Working Party considered the following distribution technologies and the appropriate interface that they should have with a broadcast ATV signal: satellite (FSS and BSS), fiberoptics, cable television, microwave (AML, FM, MDS, MMDS), VCR, and video disc.

On the following page (Fig. 4-1), the interfaces required between all of the above distribution media and a consumer's home display unit are shown in the form of a flow diagram.

Each of these technologies should deliver to the customer the highest quality signal based on optimizing both prudent business and technical factors. Thus, proponents of each technology should be free to determine what is the best transmission format for its customer base. However, WP-4 concluded that an appropriate interface should be established between ATV systems and each distribution media technology (because much programming in the future will be channeled from ATV service to an alternative distribution media).

Within the ATV feeder and distribution system environment, an "interconnection architecture" that standardizes the level of interface is required. By creating such a standardized interconnection architecture, the lowest common denominator signal standard (i.e., RGB with digital audio) would be used to join two dissimilar transmission technologies while a higher level standard would link two similar technologies. To the same effect, a "consumer electronics interconnection" standard for the home could be created to support a wide variety of connection scenarios.

Working Party 5: economic factors and market penetration

The objectives of the WP-5 were:

(a) to review the factors affecting the acceptance of ATV by consumers and, hence, the market penetration of ATV;

(b) to consider the costs and benefits to consumers of adopting ATV systems;

(c) to consider the macroeconomic implications of policies for ATV and their impact on the U.S. economy; and

(d) to determine how economic analysis and economic research could help in the formulation of a policy for ATV.

In considering the likely rate of penetration of ATV systems, WP-5 determined that the historical pattern of color television's adoption is a poor model because the penetration of color TV was stalled for several years by a lack of available color programming. By contrast, for ATV, a wealth of high-definition programming exists in the form of 35-mm film. While the matter is debatable, more suitable models for projecting the penetration rate of ATV might include the VCR and the compact disc player, both of which achieved at least a one percent penetration level in five years or less.

Although WP-5 recognized that ATV should not be introduced so as to disenfranchise existing NTSC receivers, it expressed the view that the oft-stated concern over the cost of consumer investment in television sets could be overstated. Specifically, the working party noted that the average consumer buys a new receiver every 4 to 5 years and suggested that, with the advent of ATV, the $6.6 billion spent annually on television receivers (with generally quite marginal improvements in technical quality) will be simply redirected in part to the purchase of new advanced systems. However, notwithstanding these observations, the Advisory Committee cannot overlook the investment that many consumers have in sets that will remain in use for more than 10 years. The size of this investment is clearly an important factor that must be considered in any future ATV deliberations.

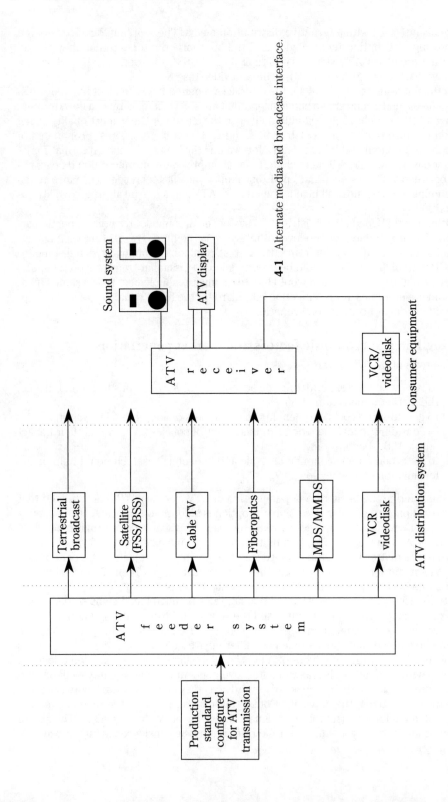

4-1 Alternate media and broadcast interface.

In considering the economics of the introduction of ATV service, WP-5 noted that a high proportion of the cost of consumer equipment is caused by the cost of the display unit. Accordingly, it was agreed that steps should be taken to ensure that the display unit itself would be common to all ATV distribution media (i.e., VCR, cable, terrestrial broadcast, etc.). To this end, the display unit should be equipped with video connections for either basic red, green, and blue (RGB) signals or standard chrominance/luminance component signals. Such an approach would provide a clear economic benefit to the consumer and would reduce the economic costs associated with the possible future coexistence of various ATV standards for different distribution media.

Today, the U.S. consumer electronic marketplace is heavily dependent on imports: net imports of television receivers and VCRs contributed over $6 billion to the U.S. trade deficit in 1987. However, changes in manufacturing technology, improvements in domestic productivity, and a low dollar exchange rate give rise to the possibility of a "second chance" for U.S. manufacturers in the ATV era. Some policies for the introduction of consumer ATV will be more conducive to the domestic production of ATV receivers and other ATV related products than others. These issues should be considered in the future work of the Advisory Committee.

Working Party 6: subjective assessment of ATV systems

WP-6 undertook to recommend test methods to be used in the subjective assessment of the proposed ATV distribution systems, and to propose guidelines for the production of subjective test material to be used as stimuli.

There were two distinct disciplines represented by members of WP-6: social scientists (market research and audience measurement experts) and psychophysicists (experimental and sensory psychology experts). Traditionally, psychophysical test methods have been used in subjective picture quality assessments. The addition of social scientists offers the potential to address different kinds of issues. For example, questions such as the perceived value of ATV to the consumer and what implications the differences among ATV systems might have for consumer behavior (i.e., willingness to pay) can be investigated, in addition to the usual task of evaluating picture quality.

Psychophysicists and engineers have developed considerable background in the area of subjective assessment, based on the characteristics of the human visual system. Extensive testing of this type has been done on current television systems and the ITU's CCIR has documented the recommended methodology. WP-6 agreed to a test methodology by relying on current studies in the CCIR committees. Based on this work, the Working Party was able to recommend test procedures to be followed for evaluating the improved performance parameters of ATV.

The subjective assessment of each proponent ATV system, when available, will follow the completion of objective hardware testing in the laboratory. The importance of such testing cannot be over-emphasized. Only through such means can comparative quality grades be assigned to each ATV system and, in turn, related to spectrum requirements and overall economics.

Specifically, the Working Party concluded that test methodology should be based on pair comparisons. A set of viewing conditions has been established that follows closely the principles laid out in CCIR Recommendation 500. These conditions, stated in the Working Party's report, include luminances, illuminance, viewing ratios, and the actual set up of the viewing displays.

The issue of test material was considered to be of such complexity that a separate specialist group was established to prepare a specification for nontechnical observers. This examination involves a wide range of subjective considerations, which, in addition to types of programming, include such matters as transfer motion and cropping. The specialist group report sets forth the recommended list of materials for use in subjective assessments of ATV. The group's basic conclusion is that all systems should be tested with a range of test material (e.g., 1125/60 HDTV and 525/59.94 component digital). It is important that there also be a large amount of source material in order to provide a wide range of comparisons under differing conditions and that all proponent systems be tested with the same material.

Advisory Group 1: creative issues

Advisory Group 1 (AG-1) set out to assess and report on the views of the creative community in relationship to the development and implementation of a terrestrial ATV transmission system in the United States. The membership of AG-1 was drawn from a broad spectrum of representatives of the creative community, included producers, directors, writers, major studios, and industrial relations representatives.

AG-1 has produced a report that makes the following points:

(a) the selected ATV transmission system should reproduce the highest quality television image and sound possible, while maintaining the artistic integrity of the creator's works;

(b) programs now in distribution should also be transmissible over a new TV system while existing NTSC sets should be able to receive transmissions during the transition period to full ATV service;

(c) the ATV system should provide an image quality equal to that of 35-mm film with no fewer than 1000 active lines resolution;

(d) the ATV system should reproduce sound quality equal to that available on compact discs;

(e) the ATV system should enable creators to preserve the artistic integrity of works originated in other formats. Specifically, programs should be transmitted in the aspect ratio in which they were originally produced; and

(f) the ATV system should be backward compatible so that existing NTSC sets can receive programs, but the system should also possess enough technical headroom to adapt readily to advancing technology.

Advisory Group 2: consumer/trade issues

In considering consumer issues, AG-2 devoted special attention to the importance of retaining the diversity of programming and local programming. AG-2 concluded that if ATV service would degrade NTSC picture quality, such programming would be difficult to justify. Additionally, consumer interests might suffer if terrestrial broadcasting of ATV lags substantially behind HDTV service on VCRs or cable.

AG-2 concluded that:

(a) the merits of the FCC's moving expeditiously to make spectrum available for ATV service are that early spectrum allocations could allow proponents to accelerate their development efforts and to optimize their systems for given bandwidth;

(b) the FCC should examine potential social benefits of ATV against the other possible uses of the same spectrum; and

(c) the choice of transmission standard should not be made until many of the technical issues have been resolved and the FCC has had the opportunity to consider the choice between single-and-multiple-standard receivers.

However, while acknowledging these considerations, the Advisory Committee is concerned that undue delay in making the spectrum allocation might:

(a) seriously disadvantage terrestrial broadcasters while non-broadcast media introduce ATV service; and

(b) encourage a multiplicity of incompatible ATV formats, counter to the interests of consumers and manufacturers.

In its study of trade issues, the AG-2 group observed that TV set manufacture in the U.S. is limited to the output of a single major American company (this is no longer true because such receivers are now manufactured and tested in Mexico) and, although many TV receivers are assembled in the U.S., most of the components are imported from offshore sources. Nevertheless, the group believed that an opportunity might exist to re-establish domestic manufacturing of receivers for ATV service.

If the development of ATV is successful, it could provide the stimulus for a revival of the U.S. consumer electronics industry, which, unlike other U.S. electronics industries, has suffered lagging output and declining employment. Given the recent decline in the value of the dollar, U.S. producers might enjoy a large share of ATV-related businesses, including encoding and decoding equipment, semiconductors, displays, and receivers.

Future priorities

While the Working Party and Advisory Group reports represent a major contribution toward the initiation of terrestrial broadcast HDTV, more remains to be accomplished. This remaining work has been described in the reports and general time periods have been suggested. The highest priority tasks are to complete the assessment of spectrum options and to develop an assignment plan. This work needs to be done while the candidate ATV systems are being defined with more precision in order to assess their ability to be integrated into the existing terrestrial television environment. The Advisory Committee and the FCC should strive to complete this effort within the next year.

As documented in the report of WP-3, such an objective requires additional analysis using the tools being developed by FCC and NTIA staffs, which include:

- similar studies to those already completed, but covering the entire United States, and taking account Canada and Mexico;
- determination of the availability of additional 3-MHz and 6-MHz channels when they are non-adjacent; and
- the effect of reduced coverage areas for the previously described situations.

If these activities are to be carried out effectively, it will be imperative to have the further support of the NTIA and FCC in extending the development of their software. Of equal importance with respect to future activity is to define, focus and accelerate the work of the attributes, testing, and subjective assessment working parties.

While the bulk of the Advisory Committee work will now shift to the Systems and Implementation Subcommittees, the Planning Subcommittee will continue to be involved in a number of important efforts. In addition to top-priority spectrum studies already mentioned, certain other activities of the Planning Subcommittee are viewed as ongoing efforts that should be continued under its leadership. In particular, as indicated, the Advisory Groups on Creative Issues and Consumer/Trade Issues will carry on their analysis of the possibilities for U.S. involvement in the manufacturing of advanced television equipment. In addition, the Working Party on Alternate Media Technology and Broadcast Interface should continue its important investigations.

The two-year life span of the Advisory Committee represents the maximum term allowed under the Federal Advisory Committee Act. However, depending on future developments and the FCC's desires, it might be appropriate to consider at some future point an extension of this term.

Congressional testimony

The second notable pronouncement by Mr. Wiley was testimony before the House Telecommunications and Finance Subcommittee on Advanced Television Technologies, which follows:

"Mr. Chairman, Members of the Subcommittee:

I appreciate the opportunity to testify today on the subject of High Definition Television (or HDTV). As you know, I am serving as Chairman of the FCC's Advisory Committee on Advanced Television Service, a committee comprised of chief executives of leading broadcast, cable, programming, and receiver manufacturing companies. To date, some 175 members of various private sector entities have contributed in some way to our efforts. In June, the Advisory Committee unanimously adopted an Interim Report to the Commission.

For the benefit of the subcommittee, I would like to briefly summarize several of our most important findings and conclusions and also discuss the committee's future work plans. In the process, I want to add a few personal views of my own.

In establishing its Advisory Committee, the FCC has initiated an activity that will affect profoundly broadcast and other video services in this country. I disagree with those who would downplay the importance of this development. In my judgment, HDTV represents potentially the most significant advance in the state of the television art since the advent of color. With the introduction of larger and wider screens in the future, it is my opinion that the differences between HDTV (which could be described as the video equivalent to 35-mm film) and our current standard (NTSC) television will become more and more pronounced. As a result, I believe that the American public increasingly will want to receive this new service.

Under these circumstances, the Advisory Committee believes that its efforts and those of the FCC should be focused on establishing, at least ultimately, an HDTV standard for terrestrial broadcasting. As indicated, it seems likely that viewers eventually will demand this level of reception quality and, as a result, non-broadcast media (with the capacity for broadband transmission) will attempt to offer it. Thus, to be competitive in the video world of tomorrow, broadcasters will need the opportunity to deliver HDTV to their audiences if they are to continue to serve as an effective outlet for local service to the public. Of course, whether full HDTV (as opposed to some kind of enhancement of the current standard) will be required must be determined by the marketplace. Accordingly, our Committee did not foreclose the possibility that so-called enhanced-definition television (EDTV), as it might evolve toward HDTV, may offer the public an acceptable, competitive alternative.

Full HDTV probably will require greater spectrum (6 MHz only with the advantage of digital compression) than the 6 MHz currently allocated for each terrestrial television channel. Thus, a second augmentation channel (with 3 or 6 additional MHz) may be required. Alternatively, some proponents have suggested a so-called 'simulcast' approach by which TV stations would continue to broadcast their current NTSC signal on one channel and a new HDTV signal on another channel (now fact, not speculation).

On the basis of very preliminary engineering studies, the Advisory Committee believes that there might be sufficient spectrum capacity in the current TV allocations to permit all existing stations to provide advanced television service through either an augmentation or simulcast approach. However, this belief is premised on an elimination of the present UHF channel-separation requirements (or 'taboos'), and the implementation of interference-protection requirements that are substantially less than those required in the current NTSC system.

Clearly, more detailed spectrum analysis is required and we and the Commission are proceeding in this direction as rapidly as possible. In the meantime, it is the committee's view that the FCC should not reallocate UHF spectrum to other uses. At the same time, we also believe that non-broadcast media should be permitted to develop their own forms of enhanced delivery, as they deem appropriate and as their audiences may demand. However, because the public undoubtedly will want to see HDTV programming via both broadcast and non-broadcast outlets, the Advisory Committee recommends that efforts be made to develop effective and inexpensive advanced television interfaces between various media—perhaps through converter devices, protocol conversions, or, possibly, a so-called 'open architecture' television receiver that might be able to accommodate different reception standards.

As enhanced forms of video delivery are introduced into the marketplace, our committee is strongly of the view that compatibility must be maintained with the nation's existing universe of NTSC television sets. The American public has made a very significant investment in receivers that use the current standard (perhaps as much as $100 billion). The committee believes that no technical improvement in the video medium can be permitted to obsolete overnight this sunk investment.

A new standard

I mentioned earlier the question of establishing a new standard for terrestrial television reception. Obviously, standard setting is a fine and sometimes controversial art. It is always difficult to decide if, and when, such a determination should be made. To act too soon, before a clear understanding of all relevant factors is possible, could result in a premature freezing of a developing technology. To act too late (or not to act at all) might retard the implementation of a new service into the marketplace (as, speaking personally, I think was the case with AM stereo). I believe that these considerations should be kept in mind as the FCC (and our Committee) continues to examine the appropriateness of a new standard, or family of standards encompassing different video media, during the next year or two.

In this connection, our committee intends to work closely with the Advanced Television Systems Committee (ATSC), and with the technology centers recently established by both the broadcast and cable industries, to test the different advanced television systems that have been proposed to date. We need to know much more about these systems and about what works and what does not in terms of spectrum, interference and related considerations. Accordingly, the Advisory Committee will be working with the FCC to design appropriate criteria that can be utilized by various private sector organizations in carrying out essential testing of the systems and examining various technical assumptions that have been suggested in this complex area. Suffice it to say that increased understanding and experience is required before the selection of any kind of advanced television standard, or standards, would be appropriate.

Finally, let me turn to an issue that I personally consider to be highly significant: this nation's involvement in the development and implementation of advanced television systems. Without question, HDTV will enhance the quality of television reception and, thus, add greatly to consumer enjoyment and benefit. But this new service also represents a tremendous economic opportunity for U.S. corporations and for American workers. We are talking about, perhaps, a $40 billion industry per year. Given this potential, my own conviction is that we should not be satisfied with simply being a passive recipient of some other country's HDTV format, programming, or video receivers and associated equipment.

Instead, I would recommend (and the Advisory Committee's Interim Report concurs) that careful consideration should be given by our government and by relevant private sector concerns to American participation in this market—specifically, to what is important, what is possible, and what is realistic. For example, does it matter, economically, whether a U.S.-oriented proponent system is selected as a standard for HDTV, and would such a system be as technically advanced as others? What about equipment manufacture? While I am skeptical that we can become a major factor in TV set manufacturing once again (given the low margins of that business and other factors), there could well be attractive possibilities in the areas of associated equipment, componentry, and receiver assembly—all of which could entail U.S. technology, U.S. jobs, U.S. dollars. Finally, we should not forget the software market. This country is far and away the world's leader in video programming, and economic opportunities for our creative community could be plentiful in the HDTV arena.

In any case, it must be recognized that the U.S. is the world's largest television market and, without doubt, will continue to occupy that position in the HDTV world of the future. With this fact in mind, it seems to me that our citizens should also benefit from the industrial, creative, and employment potential of this exciting new development.

Mr. Chairman, our Advisory Committee has completed only the first quarter of its assigned life span of two years. We look forward to working with the FCC and, indeed, with the Congress as our engineering, economic, and consumer analyses continue. Thank you once again for allowing me to appear before you today and, as an American citizen, thank you for your interest in this important area."

Planning translates into action

Now thoughtful words have turned into highly disciplined actions and committees have generally fulfilled their established objectives.

Laboratory, expert observer, and "casual" observer and cable examinations are relatively complete; the next step requiring recording the actual tests themselves, both in the U.S. and Canada. So, the next chapter offers a rather detailed account of the various procedures, limited by last-minute changes for digital approaches, but including most analog steps and a healthy description of the "test bed" of the Advanced Television Test Center located in Alexandria, VA, where your author did, indeed, participate as an expert observer in several sessions on more than one equipment.

5

The all-powerful FCC
renders decisions

The Federal Communications Commision in Washington inevitably establishes the conduct of communications, sets rules throughout the United States and, unless challenged in the courts or by Congress, becomes the law of the Land following publication in the *Federal Register*.

In following the preceding chapter, therefore, some of the objectives and proposals enunciated by Chairman Wiley of ATS, plus the FCC's own findings in both related and unrelated circumstances are printed to firmly establish the boundaries and directions high-definition television will take. To some, this slightly edited text might be rather dry reading, but to the engineering community, it's the law of the land and cannot be defied without appropriate penalties.

In printing this material, we obviously cannot include some of the appendices, nor all the various comments. But in the *Second Report and Order plus a Further Notice of Proposed Rule Making* released May 8, 1992, a point will be made of the 15-year translation date from NTSC to HDTV, including the abolition of NTSC, as well as assignments, network rules, market projections, broadcasting, etc. All of which is very ably introduced by the statement of Commissioner Ervin S. Duggan, dtd. April 9, 1992. This will be followed by a *Second Notice of Proposed Rule Making* dtd. August 14, 1992. The final report and selection of the fortunate system comes, of course, during 1994, shortly following publication of this book. By having the ensuing information, however, you will understand many of the fundamentals of this and/or these decisions and be substantially informed of the entire HDTV process. A glossary of terms completes the chapter. So let's begin with Mr. Duggan's interpretative statement and continue from there.

Statement of commissioner Ervin S. Duggan

In the *Matter of Advanced Television Systems and Their Impact Upon the Existing Television Broadcast Service* (MM Docket No. 87-268) seventeen days ago, my colleagues and I travelled to the Capitol to see the first live, over-the-air and cable-delivered glimpse of HDTV. Today, we take another significant step toward the actual inauguration of HDTV in the United States beginning in this decade. With these events, we establish Spring 1992 as the time when high-definition television moved out of the realm of theory and into the here and now.

Today, we begin to outline a vision for the transition to HDTV broadcasting. In June, we will propose a Table of Channel Allotments for HDTV spectrum. Next year, we will select the standard for this new television system. These decisions are not just significant: they are fateful. We are, in essence, decreeing the creation of a whole new broadcast television industry and the shutting down of the old one. We do not do so lightly. I believe all of us realize that the move from conventional to advanced television will be expensive, difficult, and time-consuming; that full conversion to advanced television broadcasting is likely to take more than a decade.

With all those complexities and difficulties fully in mind, we nevertheless express great confidence today: confidence that a firm set of rules and principles can be devised to keep the process orderly. Confidence that we can establish a rational process with a beginning, a middle, and an end.

The first principle we establish today is that the spectrum we grant for HDTV is for a conversion process; it is not a giveaway. When that process is complete, television licensees will keep a "conversion channel" of 6 MHz and—let us make no mistake about it—they will surrender a "reversion channel" to the public domain. The very labels we attach to the process—"conversion" channel and "reversion" channel—will serve as a constant reminder that the FCC's grant of spectrum for HDTV is not only additional: it is conditional and transitional. The spectrum we will eventually assign for advanced television developments, in short, has a strong tether attached to it; squatter's rights on the second channel are not what this commission has in mind.

A second principle is that this conversion process hinges upon a firm cutover date for the end of old-style broadcast TV and the advent of full advanced television. We must adopt a simulcasting approach that moves licensees as quickly as possible to full high-definition transmission. In the item we vote today, we express clear ideas about that cutover date and the simulcasting policy we prefer. Our intention is to make final decisions on these issues as soon as possible.

We have not come to this moment by magic, or by accident. Fortunately, we have been able to rely upon the talents of some of the best and brightest persons from the television industry on the Advisory Committee on Advanced Television Service. We owe a debt of gratitude to every one of those persons for the work they have done and will continue to do. We owe a special debt to a remarkable figure in the world of communications: Chairman Richard E. Wiley. We owe a great deal, finally, to the leadership of FCC Chairman Al Sikes. His tireless efforts to move advanced television from the drawing board to the laboratory and, eventually, into American homes and the global marketplace deserves to be remembered and honored years from now.

Let me sound, finally, a note of warning, and a summons. Until today, the development of policies for advanced television in the United States has been largely in the hands of elites: the Advisory Committee; trade associations; large broadcast corporations; and eminent engineers and lawyers. They have brought HDTV from the wild blue yonder closer to solid earth. Now it is time to move the debate from inside the Beltway to the grass roots. Now it is time for the dialogue to expand: to embrace the greatest possible number of individual television broadcasters. The burden of introducing HDTV, after all, will largely be theirs to bear—and the public interest in an orderly transition to advanced television is theirs to protect. If there are television broadcasters at the grass roots who have not yet focused fully on the implications for them of HDTV—the costs and the difficulties, and also the opportunities—now is the time for them to get involved.

Second report introduction

This *Second Report and Order/Further Notice of Proposed Rule Making (Order/ FNPRM)* decides a number of critical issues, and seeks further comment on others, affecting implementation of advanced television (ATV) service in this country. It is the fifth in a series of Commission actions since 1987 developing and refining our regulatory approach to ATV and leading to selection of a terrestrial broadcast ATV system. In November 1987, the Commission established the Advisory Committee on Advanced Television Service (Advisory Committee), comprised of industry leaders from diverse sectors, including the broadcast, cable, computer, and manufacturing industries. Testing of proponent ATV systems began at the Advanced Television Test Center (Test Center) in July 1991 and is currently progressing.

The five ATV systems being tested are: (1) Narrow MUSE, proposed by NHK; (2) DigiCipher, by the American Television Alliance (ATVA, which is composed of General Instrument Corp. and MIT); (3) Digital Spectrum Compatible HDTV (DSC-HDTV), by Zenith/American Telephone and Telegraph; (4) Advanced Digital-High Definition Television (AD-HDTV), by the ATRC; and (5) ATVA Progressive System, by ATVA. Narrow MUSE is an analog HDTV system, and the remaining four are digital HDTV systems. *Fourth Interim Report of the FCC Advisory Committee on Advanced Television Service at 4 (Apr. 1, 1991) (Fourth Interim Report); Fifth Interim Report at 6-7 n.6.* The test center is conducting objective testing of the systems. Subjective video tests are being conducted at the Advanced Television Evaluation Laboratory (ATEL) in Ottawa, Canada, and audio tests are being conducted by Westinghouse Science and Technology Center.

- We reach numerous decisions herein, the most significant of which are the following:
  - ~ We limit initial eligibility for ATV frequencies to existing broadcasters; however, we will allow others to apply for ATV allotments and licenses in communities where there are additional channels available.
  - ~ We adopt a two-year deadline for broadcasters to apply initially for a paired ATV channel, and a three-year deadline for construction of an ATV facility once assigned.
  - ~ We will consider all allotment issues and issue a draft Table of Allotments in June 1992.
  - ~ We decide (a) to use vacant noncommercial reserved channels only when no feasible alternative exists for assigning ATV channels to existing broadcasters and (b) to leave vacant noncommercial allotments without an ATV channel pair only when there is no other practicable way to award an existing broadcaster an ATV channel.
  - ~ We maintain the secondary status of low-power television service stations vis-a-vis new ATV operations, but will also continue to permit displaced low-power service stations to file noncompetitive applications for another channel in the same community. We further conclude that low-power service stations should be free to broadcast in either the ATV or NTSC mode, and we plan to initiate a proceeding to consider whether some low-power television service interference protection rules should be changed in an attempt to mitigate some of the effects of potential displacement.
  - ~ We notify broadcasters that when ATV becomes and is designated as the prevalent medium, they will be required to "convert" to ATV, i.e., surrender one of two broadcast channels and cease broadcasting in NTSC, and we conclude that we should set a firm date for conversion to ATV.

~ We conclude that we should adopt a 100 percent simulcasting requirement at the earliest appropriate point.

~ We will condition selection of an ATV system on a winning proponent's adoption of reasonable and nondiscriminatory patent licensing policies, but decline to take further action at this time.

~ We encourage the ongoing work of the Advisory Committee on compatibility issues and generally decline to take additional regulatory action on these issues at this time.

~ We direct the Advisory Committee to address new audio developments, as well as proposals for flexible apportionment of audio and data in the selection of a system; the Committee is further requested to address any analogous calls for extensibility in an ATV system standard as they arise.

- We also seek comment on various issues, including:

~ A proposal to rank the class of parties initially eligible for ATV frequencies in the event of a spectrum shortfall as follows: (a) licensees and permittees with constructed facilities and program test authority, (b) permittees with unbuilt facilities, and (c) applicants;

~ A proposal to allow broadcasters a period of time to negotiate channel assignments prior to adoption of a Table of Allotments and, where broadcasters are unable to agree, to make channels available on a first-come, first-served basis;

~ A proposal to temporarily suspend the dual network rule to permit networks to give their affiliates a second feed for ATV;

~ A proposal to require low-power television service stations to convert to ATV at the point that full-service broadcast stations will be required to do so;

~ Our tentative conclusions that (a) we should establish a firm date for conversion to ATV that is 15 years from either selection of an ATV system or the date a Table of ATV Allotments is effective, whichever is later, and (b) that we should review, in 1998, the propriety of the conversion date we will have set;

~ Our tentative conclusion that we should impose a 100 percent simulcasting requirement no later than four years after the ATV application/construction period has passed, and on proposals for affording broadcasters some initial flexibility, including a proposal to "phase in" a full simulcasting requirement in two stages;

~ The merits of Advisory Committee findings concerning new developments in ATV technology, including its findings that these new developments are not sufficiently concrete to allow timely testing and do not merit further consideration in selection of an ATV system.

Eligibility, allotment, and assignment issues

Initial eligibility As we have previously stated, "broadcast stations provide services unique in the array of entertainment and non-entertainment programs freely available to the American public." Unlike other countries, the United States has an established system of privately owned broadcast stations that have an obligation to serve the public interest and in furtherance of that objective transmit news, information, and entertainment programs of a local, regional, and national nature. As we have stated, therefore, initiating an ATV system within this existing framework "will uniquely benefit the public." In addition, because over-the-air broadcasting reaches more than 98 percent of U.S. households, an ATV terrestrial broadcast system is the medium most likely to bring this technological advance to virtually all Americans. Consequently, it is the medium most likely to result in rapid penetration of ATV receivers and, hence, to contribute to higher sales volumes and eventually lower costs for these receivers. We thus believe that the television broadcast industry should be given the opportunity to implement ATV, and we develop a regulatory approach for this implementation herein. We underscore, however, that our approach does not preclude, and indeed attempts to facilitate, provision of ATV services by alternative media. By permitting the broadcast industry to make the transition to ATV, we ensure that all competitors in the local video services market can compete on this new technological level and, hence, that the public continues to enjoy the benefits that flow from such competition.

ATV represents a major advance in television technology, not the start of a new and separate video service. The notice proposed to permit existing broadcasters to keep pace with this important technological development by restricting initial eligibility for ATV frequencies to them. Most parties commenting on this issue agree, several noting in particular their concurring view that ATV is an enhancement of existing service and not a new video service, and that additional spectrum is being used in this case to improve and expand services, rather than to create a new class of service altogether.

As we stated in the notice, Ashbacker Radio Corp. V. FCC, 326 U.S. 327 (1945), requires us to give comparative consideration to all bona fide mutually exclusive applicants for a broadcast license. It does not, however, preclude our setting licensee eligibility standards. Rather, the central issue is whether the nature and duration of any restriction on eligibility is in the public interest. As the notice stated, and most commenting parties agree, existing broadcasters' continued involvement in ATV is the most practical, expeditious, and non-disruptive way to bring improved service to the American public. Existing broadcasters possess the know-how and experience necessary to implement ATV swiftly and efficiently. They have invested considerable resources in the present system and represent a large pool of experienced talent. As initial participants in the transition to ATV, existing broadcasters will be making an appreciable capital investment in this new technology and will undertake the business risks associated with being in the forefront of such new developments. Indeed, the broadcast industry also has helped create and support the Advanced Television Test Center, investing resources and developing expertise in this new technology.

Moreover, the initial restriction will be for a period of two years only—until initial assignments have been made. Thus, the initial eligibility restriction will not indefinitely impede new entrants. Furthermore, after the initial ATV allotments and assignments are made, the table of ATV allotments may be expanded through the normal rule-making process. Any additional channels would be open to all qualified parties. Similarly, if a broadcaster failed to apply for and construct an ATV facility within the specified time, that broadcaster would lose initial eligibility for the assigned channel, which would then be open to competing applicants. Finally, this eligibility restriction is, in the long-run, spectrally efficient. It enables us to award existing broadcasters an additional 6-MHz "conversion channel" on an interim basis, giving existing broadcasters the opportunity to move to ATV technology. At the time of conversion to ATV, we will be able to reclaim one of two 6-MHz channels—the "reversion channel"—without abruptly disenfranchising television broadcast licensees. We thus find that limiting initial eligibility to existing broadcasters is in the public interest, and we adopt this restriction.

The notice includes the following in the class of existing broadcasters who would initially be eligible for ATV channels: (1) all full-service television broadcast station licensees, (2) permittees authorized as of the date of adoption of the Notice, and (3) all parties with applications for a construction permit on file as of the date of adoption of the notice who are ultimately awarded full-service television broadcast station licenses. The notice also proposed various alternatives for assigning a channel where there is insufficient spectrum to accommodate all parties in a market, such as use of decisional criteria or a lottery pursuant to 47 U.S.C. §309 (i). There does not appear to be substantial dispute regarding the composition of the class of initially eligible parties where there is sufficient spectrum to accommodate all of the groups within the class. Several parties, however, argue for ranking among the groups in case of insufficient spectrum. In affording priorities in the event of insufficient spectrum, we agree with those commenters who would rank eligible parties, according to their degree of experience as NTSC broadcasters. Such a rule would harmonize with our fundamental reason for initially restricting eligibility, to bring ATV to the public in the most expeditious and nondisruptive manner. It would do this by enabling those with relatively greater experience and expertise in broadcasting to deliver ATV service to the public first.

We thus propose to rank the eligible parties in the following order: (1) licensees and permittees with constructed facilities having program test authority, (2) permittees, and (3) applicants. We do not propose, as Public Television suggests, to afford specific types of full-service broadcasters, such as noncommercial broadcasters, priority over other types in obtaining a second 6-MHz channel. Determinations of whether the type of programming proposed by a licensee merits a special preference would be community-specific, depending on the community's existing services and its particular needs. Making such determinations among the various licensees within a market would seriously impede the delivery of ATV service to the public in a timely fashion. In the case of insufficient spectrum to accommodate licensees and permittees with constructed facilities, in our proposed first-ranked group, we would apply some other method of deciding who would be assigned an ATV channel. We seek comment on this proposal.

After initial assignments are made, we propose to assign ATV channels to (1) parties ultimately awarded a construction permit based on an allotment petition pending as of the date of the notice, regardless of whether or not the permittee had filed the original allotment petition; (2) parties awarded waivers of the current freeze on television broadcast applications in major markets and who are subsequently awarded an NTSC authorization; and (3) any other parties authorized to construct NTSC facilities in the interim period after adoption of the notice. These parties, having just been awarded broadcast facilities, have relatively less experience than the initially eligible group of broadcasters, and thus are relatively less likely to have the expertise to help speed ATV implementation. We thus propose to award these parties ATV channels only after the initially eligible group of broadcasters receives assignments. We seek comment on this proposal.

We will award existing broadcasters an additional license for the ATV conversion channel, in lieu of treating the addition of an ATV channel as a major modification to the NTSC license. Broadcasters will be operating two distinct facilities having different characteristics and, in many cases, transmitting from different locations. Treating the ATV and NTSC channels as separately licensed facilities will therefore simplify enforcement and administration. Golden Orange believes that if stations must ultimately surrender one of their two channels, rather than merely surrendering the NTSC channel, the stations should be permitted to sell that channel at an earlier point to recoup the cost of converting to ATV. However, there are likely to be important broadcast and non-broadcast uses for surrendered spectrum. Moreover, permitting the transfer of one channel of the pair to a third party for broadcasting purposes makes it impossible to recapture one 6-MHz channel and still leave existing television licensees with a broadcast outlet. Permitting such transfers could also threaten our goal of spectrum efficiency by possibly leading to widescale requests for relief from the requirement of surrender of one 6-MHz channel on the part of those who previously transferred one channel of the pair. We accordingly will not permit an NTSC license to be transferred independently of the associated ATV license, or vice versa. We also decline to adopt suggestions that we permit use of the second channel for digital broadcast of multiple NTSC channels. The reason we are awarding broadcasters a second channel is to permit them to move to an improved technology without service disruption. If a broadcaster chooses not to broadcast in ATV, there is no reason for awarding that broadcaster an additional license.

We also will not allow an applicant for an ATV construction permit to retain priority eligibility status if its NTSC license is not renewed or is revoked while its ATV application is pending. If either the broadcaster's NTSC or ATV license is revoked or not renewed, we will automatically revoke the remaining license. In this way, we will ensure that our goals in awarding broadcasters a second channel are preserved and that our goals in revoking or not renewing a license are not undermined. Permitting broadcasters to continue on their NTSC channel alone would also make the viewing public more reluctant to purchase an ATV receiver, for fear that they will be unable to receive maximum utility from their added equipment investment. Permitting broadcasters to continue transmitting their signals in ATV alone, in turn, jeopardizes our goal of graduating the transition to ATV so that consumers are not abruptly deprived of the use of their NTSC receivers. We therefore will not permit those initially eligible for ATV frequencies to retain either the NTSC or ATV license if one of then is revoked or not renewed.

We recognize, however, that permitting an unpaired ATV channel to broadcast during the transition to full ATV conversion implicates another objective, that of spectrum efficiency, by permitting the recapture of the NTSC reversion channel. We will of course permit a party awarded an ATV license not associated with an NTSC channel pair to broadcast only on its assigned ATV channel. Its broadcast helps bring new entrants into the field, enhancing diversity, and helps spur ATV implementation by expanding the ATV broadcast outlets available to the public. Thus, we will consider permitting the voluntary surrender of an NTSC channel by a broadcaster awarded a corresponding ATV channel on a case-by-case basis, considering in particular whether ATV receiver penetration in the affected community demonstrates that consumers largely will not be prematurely deprived of the use of their NTSC receivers.

Unrestricted eligibility   As stated in the notice, once ATV allotments for initially eligible parties are made, there is no reason to continue limiting eligibility for ATV frequencies. Therefore, after an allotment table is adopted, we will permit any qualified party to file a petition for rulemaking to modify the ATV allotment table to add new ATV frequencies, where they are technically feasible. In addition, we will permit any qualified applicant, not just existing broadcasters, to apply for an ATV frequency when an NTSC licensee fails to apply for and construct an ATV facility or to apply within the required time. As EIA/CEG suggests, open eligibility at such point will provide an additional impetus to ATV implementation. Existing broadcasters who fail to apply or construct in the initial priority stage will be allowed to apply for any channels which subsequently remain available on the same basis as any other qualified parties and will be given no special priority.

Beyond pairing ATV channels to those awarded NTSC authorizations in the interim period prior to the time initial ATV assignments are made, we decline to establish any new priorities for eligibility once initial ATV allotments are made. We have restricted initial eligibility to the group we conclude most likely to implement ATV quickly. We are reluctant to expand our restriction to include others who, while offering valuable services in other respects, do not appear as a class likely to spur ATV implementation in the same fashion. We thus decline requests to afford low power and translator service or noncommercial interests priority status at such point. After the time for applying for an ATV channel has passed—two years after the date of adoption of an ATV standard or of a Final Table of ATV Allotments becomes effective, whichever is later—eligibility will be completely unrestricted. An additional eligibility restriction imposed at this stage would only narrow unnecessarily the group of potentially ready, willing and able entrants who may seek to apply for and deliver ATV service to the public expeditiously.

In addition, ATV licenses will be subject to competing applications filed during the appropriate renewal window. As proposed in the notice, we will issue ATV licenses for periods concurrent with the license of the associated NTSC station (if any). License periods for all ATV licenses, whether or not associated with an NTSC channel, will be determined in accordance with 47 C.F.R. §73.1020.

Television multiple ownership rules   As the notice proposed, we will suspend application of the television multiple ownership rules, 47 C.F.R. §73.3555, for ATV stations on a limited basis. Most parties commenting on the issue agree that such suspension is necessary. We thus will permit existing licensees that are awarded an additional ATV channel to hold both their NTSC and ATV licenses, even though their signals overlap, and to permit group owners to hold both NTSC and paired ATV channels—even though nationwide ceilings may be exceeded, until such time as existing licensees are required to convert to ATV service exclusively. Our decision to establish a "use or lose" application/construction deadline should eliminate the potential for anticompetitive construction delays that FTC hypothesizes could develop from lifting the rules. Because a broadcaster must complete construction of its ATV facility within a specified time or forfeit its right to use the channel, a broadcaster will be unable to prevent others from being awarded the channel while the broadcaster itself delays construction of an ATV station. Limited suspension of the multiple ownership rules is an essential component of our regulatory approach to ATV implementation, and we therefore adopt it.

Network rules   CapCities requests suspension of the dual network rule, which prohibits a network from simultaneously operating more than one network of television stations in identical or overlapping geographic areas. According to CapCities, suspension would permit a network to operate both an NTSC and ATV network during the transition to ATV. CapCities also asks that any suspension allow a network to affiliate with a new ATV station if its NTSC affiliate fails to be awarded an ATV facility.

Temporary suspension of the dual network prohibition would appear to facilitate a smooth transition to ATV. In light of our simulcast requirements, broadcasters will be airing much of the same programming on their ATV and NTSC channels. During the transition to ATV, the networks will necessarily have to program their affiliates' two stations. Moreover, the networks are likely to be an early source of ATV programming on which existing affiliates will want to rely. Permitting the networks to supply their affiliates with ATV programming thus is likely to contribute to expeditious delivery of ATV programming to the public. We therefore propose to suspend the dual network prohibition to permit networks to give their affiliates a second feed for ATV. We seek comment on this proposal. We also seek comment on whether the suspension should extend to circumstances where a network's two feeds (ATV and NTSC) go to different licensees in a market, if so, if any additional regulatory steps would be required in such case.

Application and construction periods   To administer such rules of the Federal Communications Commission as set forth at §73.3555(c) of Title 47 of the *Code of Federal Regulations*. Departments of Commerce, Justice, and State, the Judiciary, and Related Agencies Appropriations Act, 1992, Pub. L. No. 102-140, 105 Stat. 782, 797 (1991). Section 73.3555(c) prohibits ownership of a broadcast station and a daily newspaper in the same market. This prohibition on its face does not apply to limited suspension of the broadcast/newspaper cross-ownership rule. Moreover, there is no indication that

Congress intended to preclude grandfathered television/newspaper combinations from participating on the same basis as all other television licensees in the transition to ATV.

The notice proposed that existing broadcasters would have the right to apply for a particular ATV frequency on a priority basis for three years from the time that an ATV allotment table is adopted. We also proposed to apply a two-year restriction on the time within which a broadcaster must construct a new ATV facility or forfeit its construction permit, analogous to the two-year period applicable today. Commenters are divided on these proposals. Most parties agree that a three-year application period is reasonable. Many, however, urge either deferring or extending the time period for construction.

We believe it is critical to our goal of bringing ATV to the American public quickly that we establish definite application and construction deadlines and that we give parties notice of such deadlines at this early stage. We are concerned that without such a specific timetable, some parties may unduly delay construction while waiting for others to take the lead, to the detriment of our goal of expeditious ATV implementation. We are also unpersuaded that deferral of a decision on such deadlines will enable us to obtain the information that some parties believe is essential to this decision, and which we now lack. For example, although lack of revenue forecasts is given as a reason to defer decision, no party convinces us that such data will become available within a reasonable period of time. Moreover, even if such forecasts were negative, such data would not necessarily lead us to extend our application and construction periods, as opposed, for example, to opening eligibility to others financially better able to sustain ATV operations. Our decision today will give all broadcasters ample notice of the time periods that will apply. Those broadcasters who do not apply and construct within this time (and who fail to obtain an extension of time) will lose their initial eligibility for an ATV frequency. These broadcasters may apply at a later time for an ATV channel on an equal basis with other applicants. Accordingly, we find it unnecessary to defer our decision on application and construction deadlines or extend them beyond the total five-year period proposed.

Nevertheless, we believe that we should make an adjustment to the relative lengths of the application and construction periods from those which we proposed. Upon further reflection, we do not believe that broadcasters will need a full three-year application period to arrange their financing and plan their facilities from the time an order selecting an ATV system becomes effective. Rather, we conclude that a two-year application period will be sufficient. As Island observes, this proceeding has been pending since 1987, at the initiation of a broadcast industry group. With adoption of this decision, broadcasters will have ample notice of the precise deadlines applicable to them before the application period begins to run. Broadcasters obtaining an assignment as a result of negotiations with other parties in the market, having explored potential implementation difficulties before agreeing to a pairing plan, should not need an extended time for submitting an application for that channel. Moreover, broadcasters who are unable to reach a negotiated settlement will have an incentive under the first-come, first-served approach to apply for an ATV channel early. Accordingly, adopting a two-year application period should not impose an undue burden on existing broadcasters. Moreover, a two-year period will further ensure that incumbent broadcasters take advantage of their initial eligibility priority in a timely fashion and that ATV channels are opened up to new entrants within a reasonable period of time.

At the same time, we recognize that broadcasters will be in the vanguard of those implementing ATV technology. As a result, the necessary equipment for transmission and production will have to be newly developed. Licensees will need time to solve the unique problems that pioneering construction of an ATV facility may raise. Accordingly, we will permit broadcasters an additional year from that proposed, for a total of three years, for construction of an ATV facility. In light of the modification we make to the application period, this additional year for construction will not delay the ultimate availability of ATV service to the public.

We also clarify that we intend to apply our existing definition of "construction" in this context. Thus, a broadcaster will be deemed to have constructed an ATV facility if it has the capability of emitting ATV signals, regardless of the source of these signals (e.g., local origination, pass-through of a network signal, or other signal). Studies of the cost of ATV broadcast implementation indicate that studio conversion costs are likely to be substantial. By leaving the timing of full studio conversion more to the broadcaster's judgment, broadcasters will be able to "phase-in" full ATV implementation as their individual circumstances and markets permit. At the same time, requiring transmission capability by a date certain ensures that valuable spectrum will not lie fallow and that the benefits of technological advances will be made available to the public promptly.

We underscore that the ATV application/construction time period will begin to run from the date that a Report and Order adopting a Table of Allotments or selecting an ATV system becomes effective, whichever is later. We expect that many of the asserted uncertainties regarding ATV construction that are raised today will be clarified at the point an ATV system is actually selected. However, we note that for each individual applicant, the construction period will begin to run from the actual time that a construction permit is awarded. In this way, we may appropriately compensate for time needed for application processing by commission staff. Moreover, we can ensure that those who are awarded frequencies at a relatively early point also complete construction at a commensurately early date.

Finally, not only are we allowing an additional year for construction beyond that currently permitted in our rules, but our existing policies, regarding extensions of time will afford broadcasters adequate flexibility to cope with unforeseen implementation problems. Our rules permit extensions of time to construct where (1) construction is complete and testing is underway; (2) substantial progress in construction has been made; or (3) reasons clearly beyond the permittee's control have prevented progress in construction, but the permittee has taken all possible steps to expeditiously resolve the problem and proceed with construction. We will apply these rules to grant extensions in appropriate circumstances.

For example, some speculate that local zoning problems, pendency of FAA, FCC, or other necessary government approvals, or litigation directly affecting our ATV rules will unavoidably delay ATV construction. Our existing rules, however, would provide relief in such circumstances. Similarly, some hypothesize that transmission and production equipment might not be available in a timely fashion. Our existing rules again would permit appropriate extensions. If unavoidable difficulties occur in locating an appropriate ATV transmitter site, our existing rules also provide sufficient relief. With respect to publicly-funded stations, we note that government budgetary processes can present uncontrollable circumstances specifically justifying an extension in our rules. This policy thus provides sufficient flexibility for public television stations that may experience delays in obtaining government appropriations to transition to ATV.

We thus believe that this policy on extensions affords sufficient relief to parties in unforeseen and uncontrollable circumstances. Given this policy, and the additional flexibility created by our continuing to limit the construction requirement to the ability to emit an ATV signal alone, we conclude that it is unnecessary either to extend the total time allowed for application or construction, or to undertake additional regulatory initiatives, to provide reasonable and equitable relief in extenuating circumstances. On the other hand, given the many unknown factors likely to be part of early ATV implementation, we do not believe it advisable, as Island advocates, to employ a more stringent standard than we now apply to broadcasters.

Our present rules rally do not permit an extension for inability to obtain financing. Contrary to the views of some commenters, we see no reason to modify this rule for initial ATV implementation or to defer our decision on construction periods based on concerns about future ability to obtain financing. Adequate financing is critical to prompt construction. One reason we are assigning ATV channels to existing broadcasters is our belief that they are the group most likely to have the incentive and the resources to implement ATV in an expeditious fashion. A broadcaster's inability to obtain adequate capital, therefore, will only be considered relevant under extraordinary circumstances.

We also decline to make ATV receiver penetration a factor in granting construction permit extensions or extending application/construction time beyond five years. The availability of ATV programming to the public is likely to be a major factor driving ATV receiver penetration. Unless broadcast stations are transmitting ATV programs, such programming is unlikely to be available in sufficient quantity to stimulate receiver sales. We therefore believe that broadcast transmission is likely to be a precondition for substantial receiver penetration. Thus, we cannot allow receiver penetration levels to be a factor justifying a failure to construct an ATV station in a timely fashion or moving us to extend generally the application/construction time period.

Allotment/assignment issues For the past several years, the commission's staff has been examining various approaches and methodologies for developing allotments for ATV. These efforts have been used to support the commission's preliminary positions regarding retention of reserved channels for noncommercial stations and full accommodation of existing TV stations. These studies also have provided guidance on critical spectrum parameters to ATV system designers and have aided the Advisory Committee's work in this area.

In the notice, we sought comment on general spectrum matters and two main alternatives for the initial assignment of ATV channels, including a proposal to assign channels on a first-come, first-served basis, and a proposal to also permit private negotiations among licensees for particular channels. Most commenting parties endorse an allotment/assignment approach that matches specific ATV channels with existing NTSC allotments. Broadcasters generally believe it is essential that ATV channels be assigned by the time an ATV standard is selected and that existing sites be taken into account in the assignment process. Parties disagreed, however, on the approach to be used to pair specific NTSC and ATV channels within a community. Most parties support a policy permitting pre- or post-assignment negotiations among licensees in a given community as an extension of the commission's normal allotment and assignment processes. The Joint Broadcasters also oppose an approach in which ATV channels would first be allotted to communities and then made available for broadcasters on a first-come, first-served basis. EIA, on the other hand, supports such a first-come, first-served procedure, stating that it would be the most expeditious means for implementing ATV.

The Advisory Committee has recommended that we adopt an ATV allotment/assignment scheme contemporaneously with adoption of an ATV standard, consider a site-specific assignment plan in order to promote co-location of ATV and NTSC antenna sites, and clearly define our methodology for making ATV assignments as expeditiously as possible.

We share the concerns of commenting parties that it is essential that an allotment/assignment process be in place at the time the ATV standard is adopted, and that the allotment and assignment methodology be defined as rapidly as possible. We intend to address all allotment matters related to the introduction of ATV in a separate

Further Notice of Proposed Rule Making in June of this year. This action will set forth proposed technical and policy principles and scientific and engineering concepts to be used in the allotment of ATV channels. A draft Table of Allotments based on these principles and concepts will also be included. We are aware that the Advisory Committee has also undertaken work in the allotment and assignment areas. At an informal meeting with FCC staff on February 5, 1992, representatives of the Advisory Committee and other interested parties indicated that preliminary results from this work are expected this spring. To the extent that this work becomes available, we will give it due consideration in developing our allotment and assignment proposals.

We continue to believe that negotiations among broadcasters should be an integral part of the ATV assignment process. Such an approach will ensure the most expeditious and efficient implementation of ATV service to the public. Accordingly, we have developed the following revised proposal for the initial assignment of ATV channels. This proposal will ensure that assignment and licensing procedures are in place at the time the commission adopts an ATV standard. Under this proposal, at the time the commission issues a Further Notice proposing the Final Table of Allotments, broadcasters would have a fixed period of time to negotiate with each other and submit plans for pairing NTSC and ATV channels either nationwide or on a market-by-market basis. Both commercial and noncommercial stations would be permitted to participate in this negotiation. Once the period for such industry negotiations ends, if there are markets remaining where broadcasters are unable to agree on a pairing plan, the channels in those markets would be assigned on a first-come, first served basis. In the case of simultaneously filed applications, we would apply a "random ranking" procedure, so that the top-ranked applicant would be granted its first choice, and the next-ranked applicant its highest choice that would not conflict with the first-ranked applicant, and so on. We do not agree with Joint Broadcasters that such a first-come approach would result in a "stampede" of applications because broadcasters in many markets may reach negotiated settlements among themselves. In addition, our selection of a three-year construction period, which will begin to run from the time a construction permit is awarded, should help ensure that broadcasters do not file for an ATV allotment until they are ready to construct. We seek comment on this proposed approach.

Spectrum issues

Noncommercial allotments   As the notice stated, our spectrum planning, with respect to the broadcast industry, has traditionally taken into account the important role noncommercial stations play in providing quality programming to the public and the financial constraints they face in building and running their stations. Technical studies indicate that we can continue this tradition within an ATV allotment scheme. Accordingly, in the notice we proposed that we would use vacant noncommercial reserved channels only as a last resort, to permit present delivery of ATV service, and moreover, would pair vacant noncommercial allotments with an ATV channel, except where that would preclude present delivery of ATV service.

Most parties commenting on the issue favor preserving the noncommercial reserve, with some noting that given the budgetary constraints confronting noncommercial stations, many such stations would require more time than their commercial counterparts to commence operations. Most of those commenting on the issue also favor pairing ATV channels with vacant noncommercial allotments, observing the unique role that public television plays in American broadcasting, the difficulties noncommercial interests have in competing with commercial interests for spectrum, and the importance of such reservations in maintaining the ranks of stations dedicated to public television service. Based on these comments, we conclude that we will use vacant noncommercial allotments for ATV only where there is no feasible alternative for assigning an ATV channel to an existing broadcaster. Similarly, we will leave vacant noncommercial allotments without an ATV channel pair only when there is no other practicable way to award an existing broadcaster an ATV channel. We will in no event use a vacant VHF channel allotment reserved for noncommercial purposes for commercial ATV. Moreover, only as a last resort will we delete a reserved channel, or use for commercial purposes an ATV channel that would otherwise be paired with a vacant noncommercial allotment, where that channel or allotment would be necessary to provide first noncommercial full-service Grade B coverage to a community. As Public Television suggests, if it is impossible to pair an ATV channel with a vacant noncommercial allotment, we will protect the vacant allotment with both NTSC and ATV separation requirements, provided that ATV spacing is, as anticipated, less than or equal to NTSC spacings.

Public Television also suggests that we designate relinquished NTSC channels as pairs for vacant noncommercial allotments. However, at the point that NTSC channels must be relinquished by all broadcasters—the point of conversion to ATV—our transitional channel pairing scheme will have served its purpose and will be ended. Thus, there will be no need for pairing these noncommercial reserved channels at this point. Noncommercial as well as commercial stations will have returned to broadcasting on a single 6-MHz channel.

LPTV and translator services   There is no doubt, as low-power/translator interests argue, that LPTV and translator services provide important benefits, serving minority and specialized audiences, providing locally-based services to communities, and generally furthering diversity. On the other hand, we are in the process of enabling full-service stations that, by definition, reach much wider audiences than LPTVs and translators, to bring ATV, a major technological advance in broadcasting, to these audiences on a second channel. In order to do so, these full-service stations will temporarily need a substantial allocation of spectrum. As the notice stated, it will be a challenge to provide all full-service licensees with an additional 6 MHz for ATV. Accordingly, as we stated in the notice, and the record confirms, if ATV is to succeed, it will be necessary for new ATV assignments to displace LPTV and translator stations to some degree in the major markets, although the impact is likely to be less severe in rural areas where there are fewer full-service stations. We are thus compelled to agree with those who believe that ATV implementation will require that LPTVs and translators, as secondary services, yield to new full-power ATV stations.

We thus conclude that we must continue LPTV and translators' secondary status vis-à-vis ATV stations. We do not agree with those who argue that this is impermissible and unfair because the low-power service was not established as secondary to ATV stations, but only to certain land mobile services and to the full-power television broadcast service in existence at the time the service was created. Our rules proscribe interference to "any TV broadcast station" operating on the same or adjacent channel. The low-power television service was established for the specific purpose of supplementing conventional broadcast station coverage and we have always considered low-power service stations secondary. The low-power service thus has had ample notice that it would have to yield to any full-service stations, without exception for the specific mode in which the full-service station transmit. We also do not believe that the displacement required under our rules is a restraint of trade or monopolistic, as Polar contends.

We will not deviate from established precedent and afford preference translators over low power stations should displacement be required. Our present rules balance the goals of maintaining translator service and encouraging new low power originating services. We find that maintaining such a balance is in the public interest. Our present rules also make no distinctions among low-power service applicants based on the content of their programming. We do not believe that this proceeding is the proper procedural context for development of a preference for foreign-language low-power stations or that the record before us is sufficiently developed to permit adoption of such a rule, as some parties request.

Based on Staff and Advisory Committee technical studies, we find that there is insufficient spectrum to permit LPTVs and translators to be included in the class of broadcasters initially eligible for an ATV frequency on either a primary or secondary basis or to factor in LPTV displacement considerations in making ATV assignments, as several parties argue. Because LPTVs and translators are secondary to full-service stations, we do not believe it would be appropriate for us to require full-service stations displacing low-power service stations to compensate them, as some suggest. In addition, as stated above, with the proposed exception of those awarded NTSC authorizations in the interim period extending from adoption of the notice to initial assignment, we will not grant priorities to any entity for eligibility for an ATV channel after initial assignments are made.

At the same time, we recognize that LPTVs and translators may have a role in implementing ATV. Some parties suggest that the nature of their operations may make the low-power television station transition to ATV more economical and expedient than that of full-service stations. Moreover, given the absence of multiple ownership restrictions on low-power stations, they will be free to add a second low-power ATV channel, provided no unacceptable interference to full-service stations or other protected operations occurs. In addition, we will permit LPTV and translator stations to broadcast in either the ATV or NTSC mode once ATV implementation begins.

We propose to require low-power television service stations to broadcast in the ATV mode at the time that full-service stations will be required to convert to ATV and cease broadcasting in NTSC. Such a requirement would be consistent with our treatment of full-service stations, and would help spur ATV receiver penetration by increasing the sources of ATV programming available. Moreover, requiring low-power television service to implement ATV at the time of full service station conversion gives LPTVs and translators ample time to plan their transition. We seek comment on this proposal.

Recognizing the significant benefits that low-power services bring to the public, we will, as CBA and others suggest, take such steps to mitigate the likelihood and effects of displacement as are consistent with our other objectives in this proceeding. We thus will continue to permit a low-power TV station displaced by a full-service station to apply for a suitable replacement channel in the same area without being subject to competing applications. We will also continue our present policy of permitting low power service stations to operate until a displacing full-service ATV station is operational. As Telemundo suggests, we also will continue to allow displaced LPTVs to migrate to vacant NTSC channels, including vacant reserved noncommercial channels. We stress, however, as Public Television suggests, that LPTVs' use of such vacant spectrum is secondary only. Moreover, as Telemundo suggests, we will continue to permit LPTVs and translators to file non-window displacement relief applications to change their operating parameters to cure interference to an ATV station. We also tentatively agree with arguments that certain specific NTSC interference protection rules could be reevaluated and may afford low-power service interests some measure of relief. We plan to initiate a separate proceeding to consider such changes. We decline, however, suggestions that we place additional requirements on full-service stations in order to minimize the likelihood of interference and displacement to LPTVs and translators. It is the responsibility of the low-power service, as a secondary service, to yield to full-service stations where a conflict arises.

Broadcast auxiliary service We appreciate the difficulties that broadcasters are likely to face in meeting their auxiliary service needs for both an ATV and an NTSC channel. As the Advisory Committee observes, the broadcast auxiliary spectrum is already congested, most severely in major markets, where ATV implementation will first occur. We have, however, taken pains to protect broadcast auxiliary spectrum allocations in the 1990- to 2110-MHz band, despite intense, competing need for additional spectrum by new services. Moreover, there is no additional spectrum at hand for broadcast auxiliary purposes. Additional capacity might have to be obtained by, for example, reconfiguring existing microwave links for greater efficiency, making greater use of the higher frequency bands, use of optical fiber and combined optical fiber-microwave links, and employment of digital compression techniques to allow carriage of multiple NTSC signals in a single channel. We also suggest that broadcasters may increase their use of any existing available UHF spectrum for fixed auxiliary broadcast use.

Other spectrum issues In order to ensure an adequate number of ATV channels in large border areas, some commenters urge that we initiate and/or intensify coordination efforts with Canada and Mexico. Both the Advisory Committee and the commission staff have begun informal discussions with Canada and Mexico. We plan to intensify these efforts and encourage the Advisory Committee to do the same.

Some commenters urge us to terminate Gen. Docket No. 85-172, which proposed further sharing, or reallocation, of UHF channels in eight large urban areas to private land mobile service. We suspended action in that docket following initiation of this proceeding, out of concern that we not adversely affect spectrum options for ATV. Those urging termination argue that the continued existence of Docket No. 85-172 creates an aura of uncertainty regarding the commission's commitment to ATV and, given the potentially tight spectrum conditions for ATV in certain markets, can serve no useful purpose. However, we agree with LMCC that it is premature to terminate Gen. Docket 85-172 at this time, particularly in advance of a final allotment plan confirming predictions about spectrum needs for ATV. We thus decline to terminate Gen. Docket No. 85-172.

We also find that requests for reallocation of assertedly lightly used land mobile channels for television broadcast use are beyond the scope of this proceeding. These requests are properly the subject of a separate petition for rule making. Their consideration in the instant docket would lead to undue delay and complication of the numerous and significant issues directly raised by the advent of ATV.

Conversion to ATV

Timetable for conversion Most, although not all, of those commenting on the issue agree in principle with the proposal in the notice that we require broadcasters to "convert" entirely to ATV—e.g., to surrender one 6-MHz reversion channel and broadcast only in ATV on the conversion channel once ATV becomes the prevalent medium. Requiring the surrender of the NTSC reversion channel will promote the introduction of ATV and maximize ATV coverage areas. Although, as Golden Orange states, there is a benefit to affording the public a choice between ATV and NTSC programming during the transition years, suggesting that such a choice will remain permanently available would undoubtedly inhibit the growth of ATV. More significantly, there are likely to be competing uses for this spectrum, which we will have to address. Thus, contrary to requests that we defer addressing the issue of conversion, we put broadcasters on notice that when ATV becomes the prevalent medium, they will be required to surrender their reversion channel and cease broadcasting in NTSC. By not requiring conversion until ATV achieves consumer acceptance, we allay FTC's uncertainty about whether ATV's costs will exceed its benefits to consumers.

As proposed, we will cease issuing new NTSC licenses, including noncommercial NTSC licenses, once we have completed the initial assignment of ATV channels to existing NTSC licensees, i.e., two years after an ATV standard or a final Table of ATV Allotments is effective, whichever is later. From that point forward, in order to begin the transition to ATV, we will issue new television broadcast licenses for ATV transmission only. We do not agree with Public Television that by ceasing to issue noncommercial NTSC licenses, we are defeating the purpose of pairing, where feasible, ATV channels with vacant noncommercial allotments. That pairing permits noncommercial applicants to continue applying for NTSC/ATV pairs until the point that initial ATV assignments are completed. Once that point is reached, noncommercial applicants will still be able to apply for the ATV channels that were set aside for the former NTSC noncommercial reserve. In addition, should an existing broadcaster have forfeited its initial eligibility by, for example, failing to apply and construct within the required time, we will allow that broadcaster subsequently to apply, along with any other qualified parties, for any available ATV allotment or for an available ATV channel that will enable it to switch directly to an ATV channel at the time of conversion. If it is technically possible, a broadcaster may also use its existing NTSC frequency for this purpose. Finally, we will permit modifications to NTSC facilities after adoption of a final Table of Allotments for ATV channels provided they comply with technical criteria for the protection of ATV vacant allotments, applications and assignments.

We also conclude that we should set a firm date for conversion to ATV. We agree with Zenith that use of a firm date would keep administration simple, assure progress toward freeing spectrum on a timely basis and give broadcasters, consumers, and manufacturers the benefits of a clearly defined planning horizon. Our review of the record also persuades us that complete reliance on ATV receiver penetration rates as a triggering event for conversion, on either a nationwide or market-by-market basis, as the notice also suggested, would not provide this same clear signal.

We tentatively conclude that we should establish a date for conversion that is 15 years from the date adoption of an ATV system or a final Table of ATV Allotments is effective, whichever is later. This date should permit the majority of consumers who purchase NTSC receivers prior to the introduction of ATV to get full use of their NTSC equipment. Moreover, by this point, we expect that the cost of ATV receivers should have declined from the level of initial prices, as a result of increased consumer acceptance and higher volume sales. Preliminary studies also suggest that, even absent imposition of a conversion deadline, significant numbers of consumers should have purchased ATV receivers by this point. Indeed, it is possible that alternative media such as VCRs and cable might seed the ATV receiver market even before ATV terrestrial broadcasts begin. By the time our proposed conversion point is reached, broadcasters will have constructed an ATV transmission facility and should have implemented studio production capability. It is also possible that inexpensive downconverters permitting the reception of ATV signals on conventional NTSC sets (in NTSC quality) will have become available, thereby enabling those without ATV television sets to continue to receive broadcast service without purchasing a completely new receiver. We seek comment on our tentative conclusion that a 15-year conversion date would be appropriate and on the reasoning underpinning this tentative finding.

We also invite interested parties, particularly system proponents, consumer electronics manufacturers, and professional broadcast equipment manufacturers, to comment on the availability and costs they project during this 15-year period for equipment needed in the home and in the broadcast studio to receive and produce programming in the ATV mode. In particular, we seek comment on the timing of widespread availability of ATV receivers, home downconverters, and ATV professional broadcast equipment, and what the cost of such equipment is expected to be (including any expected changes in price) during the 15-year conversion period. We also ask parties to comment on whether the possible availability of downconverters should influence the manner by which we assess ATV acceptance. Would the availability of reasonably priced ATV downconverters lessen concerns about the premature obsolescence of NTSC sets in a household?

Notwithstanding our tentative conclusion to set a 15-year conversion date, we acknowledge that, at this point, it is difficult to predict with certainty how ATV implementation will occur. Various developments relevant to the new ATV technology to a date for conversion conceivably may emerge in the next several years. Although we will establish a firm conversion date in the next stage of this proceeding, we propose to review, in 1998, the propriety of that conversion date. This review should alleviate concerns about premature termination of NTSC. It would also leave room for adjustment if ATV implementation should proceed more or less swiftly than we envision. We note that by 1998, we should have gained considerable experience concerning the transition to ATV: we will have selected an ATV system and established an ATV standard; ATV receivers should be available; and numerous broadcast stations should be transmitting in ATV. By 1998, we also should have better data regarding the development of set-top converters and other factors that are relevant to determination of a timetable for recapture of NTSC reversion spectrum. This data will in turn enable us to weigh the opportunity costs of keeping the reversion spectrum with broadcasters for some additional period of time against the costs to broadcasters and consumers of fully converting to ATV. We seek comment on our proposal to review, in 1998, the suitability of the conversion date we will soon establish in the next stage of this proceeding.

Switching frequencies We agree with Joint Broadcasters that we cannot permit stations to switch their NTSC and ATV channels on an individual, voluntary basis. As we stated in the notice, it is likely that ATV-NTSC co-channel spacing will be shorter than ATV-ATV and NTSC-NTSC co-channel spacing. Unless all stations with co-channel facilities at less than the minimum ATV-ATV spacing in a given area switch together, switching ATV and NTSC frequencies could result in ATV stations with service areas permanently much smaller than would have been the case if switching had not been permitted. Accordingly, we will permit switching of ATV and NTSC frequencies only on a case-by-case basis, after careful coordination ensuring that other ATV service areas are not adversely affected and no other negative interference consequences result, and assuming that such switching harmonizes with any long-range plan for use of television spectrum that we develop.

Commenters generally oppose the suggestion that we should require all broadcasters to switch back to their original (formerly NTSC) frequencies at some future point. Some argue that it would require significant additional investment and lead to consumer confusion. Other parties, however, advocate requiring broadcasters to switch to new channels so that all ATV operations can be reaccommodated in the most spectrally efficient-manner. These parties advocate establishment of a contiguous UHF allocation. We agree, however, with those parties who counsel that we cannot know the relative value of ATV broadcasts in the VHF band, as opposed to the UHF band until after we develop practical experience with this new technology. As ATSC states, some predict that digital transmission will virtually eliminate the advantages of VHF over UHF. In such case, we might want to avoid the added expense to broadcasters that a switch to VHF would cause, and to consider other uses for that spectrum. We will thus wait until ATV implementation is underway and we have practical experience on which to base our judgments, to decide whether, at some future point, we should require or permit broadcasters to switch frequencies.

Simulcasting

The notice stated our belief that ATV implementation should be structured to protect the existing investment in consumer equipment so that consumers are not prematurely forced to purchase new receivers to enjoy top-quality over-the-air television programming. We stated that a simulcast requirement (under which at least some amount of programming would have to be broadcast simultaneously over both the NTSC and ATV channels) would be one means of achieving this goal. We thus sought comment on the degree of simulcasting, if any, we should require and on whether there were any other equally effective ways to protect investment in NTSC equipment. After reviewing line comments on this issue, we conclude that we should require 100 percent simulcasting of the programming on the ATV channel at the earliest appropriate point. For the reasons given below, we tentatively conclude that this 100 percent requirement should be adopted no later than four years after the ATV application/construction period for preferred allotments has passed, and we seek comment on whether we should permit broadcasters some initial flexibility prior to this point.

A simulcast requirement will help ensure that consumers are not prematurely deprived of the benefits of their existing television receivers and other devices. In addition, we underscore that ATV is not a separate television service and will not result in the permanent grant of two 6-MHz channels to existing broadcasters. We intend to reclaim the reversion channel as soon as possible. Requiring simulcasting will help us to do so by minimizing broadcaster and consumer reliance on the ATV channel as a separately programmed service. Thus, we firmly disagree with Golden Orange that we should continue to permit NTSC stations to continue indefinitely and with different programming. In addition, a simulcast requirement will give added impetus to ATV receiver penetration by eliminating the need for dual-mode receivers that are capable of receiving both NTSC and ATV. It will thereby help lower the cost of ATV receivers, which in turn should spur increased penetration. Thus, simulcasting will not only protect existing consumer investment in NTSC equipment, but also facilitate consumer purchase of new ATV receivers. Our ultimate goal, therefore, is to require simulcasting of 100 percent of the programming on the ATV conversion channel as soon as is appropriate.

In this regard, we tentatively conclude that we should impose a 100-percent simulcasting requirement no later than fours years after the five-year ATV application/construction period for preferred allotments has passed. At this point—nine years after a standard becomes effective—we will have afforded broadcasters sufficient time in which to explore the potential of this new technology, and ATV should have established itself. Thus, the need to afford broadcasters some flexibility in starting up ATV operations will have diminished. On the other hand, ATV receiver penetration, and hence revenues from ATV programming, should be increasing. With the ascendance of the ATV channel, the need to protect consumer investment in existing NTSC equipment will increase. As the ATV channel begins to produce its own revenues, the need to ensure the surrender of the reversion channel also will increase. Requiring 100-percent simulcasting at this point will serve our twin goals of protecting consumer investment in NTSC equipment and ensuring spectrum efficiency. We accordingly seek comment on our plan to require 100-percent simulcasting no later than four years after the initial five-year application/construction period has passed.

At the same time, we recognize that there may be a need for some initial flexibility in programming the ATV channel to permit the development of equipment and programming for this new technology and to attract consumer interest. In the early stages of ATV implementation, it is unclear whether all stations could or will initially have the program sources or technical capability to simulcast all their programming. In addition, some parties suggest that the quantity and/or quality of ATV programming is likely to be a driving force in consumer acceptance of this new transmission mode. Moreover, broadcasters are likely to need some freedom to explore the dimensions of the new ATV technology, to use it creatively and to realize its full potential. In order to develop and produce the programming that will best exploit the benefits of ATV and attract consumers to this new technology, broadcasters might need some initial reprieve from a full simulcasting requirement. Moreover, regulation to protect consumer investment in existing NTSC equipment might well be unnecessary in the early stages of ATV implementation. In these early stages, stations will have every incentive to maintain their NTSC programming, and ATV receiver penetration (and consequently viewership and advertising revenues) will be relatively low. Thus, broadcasters will surely retain a substantial financial incentive to maintain the quality of their relatively more lucrative NTSC programs.

We therefore seek comment on one alternative that would have us phase in our simulcasting requirement, permitting broadcasters to make adjustments in a gradual fashion. Under this staggered approach, we would allow broadcasters complete flexibility in programming the ATV channel during the first two years after the initial five-year application/construction period has passed. However, as ATV implementation progresses, ATV receiver penetration is likely to increase and the need for regulatory intervention to protect existing consumer investment and ensure our ability to reclaim the second 6-MHz channel becomes more acute. Thus, starting two years after the initial ATV application/construction deadline for existing broadcasters has passed—seven years from the time a Report and Order adopting an ATV standard becomes effective—we would require broadcasters to simulcast 50 percent of each day's programming. This 50 percent requirement would continue to afford broadcasters some flexibility as they implement full ATV production capabilities, but would also prompt them to prepare for complete conversion to ATV technology by ensuring that they do not use the second 6-MHz channel to develop a separate program service. In addition, the phased-in 50 percent simulcast requirement would enable us to safeguard consumer interests in the long-term, when ATV overtakes NTSC, by protecting the public's investment in NTSC technology. For the reasons discussed above, the 50-percent simulcasting requirement then would be increased to a 100-percent requirement two years later, at a point nine years after an ATV standard becomes effective. We seek comment on this proposed approach.

We also seek comment on other alternative schedules, including an approach that would adopt a full simulcasting requirement earlier than four years after the application/construction period has passed. An earlier adoption of a 100-percent simulcast requirement would appear to strengthen our ability to reclaim one 6-MHz channel at conversion. If the necessary production and conversion equipment is available two years after the initial five-year application/construction ends, or even earlier, it might be technically feasible to move to a 100-percent simulcast requirement at such point. We seek comment on such an approach and the projections as to the availability of necessary hardware and software that underlie it. We also ask interested parties to comment on whether broadcasters would, regardless of technical feasibility, need some reprieve from a 100 percent simulcast requirement after the initial application/construction period passes to explore the creative potential of the ATV mode, to attract viewers to ATV, and to ensure their ability to recoup their investment in ATV implementation.

We also seek comment on other proposed approaches to affording broadcasters flexibility in developing ATV technology. For example, we might require a broadcaster to air the same programming on the ATV and NTSC channels, but permit flexibility, with respect to time of airing or material included. The guiding policy under such an approach would be to ensure that the NTSC viewer had an opportunity to receive the same programming available to ATV viewers during the early phase of ATV implementation. Under this approach, we would broadly define the "same time" at which simulcast programs are required to air, e.g., as the same 24-hour period. As Joint Broadcasters suggest, we would define the "same program" as one which has as its basis the same underlying material. Thus, variances between programs accommodating the special nature of ATV or NTSC, such as different aspect ratios, angles or numbers of cameras, or commentary would be permitted. We might also define "program" to exclude commercials and promotions and to include primary material, such as movies, news, sports, and entertainment shows. We also seek comment on whether programming subject to a simulcast requirement should be of some minimal length and, if so, what an appropriate length would be. For example, would it be appropriate to apply a simulcast requirement to programs of five minutes or more in length? Should the obligation be even broader, encompassing one-minute news breaks for example, or narrower, applying to programs perhaps of 15 minutes or more in duration? These proposed definitions regarding the timing and content of simulcast material would give broadcasters added flexibility and would alleviate concerns that a simulcasting requirement will have a chilling effect on program content or raise First Amendment concerns. We seek comment on these proposals. If we do adopt such an approach, we seek comment on whether it would remain necessary to "phase in" a full simulcasting requirement, as proposed above, to afford broadcasters the flexibility they might need to implement ATV.

As CapCities suggests, we also tentatively conclude that, from the outset, upconverted NTSC programming on broadcasters' second 6-MHz channel must be simulcast programming. We are awarding broadcasters a second 6-MHz channel on an interim basis to permit them to make a transition to ATV. We see no reason to permit use of the second channel for non-ATV programs that differ from those broadcast on the associated NTSC channel. Thus, in the event we adopt a phased-in simulcast requirement, we would nonetheless expect programming on the ATV channel to take full advantage of the technical capabilities of the ATV mode. We seek comment on these tentative conclusions. We also seek comment on the types of programming that would take such full advantage of the ATV mode. For example, such programming might include: (1) programs produced in film and directly converted to the ATV mode; (2) programs originally produced on tape in the ATV mode; and (3) programs produced in the ATV mode live. We ask interested parties to comment on what other types of programs, in addition to these three categories, would take full advantage of the technical capability of the ATV mode.

As we assess the impact of the various alternatives for adopting a simulcast requirement, we are particularly interested in their effect on consumer interest in ATV and on ATV receiver penetration. The more swiftly ATV receiver penetration increases, the more rapidly we will be able to reclaim one 6-MHz channel. We thus are most concerned that we receive detailed comments from electronics manufacturers on the desirability of any given simulcast approach. In addition, we seek detailed comment, especially from professional equipment manufacturers, regarding the speed with which cost-effective equipment permitting upconversion of NTSC programming and downconversion of ATV programming will be available. We also ask for detailed information, particularly from consumer equipment manufacturers, regarding the extent to which inexpensive downconverters for home use are expected to be readily available. We ask interested parties, particularly consumer equipment manufacturers, to comment on the likelihood that dual-mode ATV/NTSC receivers will be developed, and the relative cost of such a dual-mode receiver, as compared with an ATV-only receiver. Finally, we ask interested parties, particularly the programming community, to comment on whether and when a supply of ATV-capable programming is expected to be readily available to broadcasters and consumers.

In a related matter, CapCities requests suspension or waiver of commission rules governing the network/affiliate relationship and contractual negotiations to permit a network to link affiliate clearance or preemption of a program in one format (NTSC or ATV) to clearance or preemption in the other format. These particular rules are at issue in a pending commission proceeding addressing the need to reform our existing broadcast rules. We will therefore not consider relaxation of these rules in this docket at this time. After a decision has been reached in the TV Marketplace proceeding, we will consider in this rule making any specific ATV-related questions that remain, if necessary.

Patent licensing and related issues

The notice stated our belief that, in order to generate the volume of equipment necessary for ATV service to develop widely, the patents on any winning ATV system would have to be licensed to other manufacturing companies on reasonable terms. The consensus among the commenters is that the winning proponent should adopt such reasonable patent licensing policies. There is, however, some divergence of opinion as to the degree to which regulation is required, either now or at some future point, to ensure that reasonable patent licensing policies are indeed adopted. The ATV testing procedures already require proponents to submit, prior to testing, a statement that any relevant patents they own would be made available either free of charge or on reasonable, nondiscriminatory terms. Contrary to the views of those advocating greater regulatory involvement, we find that these requirements adequately safeguard the consumer and competitive interests in reasonable availability of relevant patents, so far as is currently possible.

One party suggests that there will be powerful marketplace incentives that will induce a winning proponent to adopt reasonable patent procedures. Although this might well be true, this issue is critical to ATV implementation and to the consumer and competitive interests implicated. When we officially select an ATV system, therefore, we will condition that selection on the proponent's commitment to reasonable and nondiscriminatory licensing of relevant patents. Nonetheless, we find it premature to decide now, as some commenters advocate, whether we can or should exercise greater regulatory control over a selected system's patent practice. Finally, we recognize that prompt disclosure of a winning system's technical specifications may be necessary to permit the mass production of ATV equipment in a timely fashion. The Advisory Committee indicates that industry efforts are underway to designate a standards-setting group to undertake the formulation of such specifications. We encourage such efforts and will monitor the progress of this industry activity.

Second further notice of proposed rule making

Here the commission examines the critical selection of channel awards (allotments) and has developed an allotment table example that will serve as a serious proposal for all existing TV transmitters from which the broadcast industry can study and express their agreement or otherwise. Because it is both many pages long and not yet official, the tables will not be printed in this chapter. But you will see the FCC's approach to the problem and how it intends to solve at least part of it. The final ATV selection could be very different from that proposed, affecting the various communities throughout this country in many ways and possibly not at all as initially outlined. So, we'll just print the major portion of the text and not the preliminary tables.

In further reading, note that the FCC might actually eliminate many UHF taboo channel spacings and locate some co-channel ATV broadcasting possibly as close as 100 miles. So these are actually radical considerations based upon initial studies under consideration by both the FCC and its industry advisory committee, known as ATV.

The final outcome of these deliberations should appear late in 1992 or early 1993 because final comments are due by October 1992 with replies scheduled later in November.

Background

On April 9, 1992, the Commission adopted a *Second Report and Order/Further Notice of Proposed Rule Making (Order/FNPRM)* in this proceeding. In that action, we adopted policies and rules regarding a number of legal and policy issues associated with the initial implementation of ATV service by existing TV broadcasters and sought comment on proposals regarding other ATV legal and policy implementation issues.

In the *Order/FNPRM*, we, *inter alia*, determined that ATV represents a major advance in television technology, not the start of a new and separate video service. We also found that existing broadcasters possess the know-how and experience to implement ATV swiftly and efficiently. We further recognized the value of the service provided by the existing broadcast television industry and its benefits to the public. For these and other reasons, we therefore concluded that broadcasters should have an opportunity to implement ATV and presented a regulatory approach for that implementation. This plan consists of a transition program in which broadcasters will maintain service to existing NTSC receivers until ATV becomes, and is designated as, the prevalent television medium. To facilitate the transition, broadcasters will temporarily be provided with a second channel to allow them to operate both ATV and NTSC services. At the end of the transition period, broadcasters will relinquish one of their channels. We described the channel that the broadcasters would keep at the end of the transition period as the "conversion channel" and the channel to be relinquished as the "reversion channel."

With regard to ATV allotment policy, in the *Order/FNPRM*, we agreed with commenting parties that it is essential that an ATV allotment/assignment process be in place at the time the ATV standard is adopted and that the policies and methodology for this process be defined as soon as possible. The commission proposed that negotiations should be an integral part of the ATV allotment and assignment process; and that, at the time it proposes a "final" ATV Table of Allotments, broadcasters would be provided a fixed period of time to negotiate and submit plans for pairing NTSC and ATV channels. It further proposed to permit both commercial and non-commercial stations to participate in such negotiations. If there are markets remaining where broadcasters are unable to agree on a pairing plan, the commission proposed that channels in those markets would be assigned on a first-come, first-serve basis.

In the *Order/FNPRM*, the commission deferred action on a number of issues relating to ATV allotments that were raised by parties filing comments in response to the *Notice of Proposed Rule Making (Notice)* that preceded the *Order/FNPRM*. The commission stated that it intended to address those and all other, ATV allotment issues in another Further Notice of Proposed Rule Making, *i.e.*, the instant action.

Discussion   This further notice is the first in the planned series of actions leading to the adoption of a final ATV Table of Allotments. The commission will consider information from the comments and other sources, such as data from the testing of the proponents' technical systems, in finalizing its ATV allotment policies and preparing its proposal for a "final" ATV Table. Interested parties are also advised that we intend to consider alternative proposals for the underlying principles set forth herein that will guide the development of the ATV Table, and request interested parties to submit specific proposals for such alternative approaches.

The purpose of the draft ATV Table of Allotments proposed herein is to aid broadcasters and other interested parties in focusing their comments on the policy proposals presented below. Interested parties are asked to examine this table in formulating comments and alternative proposals regarding ATV allotment and assignment policy issues. We emphasize that the final ATV table could change significantly from the table proposed herein because of factors, such as changes to our ATV allotment policy proposals, the final performance characteristics of the ATV technical system, and the results of our international coordination of ATV allotments with Canada and Mexico. We therefore do not seek comments on the specific conversion-channel allotments indicated on the draft table attached to this further notice. Rather, it is our tentative plan, at the time we propose the final ATV Table, to provide opportunity for comment on individual channel allotments, as well as a specified period of time for broadcasters to negotiate and submit allotment/pairing plans for ATV. Any such negotiated plans would then be included, to the extent practicable, in the final ATV table that we adopt.

Allotment policy

ATV allotment objectives In order to guide the ATV allotment process, we are proposing four broad allotment objectives. These objectives are discussed below in the order of their priority. The application of these objectives to the allotment process is discussed more fully in the section on Allotment Methodology.

Full Accommodation. In the *Order/FNPRM*, the commission decided that all existing TV broadcasters will be eligible for ATV channels. Parties commenting in response to the earlier notice support providing sufficient ATV channel allotments to accommodate all eligible broadcasters. For example, the Advanced Television Systems Committee (ATSC) and the Joint Broadcasters state that it is essential that all existing broadcasters be able to participate in ATV. ATSC endorses a commission plan to amend the Table of Allotments to provide ATV conversion channels for each local community now served by a local television station.

We agree that there should be sufficient ATV allotments to accommodate all eligible broadcasters. This approach would ensure that all broadcasters have an opportunity to participate fully in the transition to the new television technology. This would benefit the public by preserving the service of all the existing TV broadcast stations. In view of the expected expense of implementing ATV service and the need to develop associated programming and production resources, we also believe it is important to minimize the impact of the implementation of ATV on other aspects of the industry's structure. Accordingly, we are proposing that our primary allotment objective be to accommodate all eligible broadcasting entities.

ATV Service Areas. In comments responding to the notice, the Joint Broadcasters and other broadcast industry representatives submit that the commission should base channel pairings, to the greatest extent feasible, on technical and engineering considerations that optimize ATV allotments and maximize service to broadcasters' audiences. The commission's Advisory Committee on Advanced Television Service (Advisory Committee) takes a similar position in its "Fifth Interim Report." The Joint Broadcasters further submit that the channels necessary for ATV should not be obtained by reducing the size of ATV service areas below that needed to achieve maximum ATV coverage or by creating additional interference to NTSC channels.

The Advisory Committee and parties representing a number of broadcast interests, including the Broadcast Caucus, MSTV and others, also suggest an allotment approach that would pair ATV channels with existing NTSC stations based on a "service replication/maximization" plan. Under this approach, the allotment process would attempt to provide ATV coverage areas comparable to existing NTSC coverage areas, taking actual interference into account. Consistent with the comparable coverage objective, the service replication/maximization approach would match ATV channels with existing NTSC channels to create channel pairings/assignments. The goal of this approach would be two-fold: 1) to provide ATV coverage, comparable to a station's entire current coverage area and 2) to provide the best correspondence between the size and shape of the proposed ATV channel's coverage area and the station's existing coverage. MSTV argues that the service replication/maximization plan would be "more equitable, more spectrum efficient, more supportive of the rationale that ATV is an enhancement of existing service and more likely to achieve simulcast service" than the first-come/first-serve, random selection procedures proposed for determining ATV assignments in the *Order/FNPRM*.

On the other hand, representatives of public television stations (Public Television), Fox, Inc., and others submit that, rather than allotting ATV channels based on current NTSC coverage, the commission should attempt to improve the coverage areas of UHF stations and end the UHF/VHF disparity. These parties propose that the allotment plan be guided by the principle of equalizing ATV coverage within markets.

We agree with the commenting parties that it is important to allot conversion channels in a manner that will maximize the service areas of ATV stations to the extent possible. We are concerned, however, that the service replication/maximization objective suggested by the Advisory Committee and others might not be attainable. In particular, we tentatively believe it is likely that a significant number of cases would be encountered in which an acceptable degree of service replication could not be obtained and that all licensees might not be satisfied with the allotments and assignments the plan would produce.

We therefore are proposing an approach that would maximize the service areas of all ATV allotments. Along with a general maximization of service objective, we further believe it is important to enable ATV stations to serve geographic areas that encompass their communities of license and surrounding market areas. For this reason, we also intend to establish a minimum ATV service area objective. We believe that, at a minimum, ATV stations should have the capability to provide service to an area within a radius of 85 to 90 km (about 55 miles) of their transmitter sites. We, therefore, are proposing that the second primary objective of the ATV allotment process be to attempt to maximize the expected service areas of new ATV stations and to ensure that all such stations are able to meet an 85- to 90-km minimum service area objective.

We also request comment on the service replication/maximization concepts described above. In particular, interested parties are asked to address how, under such a plan, choices regarding allotments and service areas should be made across adjacent markets and densely occupied regions where the choice of channels in one market affects the choice of channels in markets located beyond the minimum spacing requirements through a "daisy chain" process. We further request comment on how NTSC interference-limited coverage should be defined with regard to both the existing NTSC service and the new ATV service, taking into account the fact that many existing stations operate at less than the maximum facilities they could be authorized and could, with a minor modification, increase to the maximum. We emphasize that we plan to provide parties an opportunity to develop and work out allotment and assignment matters with other broadcasters in the negotiation period that will be provided after we propose a final ATV Table.

Use of UHF Channels. It is our preliminary view that the implementation of ATV service would be enhanced if all ATV operations were located in the same area of the spectrum, in particular, in the UHF band. This would help to simplify ATV equipment design and to reduce technical disparities between stations. For example, use of a single contiguous band would simplify the design of TV receivers and antennas by removing the need for tuning signals in more than one band. These simplifications could be expected to lower the cost of consumer TV receiver system equipment.

Our ATV allotment studies to date indicate that the majority of ATV conversion channels will have to be allotted from the UHF band. These studies further indicate that only a few VHF channels could be made available in each of the large, congested markets. Generally, we believe the UHF band will prove quite suitable for ATV service. The design of the ATV technical standard is expected to allow ATV UHF stations to serve the same geographic area as NTSC UHF stations, but with substantially less power. This will result in considerable savings in power costs for ATV UHF operations. In addition, the transmission properties of ATV signals and the use of signal processing in ATV receivers should generally render the propagation differences between UHF and VHF frequencies less important. Further, ATV signals are expected to be much less susceptible to multipath and flutter than NTSC signals. We, therefore, are optimistic that the disparity that currently exists between the UHF and VHF bands will be much less significant for ATV service. In view of these considerations, we propose, as our third ATV allotment objective, to make ATV allotments exclusively to the UHF band.

An examination of the proposed ATV table indicates that very few, i.e., 17, ATV VHF allotments would be needed to achieve full accommodation. We also observe that the few ATV VHF allotments included in this table are located in areas where there are one or more existing NTSC stations on UHF channels that meet the proposed ATV-to-ATV spacing requirements. We, therefore, believe that ultimately it will be possible to provide a UHF channel for ATV operation by all of the existing stations that would be assigned ATV VHF allotments. We are proposing special transition provisions to ease the change to ATV for those stations. First, we propose to allow existing NTSC UHF stations assigned ATV VHF channels to switch their NTSC channels to ATV operation before the conversion date. Second, in cases of existing VHF stations or where a direct switch from NTSC to ATV operation by a UHF station otherwise might not be feasible, we propose to make an additional, suitable UHF channel available for the station's ATV operation from the vacated NTSC channels in its area once the conversion occurs. Application for such specially created channels would, of course, be limited for a certain period to existing stations assigned ATV VHF channels in the market. We anticipate that the specific channels to be made available under this policy would be finalized at least two years before the conversion date, so that the affected stations would have adequate time to construct their ATV station and prepare for its operation before the conversion occurs. We request comment on this approach for completing the transition to an all ATV UHF service. Interested parties are also asked to address the point at which early conversion of existing UHF stations to ATV operation should be allowed to occur and to submit proposals for other ways to ease the conversion of ATV VHF stations to UHF channels.

We recognize that the all-UHF approach would represent an important change for the television industry. In particular, it would tend to equalize the expected coverage areas and reception characteristics of all stations. Location of all TV stations in a single band could also be expected to reduce or eliminate differences in viewers' perceptions of stations that might be based on whether stations operate on UHF or VHF channels. Such a change also could affect the current market position of the existing VHF stations. Nonetheless, we tentatively believe the changes in the industry structure that would result from an all UHF service would be beneficial for the public. We request comment on this proposal and its expected impact on the broadcast television industry and television viewers. Alternatively, we seek comment on whether we should maintain some UHF/VHF distinction.

ATV Allotment Preference. We propose, as our final objective, to give a relative preference to new ATV operations over NTSC operations in the allotment process. In most instances, the choice of channels for an ATV allotment will involve consideration of other nearby ATV allotments and existing NTSC stations. Because ATV is proposed to be the medium for television service in the future, we believe ATV service should be preferred over existing NTSC service. That is, where a choice must be made between providing greater service area for a new ATV allotment or minimizing interference to an existing NTSC allotment, we are proposing to choose in favor of the ATV allotment. We request comment on this proposed objective.

Expected performance of ATV systems Our earlier ATV allotment studies indicated that in order to accommodate all existing stations with an ATV channel, it would be necessary to locate some co-channel ATV operations at distances to other NTSC and other ATV stations as close as 160 km (100 miles), with perhaps a very few stations at slightly closer spacings. These studies also indicated that ATV-to-NTSC co-channel spacing is by far the dominant consideration in achieving full accommodation. Our earlier studies further indicated that we will need to eliminate or significantly alter the existing adjacent-channel and UHF taboo-channel spacing requirements. In particular, these studies indicated that to achieve full accommodation, it will be necessary to co-locate or reduce spacings between adjacent channels in some instances and to eliminate many of the UHF taboo channels. FCC staff studies of NTSC receiver performance and spectrum availability also indicate that it appears possible to use the UHF taboo channels for ATV service.

Understanding these considerations, the proponents of the five HDTV systems being evaluated by the Advisory Committee as candidates for selection as the ATV technical standard have designed their systems to operate at the necessarily closer spacings. The proponents claim that their systems can provide service at 160- to 184-km (100 to 115 mile) co-channel station-to-station distances. At these spacings, ATV stations would be able to provide service that extends nearly as far as the service of co-channel NTSC stations located at the current minimum spacings. The system proponents also indicate that their systems can provide this range of service at the closer spacings while causing no more interference to existing NTSC service than is caused by another NTSC station operating at the current minimum spacings for co-channel NTSC UHF stations. These estimates generally are based on system-independent service area planning factors consistent with those recommended by the Advisory Committee.

We, therefore, expect that the technical system chosen as the ATV standard will be able to provide satisfactory service and interference performance at the co-channel spacings we will need to use in allotting ATV channels. The actual performance capabilities of the proponents systems are being evaluated by the Advisory Committee. The information from these evaluations will be considered in developing the final ATV table.

Allotment methodology and approach In this section, we address the specific methodology and criteria to be used in allotting ATV channels to meet the broad objectives presented above. Interested parties are invited to comment on these proposals and to suggest alternatives.

Use of Spacing Standards. The Advisory Committee, the Joint Broadcasters and others support use of minimum spacing standards for the allotment of ATV channels. This approach is similar to the approach currently used with NTSC TV and FM radio allotments.

We concur with this view and therefore propose to allot ATV channels using geographical spacing criteria in the same manner that we currently allot to NTSC TV channels and FM radio channels. This traditional approach has proved to be an efficient, effective means for managing interference between stations and the implementation of new allotments and assignments. Moreover, the geographical spacing approach allows considerable flexibility in the specification of station operating parameters such as power and antenna height in meeting coverage objectives. To maximize the expected coverage areas of ATV stations, our allotment decisions will attempt to optimize the distances between new ATV allotments and between new ATV allotments and existing NTSC stations.

Spacing Proposals. Consistent with our broad ATV objectives, we are proposing minimum spacing standards that we believe will ensure that ATV stations are able to serve areas comparable to NTSC UHF stations, i.e., areas within 85 to 90 km of their transmitters. As is the case for NTSC service, the most difficult area for locating ATV allotments is in Zone I, particularly the northeast corridor of the United States. The projected ATV system performance information indicates that our ATV service goals can be achieved through the following minimum spacings:

1. ATV-to-ATV co-channel stations: 200 km (125 miles)
2. ATV-to-ATV adjacent-channel stations: more than 88 km (55 miles) or less than 8 km (5 miles)
3. ATV-to-NTSC co-channel stations: 184 km (115 miles)
4. ATV-to-NTSC adjacent-channel stations: more than 88 km (55 miles) or less than 8 km (5 miles)

Accordingly, we propose to establish the above criteria as the minimum spacing requirements for ATV stations. Consistent with our goal of maximizing the coverage potential of the ATV allotments, we will endeavor to separate co-channel stations as far as possible, up to a distance of 250 km (155 miles). We believe that this approach will balance the overall quality, e.g., expected coverage areas, of the allotments in adjacent markets. We recognize that additional data on spacing needs will be forthcoming from the Advisory Committee's testing process and we will consider that data when it becomes available.

The minimum spacing needed between stations on adjacent channels and on channels separated by the UHF taboo relationships will be affected by the selectivity of the tuners used in consumer ATV receivers. We, therefore, intend to pay careful attention to the Advisory Committees adjacent and taboo channel testing and the likelihood of building economical tuners to perform to, or improve upon, those results in developing the final table. Based on our own earlier receiver studies, we believe that most of the UHF taboos can be largely ignored in allotting ATV channels. Accordingly, at this time we are not proposing spacing rules to protect for UHF taboo effects. Interested parties are requested to address the relationship between economical tuner designs and acceptable spacings between stations on adjacent and UHF taboo channels and the possible need for maintaining specific taboos.

We request comment on the above spacing proposals. Parties suggesting alternative spacing requirements are asked to submit data and analyses that support their proposals. Commenting parties are also invited to examine the forthcoming Advisory Committee data and comment on its implications for minimum spacing requirements. We also request comment on whether it is necessary to specify alternative minimum spacing requirements for Zones II and III, as we do for NTSC service.

Short-spaced Allotments. Because our primary objective is full accommodation of all existing television stations, our first concern will be spacing stations at distances necessary to provide channels for all existing stations in the initial ATV Table. In implementing this priority with our objective to maximize service areas, our approach will be to attempt, first, to allot channels at distances that meet or exceed the minimum spacing requirements stated above. However, in order to accommodate all existing stations with ATV channels, it will be necessary to locate some allotments at co-channel spacings that are closer than the minimum standards. In fact, it will be necessary to locate some co-channel ATV and NTSC stations as close as 156 km (97 miles) apart. The service range of such short-spaced stations likely will be reduced in the direction of a line between the two stations. Nonetheless, we believe the benefits of providing full accommodation of all existing stations warrant the relatively small loss in total service area that will occur in such cases. We intend to make every effort to minimize the use of short-spacing and its effect on neighboring stations. We also note from the ATV Table proposed herein that most of the short-spaced situations will be between ATV and NTSC stations. As the ATV-NTSC short-spacings will be present only during the transition period, most of the effects on service areas from short spacings will not be present after that time.

We also propose to allow short-spaced allotments only during the initial assignment phase for existing stations. Subsequent additions to the ATV Table for stations to be operated by new applicants would be required to comply with the minimum spacing requirements. After the two-year initial application period, we propose to delete all short-spaced allotments that have not been activated by an eligible broadcaster.

Use of Existing Sites. The Advisory Committee and the majority of broadcasters take the position that ATV channels should be allotted on the basis of current transmitter sites, rather than the reference points of communities. The Joint Broadcasters believe this approach would help maximize the coverage areas of ATV stations, while minimizing potential interference to other, including secondary, stations. These parties further state that deviations in the service areas that are possible within the group of channels available to allot to a given community argue strongly for pairing on the basis of existing transmitters sites. Joint Broadcasters also submit that most stations will find it cheaper and easier to co-locate their ATV transmitters at their existing transmitter sites, and that this would reduce implementation expense and expedite the introduction of ATV service. They acknowledge, however, that some stations will have tower loading problems, at least in the short run, and that others might find their existing sites relatively inferior. Great American Television and Radio Company, Inc. (Great American) requests that the commission establish procedures that would permit stations, for good cause, to request that their allotment be located at a site different from that of their existing transmitter. Great American points out that in some cases the licensee might not be able to locate a second transmitter and antenna at an existing site or might have identified a preferred alternative site.

du Treil. Lundin and Rackley, Inc. (dLR), the Telemundo Group, Inc. (Telemundo) and others ask the commission to consider clustering ATV allotments at one location in a community to facilitate a common antenna location for stations and thus reduce transmission costs. Telemundo also states that co-location of the ATV operations in an area would eliminate UHF taboo concerns. Bradenton Broadcast Television Company, Inc. (Bradenton) urges that channels be allotted on a "whole market" basis, rather than to the specific communities to which NTSC stations are currently licensed. Bradenton states that this would allow fringe-area stations to compete with the more centrally located stations in their market for the more desirable channels.

We agree with those parties who suggest that there are advantages in taking into account existing transmitter locations in the ATV allotment process. Using the locations of the existing transmitter sites as reference points for the initial ATV Table would facilitate more efficient spacing of ATV allotments. It also would ensure that, where otherwise feasible, broadcasters can realize the cost savings from co-locating their NTSC and ATV operations. We disagree with those parties who suggest that all of the channels in a market or community be located at a single site or that channels be allotted on a whole market basis rather than to specific communities. These approaches would reduce allotment flexibility and might tend to limit the number of channels that could be allotted. Moreover, we see no reason to expect that all the stations in a market would generally seek to operate their ATV service from a common location. Accordingly, we propose to allot ATV channels on the basis of current transmitter sites, rather than community reference points. The current NTSC transmitter sites would be used to develop the ATV Table and to determine whether potential ATV allotments meet the proposed minimum separation requirements. We request specific comment regarding any circumstances where it might be desirable to evaluate ATV allotments on the basis of sites other than those occupied by existing TV stations.

For purposes of this proposal, we would assume that an existing site location is the area within a three-mile radius of the actual transmitter location. In accordance with our established practice for broadcasting, we propose to permit a licensee to operate its ATV station at a site different from that of its NTSC operation where the alternate sites would meet the proposed ATV minimum spacing requirements and the station would continue to serve its community of license. Such site relocations could include movement to a common local TV transmission site.

Other allotment policy and process issues

Existing vacant allotments and new applications   dLR submits that all commercial TV allotments that are not currently being used or for which there are no pending applications should be deleted from the existing TV Table of Allotments. dLR also asks the commission to extend the current freeze on acceptance of applications in the most densely occupied markets. Joint Broadcasters state that the commission must at some point "freeze" the pool of eligible existing stations and the locations of those stations. They further state that a limited exception to this freeze might be appropriate for new NTSC noncommercial stations in areas not yet receiving noncommercial service. MSTV, in reply comments, submits that the commission should institute a freeze, for planning purposes only, on all modifications of existing stations' technical and engineering parameters that could affect the determination of both existing and proposed HDTV coverage and interference areas. Under this suggestion, licensees would, in fact, be allowed to seek modifications that would affect their coverage and interference areas. The commission would ignore any such changes in its planning work, however. MSTV says the "planning freeze" would allow the commission to design ATV allotments with a first priority of achieving coverage comparable to NTSC coverage.

We see no need to implement dLR's suggestion to delete from the existing TV Table of Allotments all commercial TV allotments that are not currently being used or for which there are no pending applications. It does not appear necessary to eliminate all of the existing vacant NTSC allotments in order to implement our ATV plan. We also see no need to impose a general "freeze" on the pool of NTSC stations eligible for ATV channels or on the locations of existing stations. As noted above, we have already issued an Order freezing applications for new stations in the 30 major cities where our earlier studies indicated that a shortage of spectrum for operation of ATV stations might exist. We continue to believe there is adequate spectrum available in markets outside these 30 to accommodate ATV channels. Thus, the existing freeze appears adequate to ensure that spectrum is available for ATV channels. Similarly, we see no purpose in employing MSTV's "planning freeze" with regard to modifications of existing stations. Accordingly, as indicated in the Order/FNPRM, we will accept applications for new NTSC stations during the course of the development of the ATV table and until the end of the initial ATV assignment process.

We propose, however, to delete vacant NTSC commercial allotments where necessary to facilitate creation of an ATV allotment. To the extent that it would be necessary to displace specific existing vacant allotments to create an ATV allotment, we would not accept applications for those existing allotments. This policy would become effective at the time we propose the final ATV Table of Allotments.

In keeping with our decision in the Order/FNPRM, we will attempt to maintain existing vacant noncommercial NTSC allotments and to provide new ATV channels for such allotments. We will eliminate vacant noncommercial allotments only where no feasible alternative exists for allotting ATV channels for eligible broadcasters. We also will provide vacant noncommercial reserved allotments with an ATV channel except where all of the available ATV allotments are needed by existing broadcasters and careful engineering analysis reveals no other practicable alternative.

Low-power and TV translator stations In the Order/FNPRM, we determined that if ATV is to succeed, it will be necessary for new ATV assignments to displace low-power TV (LPTV) and TV translator stations to some degree in the major markets. We observed that the impact on low-power stations is likely to be less severe in rural areas, where there are fewer full-service stations. This determination was based on studies by our staff and the Advisory Committee that indicate there is insufficient spectrum available in the broadcast TV bands to factor in low-power displacement considerations in making ATV assignments. We observed that, in fact, it will be a challenge just to provide all full-service licensees with an additional 6 MHz for ATV. We, therefore, reluctantly concluded that we must continue LPTV and TV translators secondary status vis-a-vis ATV stations. In view of the important benefits that LPTV and TV translators provide to the public, we also took a number of steps to mitigate the likelihood and effects of displacement on low-power stations.

Consistent with the determinations and actions in the Order/FNPRM, the ATV allotment process generally will not attempt to protect low-power stations from interference from potential ATV stations. Also, as indicated in the Order/FNPRM, some of these stations, particularly those in the more congested areas of the nation, may be required to make changes in their operation, including the possibility of ceasing operation, to avoid interference to ATV stations.

Use of TV channels 3 and 4 In its reply comments, MSTV submits that, because channels 3 and 4 are used as the output frequencies of cable terminal equipment and VCRs, caution should be exercised in allotting both of these channels to the same community. MSTV is concerned that cable terminal equipment and VCRs might be vulnerable to interference from ATV signals operating on the output channels used by this equipment.

Although, at this time, we are proposing to use the UHF frequency band for ATV and the proposed ATV table does not use TV channels 3 and 4, we are aware of the potential interference concerns mentioned by MSTV with regard to use of these channels in the same community. In general, we believe the output signal levels of cable terminal devices and VCRs can be expected to be significantly higher than the off-air levels of an ATV signal on the frequency on which this equipment would operate. Moreover, the amplified output signal of cable terminals and VCRs would be coupled by cable directly to the input terminal of a TV receiver's tuner circuit. The interfering ATV signal, on the other hand, would be present only through direct pickup within the TV receiver itself, and therefore would be at a significantly lower level of power. An off-air ATV signal is therefore not likely to interfere with the operation of a cable terminal or VCR. Conversely, if the connection between the output of a cable terminal or VCR and a TV receiver is properly shielded, the output signal will not interfere with reception of off-air signals through the VCR, suitably equipped cable terminal or other device for switching program sources. Thus, we believe that channels 3 and 4 generally can be used for NTSC and ATV operations in the same area without conflicting with the operation of cable terminal devices and VCRs. Nonetheless, if it is decided to use the VHF frequencies for ATV, we propose to avoid the allotment of both channels 3 and 4 within the same community wherever possible.

TV channel 6 allotments If we decide to use the VHF channels for ATV, we will need to protect against possible interference from TV channel 6 operations to FM radio service on FM channel 253 and to TV channel 6 from FM radio service on noncommercial educational FM channels 201-220. To avoid situations where such interference could arise, we propose to make ATV allotments to TV channel 6 only where there is no other readily available allotment opportunity that would meet the minimum spacing requirements. We propose to apply an appropriate standard similar to that currently specified in the rules to protect against interference between NTSC channel 6 and FM radio. We note the sample ATV table set forth herein does not use channel 6 for any ATV allotments.

Land mobile sharing channels We also need to protect against possible interference between ATV stations and land mobile operations on TV broadcast frequencies in certain areas. The rules authorize land mobile sharing operations on frequencies in the range of UHF channels 14 to 20 in 13 urbanized areas, the Gulf of Mexico offshore region, and Hawaii. Because ATV stations are expected to operate with 10 dB less power than NTSC stations, we believe we can allow ATV stations to be located somewhat closer to land mobile operations than is permitted under our current policy. Generally, we believe that it would be possible to allow ATV stations to operate at co-channel and adjacent-channel spacings to the city-center of land mobile operations as close as 250 km (155 miles) and 176 km (110 miles), respectively. We request comment on whether these shorter spacing standards would adequately protect against interference between land mobile operations and ATV stations. We also invite interested parties to submit proposals for alternative minimum spacing requirements for ATV and land mobile stations.

All but one of the allotments on the draft ATV table would comply with the proposed 155-mile co-channel spacing requirement between ATV allotments and land mobile operations. That is, only one of the ATV allotments on this table would be short-spaced, with respect to co-channel land mobile operations. The draft table does, however, include five cases where ATV allotments would be located at distances less than 110 miles from the city-center of an adjacent-channel land mobile system. In order to achieve full accommodation of all existing TV broadcasters, it might be necessary to make special accommodations in the few situations where short-spacing is necessary between ATV allotments and land mobile service. Such accommodations could take the form of conditions on either ATV or land mobile operations in the affected areas. We request comment and information regarding the specific conditions to be applied in such types of cases and the manner in which such conditions should be applied to achieve an appropriate balance between ATV and land mobile interests.

In the case of Detroit and Cleveland, our existing border agreements with Canada preclude activation of land mobile stations on UHF channels in those markets. It also appears that it would further our full accommodation and service area goals to use the land mobile reserved channels in these markets for ATV. Accordingly, we are proposing to make channels 15 and 16 in Detroit and channels 14 and 15 in Cleveland, which are now reserved for land mobile use, available for allotment as ATV channels.

International coordination We have initiated coordination activities with both the Canadian and Mexican governments for proposed ATV allotments in the border areas. We expect to address coordination arrangements with these governments for ATV allotments in the border areas in a time frame consistent with our allotment and assignment schedule.

Certain ATV issues resolved: further comment sought on other issues (MM Docket 87-268)

Excerpted here from the FCC News *report, dated September 17, 1992 are other issues that have been resolved concerning HDTV.*

The commission has resolved, and in some cases reconsidered, a number of outstanding issues and has solicited further comment on other issues fundamental to implementation of an advanced television (ATV) service in this country.

In today's action, in response to petitions for reconsideration or clarification of the Second Report/Further Notice, the commission:

- reconsidered in part its decision regarding the application and construction permit. As a preliminary matter, it extended the application deadline to three years after the time that an ATV Allotment Table or an ATV standard is effective, whichever is later, and permitted a total of six years for both application and construction. Licensees who apply before the end of the initial three-year application period will be given to the end of that three-year application period plus three years in which to become operational;
- declined to modify policy regarding the secondary status of low-power television service stations or to restrict competition for licenses in order to favor these stations;
- adhered to its decision that a firm date for conversion for all broadcasters must be established;
- adhered to its determination that a 100-percent simulcasting requirement should be adopted at the earliest appropriate time.

On the basis of the comments and replies received in response to the Second Report/Further Notice, the commission took the following actions:

- reaffirmed its decision to limit initial eligibility for ATV frequencies to "existing broadcasters."
- temporarily suspended the dual network rule during the transition period to permit networks to give their affiliates a second feed for ATV and provided for review of this temporary suspension;
- deferred its decision on an assignment methodology until it determines the allotment approach that it will adopt;
- agreed to create a noncommercial reserve of ATV spectrum;
- declined at this time to mandate low power television service conversion to ATV by a date certain;
- adopted, as a preliminary decision, a deadline for conversion that is 15 years from the date that ATV system selection or a final table of ATV Allotments is effective, whichever is later. Clarified that broadcasters will have to cease broadcasting in NTSC at the final conversion date;
- declined to adopt production standards for ATV;
- adopted, as a preliminary matter, a 50-percent simulcasting requirement to be imposed one year after, and a 100-percent simulcasting requirement to be imposed three years after, the six-year construction/application period ends;
- In addition to scheduling a review of the application and construction period at the time standard selection or an ATV Allotment Table, whichever is later, adopted a timetable for periodic review of the regulatory approach to conversion and simulcasting, including a review of the presumptive simulcasting and conversion deadlines. The periodic reviews would be conducted by notice and comment proceedings.

Preliminary decisions would not be modified without substantial showings based on specific data that such change was in the public interest;

- defined simulcasting as the broadcast on the NTSC channel of the same basic material broadcast on the ATV channel, excluding commercials and promotions, within 24 hours. It did not permit subscription services only on the ATV channel of an ATV-NTSC pair;
- endorsed the Advanced Television Systems Committee's agreement to document technical specifications once an ATV standard is selected.

The commission also sought comment on the following issues:

- whether a renewal challenger should be permitted to file a supplemental application for the ATV channel, which would be contingent upon the grant of the challenger's NTSC application; also, whether that contingent ATV application should not be subject to a second comparative hearing;
- whether some additional measure of relief or further action should be taken on behalf of noncommercial stations, with respect to the presumptive six-year application/construction deadline;
- a proposal to assign an existing broadcaster's ATV channel the same callsign as its NTSC channel, with the addition of an appropriate two-letter suffix;
- whether future advances in technology that are compatible with any ATV standard selected should be permitted on the conversion channel; and
- whether to permit use of ATV channels for ancillary purposes in a manner similar to what is now permitted on NTSC.

Glossary

ACTV Advanced Compatible Television. The only Enhanced Definition Television system on the test schedule, proposed by the Advanced Television Research Consortium.

Advanced Digital High-Definition Television One of the digital HDTV systems on the test schedule, proposed by the Advanced Television Research Consortium.

Advanced Television (ATV) Any television technology, including High-Definition Television and Enhanced Definition Television, that provides improved audio and video quality or enhances the current television broadcast system.

Advanced Television Evaluation Laboratory (ATEL) Organization located in Ottawa, Canada, undertaking the subjective video testing of the proposed ATV systems.

Advanced Television Test Center (Test Center) Organization formed by the Advisory Committee on Advanced Television to conduct broadcast testing of the qualified proposed ATV systems.

Advisory Committee on Advanced Television Service (Advisory Committee) Panel formed by the Federal Communications Commission in 1987 to advise the agency on the technical and public policy issues concerning Advanced Television. Membership is comprised of industry leaders from diverse sectors, including the broadcast, cable, computer, and manufacturing industries.

Allocation, Allotment, Assignment As a technical matter, spectrum space is "allocated" to a particular service. The allocated channels are then "allotted" to specific geographic areas, and the allotted channels are then "assigned" to a licensee.

ANSI The American National Standards Institute, which establishes patent policy adhered to in the ATV Test Procedures Test Management Plan.

Aspect Ratio The ratio of picture width to picture height.

ATRC The American Television Research Consortium, proponent of the Advanced Compatible Television system and the Advanced Digital High-Definition Television system. Membership consists of the David Sarnoff Research Center, North American Philips, Thomson Consumer Electronics, NBC, and Compression Labs.

ATVA The American Television Alliance, proponent of the DigiCipher system and the ATA Progressive System. Membership consists of General Instrument Corporation and the Massachusetts Institute of Technology.

ATVA Progressive System One of the digital HDTV systems on the test schedule, proposed by the American Television Alliance.

Broadcast Auxiliary Spectrum Microwave frequencies allocated for use by television stations to convey their signals on a point-to-point basis from fixed or mobile facilities.

Cable Television Laboratories, Inc. (CableLabs) Organization sponsored by the cable industry, which is conducting tests of the cable-related performance of the proposed ATV systems.

Closed Captioning Technology that allows captions to appear on a specially equipped receiver screen at the same time the words are being broadcast, generally used so that dialogue can be followed by deaf viewers.

COHRS The Committee for Open High Resolution System.

Conversion The point at which broadcast licensees would cease broadcasting in NTSC and "convert" entirely to ATV programming (i.e., surrender one 6-MHz channel and broadcast only in ATV).

Conversion Channel One of the two 6-MHz channels that will be assigned to broadcasters to enable them to transmit in both ATV and NTSC for the interim period prior to conversion to ATV alone.

DBS Direct Broadcast Satellites.

Decoder Act The Television Decoder Circuitry Act of 1990, which requires television receivers with screens 13 inches or larger that are manufactured in or imported into the United States, to contain built-in decoder circuitry for closed captioning display, and that the commission ensure continued closed captioning service.

Descriptor A descriptor identifies the technical characteristics of the data in a digital signal.

DigiCipher One of the digital HDTV systems on the test schedule, proposed by the American Television Alliance.

Digital Spectrum Compatible HDTV (DSC-HDTV) One of the digital HDTV systems on the test schedule, proposed by Zenith and American Telephone and Telegraph.

Downconversion Changing a program from the HDTV format to the NTSC format.

Dual Network Rule Commission rule (47 CFR §73.658(g), which prohibits a network from simultaneously operating more than one network of television stations in identical or overlapping geographic areas.

Enhanced Definition Television (EDTV)   Television systems that provide limited improvements over the current NTSC broadcasting system.

Extensibility   As defined by the Advisory Committee, a property of a system, format, or standards that allows future improvements in performance or format within a common framework, while retaining partial or complete compatibility among systems that belong to the common framework.

Five-channel Audio   A system characteristic that provides for a right, center, and left front channel, plus a right and a left rear channel (or surround channel).

Harmonization   As defined by the Advisory Committee, the coordination of different advanced image standards in an orderly process.

Header   A sort of digital label that identifies the type of data and type of processing performed on the data that follows.

High Definition Television (HDTV)   Television systems that aim to offer approximately twice the vertical and horizontal resolution of the existing NTSC receivers and to provide picture quality approaching that of 35-mm film and audio quality equal to that of compact discs.

Interoperability   As defined by the Advisory Committee, the capability of providing useful and cost-effective interchange of electronic image, audio, and associated data: among different signal formats, among different transmission media, and among different performance levels.

IS/WP1   Working Party 1, Policy and Regulation, of the Advisory Committee's Implementation Subcommittee.

IS/WP2   Working Party 2, Transition Scenarios, of the Advisory Committee's Implementation Subcommittee.

Low-Power Television (LPTV)   A broadcast television facility with secondary service status that is authorized to retransmit the programs and signals of a TV broadcast station and that may originate programming and/or operate a subscription service.

Narrow MUSE   The analog HDTV system on the test schedule, proposed by NHK.

NHK   The Japan Broadcasting Company, proponent of the Narrow MUSE HDTV system.

NTSC   The existing broadcasting system, named after the National Television Systems Committee.

PS/WP3   Working Party 3, Spectra Utilization and Alternatives, of the Advisory Committee's Planning Subcommittee.

PS/WP4   Working Party 4, Alternative Media Technology and Broadcast Interface, of the Advisory Committee's Planning Subcommittee.

PS/WP5   Working Party 5, Economic Factors and Market Penetration, of the Advisory Committee's Planning Subcommittee.

Reversion Channel   One of the two 6-MHz channels assigned to broadcasters during the transition to ATV. This channel will be reclaimed by the commission after full conversion to ATV.

SBCA   Satellite Broadcasting and Communications Association.

Scalability As defined by the Advisory Committee, the degree to which video and image formats can be combined in systematic proportions for distribution over communications channels for varying capacities.

Studio-Transmitter Link (STL) A type of broadcast auxiliary channel used for transmissions between a television station's studio and the station's transmitter.

Terrestrial Broadcast Station Broadcast stations that transmit from a tower located on the surface of the earth, as opposed to a satellite system with a space station.

Translator A low-power TV station that does not originate programming and acts only to retransmit the signals of a full-service TV station.

Upconversion Changing a program from NTSC to HDTV format.

Vertical Blanking Interval That portion of the TV signal that appears as a black bar when the picture rolls. The commission's rules currently provide that closed captioning of NTSC programs for the deaf may be transmitted on line 21 of the vertical blanking interval.

6

Companding—the secret of HDTV transmissions

This chapter title might be somewhat presumptuous and slightly misleading, but without companding there would be no 5-channel audio and 30-MHz video. So, take this statement to task, if you will, but do read on and absorb a bit of the interesting detail with which we will try to enliven this short chapter.

Admittedly, some of the information has already been discussed among the individual system writeups, but we do have a couple of supplementary references that can illuminate the subject somewhat further and possibly promote additional understanding—at least a rather diligent attempt will be made and the result evaluated solely by the reader. Regardless, we'll do our best for dear young HDTV and allow the artifacts, glitches, and mega-bit streams to fall where they may.

Brief system descriptions

The objective broadcasting wideband video accompanied by superior audio is placing an electromagnetic signal on the air with a minimum of processing. According to Wayne Luplow of Zenith, digital information can be transcoded, but the difficulty lies in execution without artifacts. Maximum data rates in several systems use discrete cosine transfer and vector quantization compression in addition to motion compensation and spatial redundancy. Zenith, for instance, has also introduced bi-rate coding so that critical sequences are encoded in binary, with much of the remaining intelligence carried on a 4-level bit stream, which, it's said, produces fewer errors approaching maximum signal range.

ATRC (the NBC, Sarnoff Labs, Compression Labs, Philips, and Thomson consortium) has unilaterally adopted motion-picture experts group MPEG as its digital compression standard, expanding that technology to MPEG++ for "excellent HDTV performance," as well as recording, VCR, disc, and computer compatibility. It establishes a "seam" between the "Standard Priority Channel" and High Priority channel (Fig. 6-1) to prevent video interference and project stronger visual and sound at 4.8 Mbps, with additional picture information in the standard priority carrier at 19.2 Mbps at a total data rate of 24 Mbps/sec and CD-quality sound. A drawing of this SS-QUAM spectrum, compared to NTSC is illustrated in Fig. 6-1, with both transmissions within the allotted conventional 6-MHz/channel VHF/UHF passband. This scheme offers dual-pass encoding, allowing bit allocations with perceptual weighing, reducing artifacts and improving picture quality. Its prioritized data transport supplies a stronger carrier for high-priority sound, and picture and system packaging permits separate video, audio, and auxiliary data entities to be mixed and varied dynamically for suitable combination transmissions. The system was broadcast during late September 1992 over WRC-TV in Washington, DC in simulcast with NTSC (Fig. 6-2).

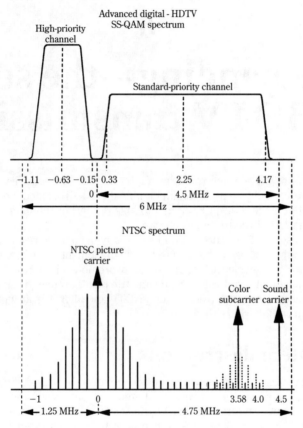

6-1 Sarnoff Consortium's spectrum compression compared to standard NTSC.

General Instrument is offering two HDTV systems in cooperation with the Massachusetts Institute of Technology (MIT).

DigiCipher/G.I. is a predictive/transform compression algorithm that is delivered in either 32 quadrature amplitude modulation or 16 QUAM. Receivers will decode either, although 16 QUAM has somewhat lower picture quality, but is superior where transmissions face co-channel spacing and power problems. So, 32 QUAM is covered here instead.

Data, audio, and video are multiplexed into single data streams at 18.22 Mbps, with error correction expanding delivery to 24.39 Mbps. Motion-compensated predictive coding DCPM takes care of temporal correlation and discrete cosine transforms operate on

6-2 Simulcasting NTSC and HDTV from the same tower with multiple antennas.

spatial correlation. Frame-to-frame redundancy is eliminated by DPCM or, if DPCM is less effective than PCM, switching to PCM occurs for intraframe coding. And when frequency-domain images are not readily seen by the viewer, discrete cosine transform (DCT) offers further bit reduction. Chroma and luminance information are processed together by DCT, but 8 luminance blocks pass while only two chroma blocks continue. Short words are frequently re-occurring values while longer words are infrequent and all are quantized accordingly via Huffman coding.

While one DigiCipher/G.I. operates at a frame (video) rate of 29.94 Hz, 2:1 interlaced, and single frames of 960 lines, the second MIT/G.I. system delivers 787.5 RGB lines at 59.94 fps in progressive scan format. There's motion estimation and compensation, quantizing, entropy encoding with multiplexing/modulation, as well as matrix conversion, subband analysis, and muxing for auxiliary data and digital audio. The receiver then delivers a 3:2 pull down from 60 frames for the frame display plus decoding, transform/subband synthesis, motion compensation and vectors, then converts into regular RGB.

Generalizations

What you have read so far are shave-tail specifics from the remaining digital systems. But we're going to add some generalities that, hopefully, can make the subject somewhat lighter and more understanding. In other words, not binary, hexadecimal, or octal details in GPIB printouts, but a few of the ordinary procedures applicable to many current digitizing efforts in television. If this helps, so much the better; if not, return to the individual, long descriptions among the early chapters and struggle on. Fortunately, we didn't promise a "Rose Garden"... so "The Beat Goes On."

Bandwidth compression has often consisted of Sub-Nyquist sampling with (or without) motion compensation, lowpass or bandpass component filtering, and timing operations on components to reduce bandwidths, in addition to more modern source and channel codings. Source coding shrinks and compacts video, while channel coding transmits this information over the air. Here, as in several systems, redundant information is not broadcast while necessary video is constricted to an RF total of 6 MHz across the channel. Visual perception is also involved because the eye cannot see details in color as well as black and white—that's why fine detail is especially important in monochrome. Thus, nonessential color is removed prior to transmission, thereby conserving bandwidth. Then, only newly-generated picture information reaches succeeding frames, followed by motion compensation as information or objects appear to move across the picture.

General Instrument and its DigiCipher observe that most of the energy in pictures consist of low-frequency images occupying large areas, so they represent small picture portions as "sets of frequencies" and much high-frequency intelligence "can be discarded with no loss of picture quality." This, of course, is further video compression.

Now, as pictures become busier, more of it fails to transmit, but since visual perception isn't that keen, the viewer sees little resolution change because of continued picture movement. And in scene changes, DigiCipher transmits coarse information upon any scene change and refines it rapidly before the eye reacts unfavorably.

Thereafter, highly compressed digital is coded and transmitted, delivering at least half of the total compression. In this system, transmission occurs at either 16 or 32 quadrature amplitude modulation (QUAM) as a digital bit stream. Once this reaches the home receiver, the process is basically reversed, decoding and demodulation takes place, digital skips are filled and D/A (digital-to-analog) conversion takes place so that a high definition picture covers the 16:9 extended horizontal/vertical ratio-proportioned screen.

The transmitter must guard against digital coding errors and the receiver has to correct for multipath (ghost) distortions—both of which techniques are now available.

HDTV transmissions operate at much less power than standard NTSC and transmitters can often share towers (Fig. 6-2) with analog NTSC because they are usually confined to UHF (channels 14 to 69) and normally use smaller antennas of diminished bulk.

As stated, specific details of all surviving systems have been set forth previously in considerable detail, so we feel that this short, pithy explanation of at least one basic operation in virtually laymens' terms should bring you up to virtual gravity-release speed and permit easier reading for the remainder of the book.

7

HDTV and CATV testing

With more than considerable thanks to Peter Fannon (TV) and Brian James (Cable), we now have much of the vital information on laboratory testing that has gone forward over these many months past—occasionally painfully, but always in forward progress and normally within scheduled parameters. These were actually prodigious undertakings because they were examining analog and digital equipments never before available to either the U.S. or the rest of the world. Therefore, highly specialized instruments were needed, and some even had to be designed or interlocked from scratch to produce accurate assessments of general and specific HDTV and CATV performance under stringent operating conditions.

Unfortunately, we cannot describe all these operations in either basic electronics or laymens terms because of very new and extended technology that sometimes can be only understood by the very testers themselves. So, rather than stretch both our imaginations, we'll stick to the excellent, but often involved, material presented in the public domain, doing our best to interpret whenever or wherever possible along with illuminating line-cut illustrations furnished by the test bed originators.

Test beds

With such "basis in fact" to begin, the first diagram you see is that of the necessary Functional Requirements (Fig. 7-1). Here you see the status, control, database, distribution system, and error/time logs for the TV system. Observe all the recorders, synthesizers, test projections, supervisor controls, and the various human/machine interfaces.

Expanding the foregoing outline further, you now are made aware of not only the RF Test Bed (Fig. 7-2), but also the Technical Operating Center, as well as the Viewing Room, which was always used by the Expert Observers examining the various systems' performance for signal levels, interference with adjacent HDTV or NTSC, artifacts, and the anything-term, known as *glitches*.

Fortunately, Advanced Television Test Center Executive Director Peter Fannon has not only furnished photos of the testing areas, but also some worthwhile information to go with them, which we will happily include as the description continues and expands. There isn't room enough word-wise to include individual system testing, but we will conclude the TV portion with a system-specific test procedure for G.I./DigiCipher system,

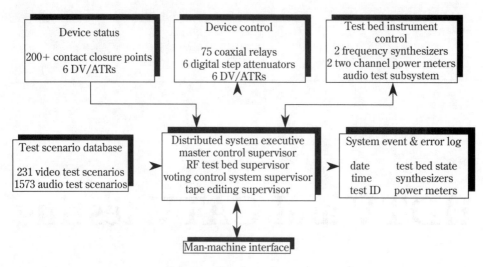

7-1 Functional requirements.

which is partially applicable to other all-digital proposals as well. So, really, this is a well-rounded discussion of who, what, why, along with some how that might hold your attention for a while longer. Just remember, months of examining the various proponents' systems with all their differences and requirements isn't the easiest of tasks—especially because it all began July 12, 1991 and was only completed during October 1992 at a cost of $5 million for the test bed out of a total $17 million commitment by television broadcasters and receiver manufacturers. Sponsoring members include Capital Cities/ABC, Inc; CBS, Inc.; NBC, Inc.; Public Broadcasting Service (PBS); The Association of Independent Television Stations (INTV); the Association for Maximum Service Television (MSTV); Electronic Industries Association (EIA); and the National Association of Broadcasters (NAB). Individual system proponents themselves paid out over $300,000 each for required tests. As you can see, considerable money and a maximum effort was needed to complete the task, which even extended to Canada for the many "lay" observers collected from among available college students there.

So, before we fully enter the realm of specifics, let's view selected pictures offered by the ATTC and explain certain captions as we go along. Figure 7-3 illustrates the official viewing room at ATTC with its Hitachi 16:9 aspect ratio HDTV 65" diagonal projector and lenticular screen used here and in Canada. The Hitachi multi-scan could display all four HDTV formats and also accommodate five expert viewers across a 60° viewing angle. There was also a 35" NTSC direct view receiver in the room to verify interference (if any) of ATV into NTSC for both ATTC and lay viewing in Canada.

Figure 7-4 illustrates three of the Sony HDD-1000 digital video tape machines with transport at rack top and processor on the bottom. While these were originally built for the 1125-line 60-Hz interlaced Japanese format, the ATTC format converter changed them into multi-format units that recorded and played all four of the several ATV formats. These included 1125/60 interlaced, 1050/59.94 interlaced, 787.5/59.94 progressive, 525/59.94 progressive, and even the European 1250/50-Hz format with enhancements.

Observe that in the middle of each rack above the Sony tapes appears the ATTC Format Converter (Fig. 7-4). This is not Japanese equipment, but was invented by ATTC chief scientist Charles Rhodes and was designed and manufactured by Tektronix, Inc.

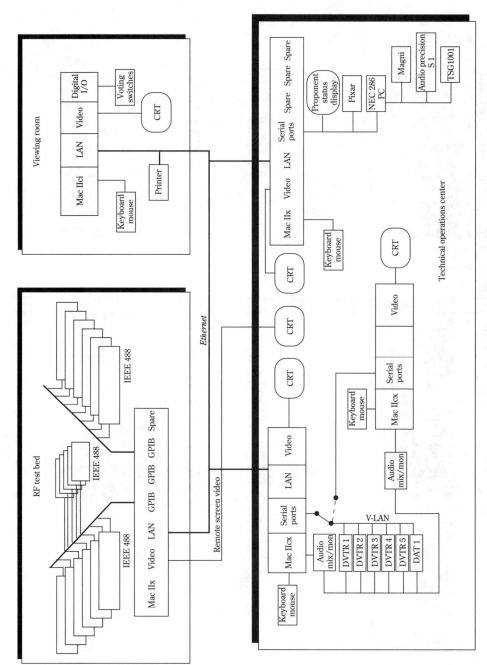

7-2 ATTC control system architecture.

7-3 The ATTC viewing room.

7-4 Sony's digital 1125/60 tape machines with ATTC's special U.S. format converter above.

Without this converter, the different formats could not have been tested, no repeatable or comparable pictures, no archive records, no workload sharing between the U.S. and Canada, artificially limited motion pictures, and only live camera and computer sources plus extended testing times could have existed.

This converter automatically reads the playback format and allows convenient switching from one format to another. It translates RGB incoming from camera or other analog source into a digital bit stream, bypassing the HDD-1000 Sony codec and multiplexing Y, Pr, and Pb, arranged so the digital storage/digital tape equipment will accept and retain. In playback, The format converter reverses the process into analog RGB.

Figures 7-5 through 7-7 are prime examples of the composite test bed illustrating various instruments—even including the VHF transmitter for channels 11, 12, and 13.

7-5   A major portion of the ATTC's TV test bed.

Functions of these multiple equipments are illustrated in the VHF and UHF simplified test bed block diagrams that follow. In Fig. 7-8, you see the VHF NTSC arrangement with its synthesizers, up-converters, noise generators, the various video, audio, SAP (second audio program), delay line, IF input, and an IF external input amplified and up-converted for channels 11, 12, and 13. Finally, attenuators and amplifiers process the signal through a 3-dB hybrid coupler to another attenuator, as well as a directional coupler and on to the viewing rooms.

Figure 7-9 is also NTSC for UHF, except for the higher frequency up-converter serving various channels between 15 and 38. Noise sources, however, are not included, but there is also a BTSC encoder (for stereo), as well as a second audio program (SAP) 10-kHz maximum unit, both of which, as in the VHF block, feed Harris' NTSC exciter. Another difference noted would be the adjustable delay line from 0 to 20.48 µs, rather than one that's fixed at 20.47 µs for the VHF unit.

7-6 A view of the UHF transmitting equipment.

Figure 7-10 now brings us up to date with a functional block diagram that is applicable to both ATV, as well as CableLabs, in addition to the expert viewers area, test instruments, test signals, and HD/RGB introduction and the special ATTC Format Convertor. Observe that the various proponents furnish their own ATV encoder and modulator, as well as their ATV demodulator and decoder. Here, also, are the impairment (interference) signal introductions, such as noise, multipath, airplane flutter, etc., which are all portions of the rigorous and exacting test procedures.

The foregoing should be a reasonable introduction to the various enterprises within ATTC in Alexandria, VA and we'll try to bring you considerably more as the chapter develops. At the end, we'll also list a table of the several transmission systems, as well as a general inventory of the various hardware contributors—especially the television receivers and VCRs. Then, we'll bring you fully up to date with special test procedures out-

7-7 A view of the VHF transmitting equipment.

lined for the CC-DigiCipher system, which are somewhat applicable to others. Naturally, some of the available material is omitted due, in large part, to its considerable volume.

Before continuing, however, we'd like to comment on the special RF facility in the test bed that simulated the numerous impairments, which could be found in virtually any (but not all) over-the-air broadcast conditions. Built by Harris Corp. it operated "at vastly tighter frequency and control tolerances" than are actually experienced in ordinary broadcasts. Additionally, inexpensive Apple/MacIntosh computers operating on over 600 especially formulated programs based on National Instrument's LabVIEW supplied the unique ATTC computer-control system that managed the laboratory plant, highly complex RF test bed settings, plus multi-signal and taping equipment for exciter stimulus and data recording.

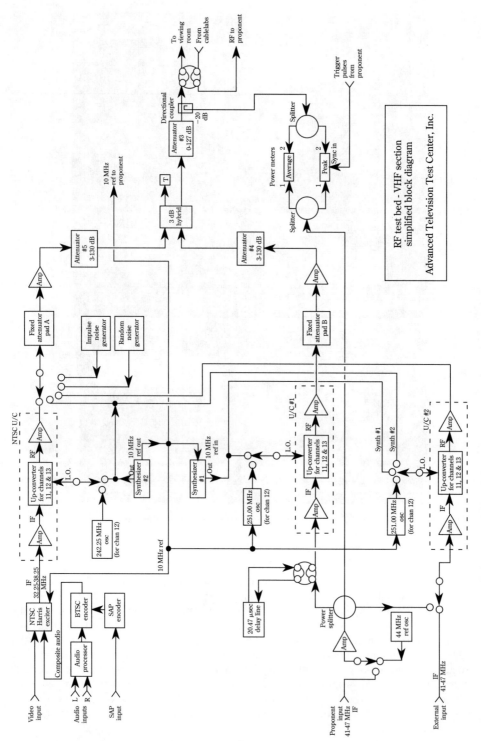

7-8 RF test bed: VHF section simplified block diagram. *Advanced Television Test Center, Inc.*

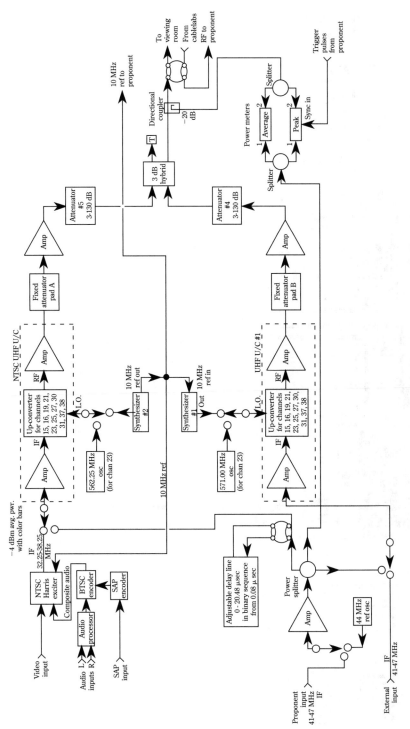

7-9 RF test bed: UHF section simplified block diagram. Advanced Television Test Center, Inc.

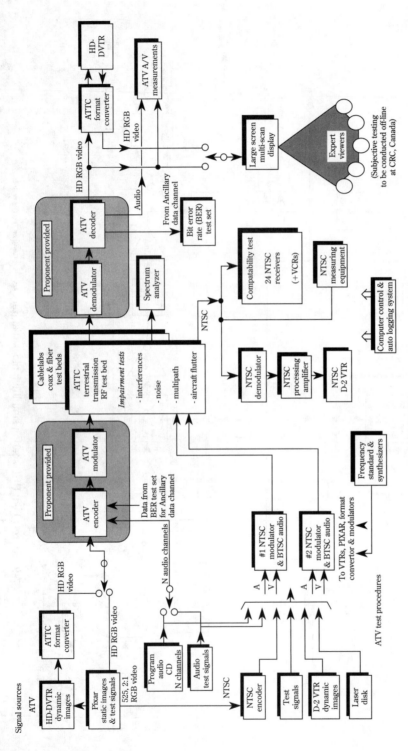

7-10 Functional block diagram of cable test bed operations.

Test conditions and goals

In the end, there were only four fully digital systems remaining for HDTV contention: two by General Instrument & partners; one by Sarnoff and the Consortium, and one by Zenith/AT&T. Narrow MUSE (Japanese) would also perform as a simulcast arrangement, but broadcast analog video. The FCC will undoubtedly select an all-digital system for previous reasons given, as well as assign the honor to an all-American (or nearly so) winner because of prestige and the patent royalties, which will accrue. So the remaining four are GI/DigiCipher™, DSC-HDTV, AD-HDTV, and Channel Compatible DigiCipher™ and MIT. These are all called out in Table 7-1, as well as their test times in Alexandria at the ATTC.

Although all proponents were initially required to deliver complete systems to ATTC for complete testing, audio system(s) were initially withheld because 4-channel stereo with a 5th for surround sound has now become the rule—a subject discussed in detail later in chapter 11. Excluding audio, then, each system delivered to the ATTC for testing was required to "operate in real time, with no simulations, and without staff operating support or intervention, except for maintenance and repair." Each represented every part needed for the complete HDTV signal for transmission from a TV station or cable system, plus hardware that would decode, demodulate, and display a home-type television picture. No government was involved, each proponent paid approximately $350,000 for complete (but not additional) testing, and ATTC's sponsors picked up the rest because this amount represents only about 10% of the actual cost. If proponents (such as Zenith and G.I./MIT) require further examination, the charge to that proponent has been $25,000/day. Prime purpose of such tests was to determine how the HDTV systems would work alongside NTSC, with each other, if NTSC would interfere, and single co-existence should and when it becomes the new standard after the turn of the century.

With tests underway, engineers, producers, industry specialists, and FCC analysts observe problems or advantages of each HDTV system so that results could then be recorded on digital video tape and could be further observed by non-expert viewers at the Advanced Television Evaluation Laboratory (ATEL) in Ottawa, Canada. Each system is then rated, according to performance regarding quality and/or difficulty. Audio portions were also taped and evaluated by expert listeners at the Westinghouse Science and Technology Center in Pittsburgh, PA.

Meanwhile, cable-specific tests were ongoing during one week of the eight assigned each test period at CATV laboratories in Boulder, Colorado. Various impairments (or not) were examined there during transmissions and distribution for both coax. as well as fiberoptics, encoding capacity and encryption conditions. All this combines with Alexandria ATTC tests and results forwarded to the Federal Communications Commission for its final evaluation during 1994.

A timely decision, and a good one

Since ATTC tests in foregoing publications described primarily analog procedures for HDTV examinations (and because we do have both system-specific information on DigiCipher and CableLabs) these two evaluations will be included almost completely and analog exact procedures left to other historians who might install them in several volumes for some purpose we can't conceive of at the moment. Therefore, hereafter, we'll stick with digital for all seasons.

The first concerns General Instrument's CC-DigiCipher, a very up-to-date test scheme gathered and set forth by John Henderson of Hitachi, formerly Sarnoff Labs in Princeton, NJ. It's an excellent directive and I see no considerable reason for editing, therefore there is none. The remainder is just the way John wrote it for The Advanced Television testers:

Table 7-1. ATTC viewing room NTSC television receivers.

High Definition (HDTV) Television Transmission Systems*
under consideration by the
FCC Advisory Committee on Advanced Television Service

HDTV System/Proponent	Scanning Format[1]	Type	Transmission Form	Testing at Advanced TV Test Center (actual/estimate)
(Testing Order)				
Narrow-MUSE NHK/Japan Broadcasting Corporation	1125/60.00, 2:1	Simulcast HDTV	Analog	Sept. - Nov. 1991
DigiCipher™ General Instrument Corporation/ATVA[2]	1050/59.94, 2:1	Simulcast HDTV	Digital	Dec. 1991 - Feb. 1992
DSC-HDTV: Digital Spectrum Compatible HDTV Zenith Electronics Corporation/AT&T	787.5/59.94, 1:1	Simulcast HDTV	Digital	March - May 1992
AD-HDTV: Advanced Digital High Definition Television North American Philips/ATRC[3]	1050/59.94, 2:1	Simulcast HDTV	Digital	June - July 1992
Channel Compatible DigiCipher™ Massachusetts Institute of Technology/ATVA[2]	787.5/59.94, 1:1	Simulcast HDTV	Digital	Aug. - Oct. 1992

* ACTV: Advanced Compatible Television, from David Sarnoff Research Center/ATRC[3], was tested July - September 1991. It is not HDTV, but an "enhanced NTSC" system, analog, 525/59.94, 1:1. It was withdrawn from FCC Advisory Committee consideration at request of proponent, March 1992.

[1] Scanning formats include: Number of lines per picture/rate of images per second at 2:1 = interlaced scanning (i.e. 2 fields per picture or approx. 30 pictures/second) or at 1:1 = progressive scanning (i.e. one field per picture or approx. 60 pictures per second).

[2] ATVA - American Television Alliance (GI, MIT)

[3] ATRC - Advanced Television Research Consortium (NBC, Philips, Sarnoff, Thomson, Compression Laboratories)

Digital specific tests: supplemental information

Threshold characteristics

The intent of this test is to characterize the differences in threshold behavior among the digital proposals. The test should explore image quality at C/N values and at NTSC $\rightarrow$ ATV co-channel levels from TOV to and beyond POU; they should also include video of varying complexity to determine if source material affects thresholds. Suggested video sequences are *Rotating Pyramids* (difficult), *Texas Dude* (modest), *Lamp* (easy), and *Woman with Roses* (still).

Procedure Separate tests must be performed with RF channel noise and with NTSC co-channel as impairments. For the random RF noise test, the desired ATV level should be strong. The co-channel test should be performed at both moderate and weak ATV levels. For each test, observers should note both TOV and POU and comment if there are differences among the images. Observers should increment or decrement the impairment between TOV and POU in step sizes that seem appropriate to the observers at test time. The intent is to collect data adequate to characterize the shape of the threshold curve for the different images.

Time-varying channel impairments

In addition to the original test, this test should also be performed in the manner implemented for the added test of the Zenith/AT&T system and of AD-HDTV in order to characterize threshold performance. Therefore, the time varying signal should be created using the 0.1-Hz offset; this signal should be added at increasing levels from a low-level start and comments made on resulting performance. The original test's added noise level (–55 dBm) and the strong (–38 dBm) desired level should yield a starting point near the TOV. A low level (suggest 20 dB below the desired signal) starting point for the added offset signal should allow useful exploration of signal fading conditions, starting from a near-threshold condition, and continuing until observers decide no more useful data is being collected.

Special instructions for existing digital-specific tests

Visibility of panel boundaries during scene cuts Use the scene cuts tape to observe the effect of rapid scene cuts on the visibility of panel boundaries. *Special instruction for 1.2.1.1 (scene cuts).*

Visibility of panel boundaries during stressful scenes Use the active video gate to add various levels of white noise to the free-form viewing tape. Observe panel boundaries. *Special instruction for 1.2.2-free-form viewing and source noise.*

System-specific tests for channel-compatible DigiCipher HDTV system television

The free-form viewing test of the System-Specific Tests for Digital Systems, should be performed before any of the following tests are undertaken. This will allow the viewers to become familiar with the system. The time for this free-form viewing is not part of the two days for System-Specific Testing.

Written record of observations A written record should be made for each of the system-specific tests. If an effect under investigation cannot be discerned, that fact should be noted. For each observation, the test signal(s) or video sequence(s) used should be identified and, where useful, any portion of a particular scene that was of special interest.

Viewing distances   The expert observer should be free to examine images from any distance. In some cases, very close observation might be required in order to observe or describe adequately a particular effect.

However, all tests should as a minimum include observations made from standard viewing distance. For each test, close observation should occur after standard viewing distance observation for that test has been completed and recorded.

Motion sequences and stills   For some tests that utilize motion sequences and stills, descriptions of the desired types of signal conditions are given in the procedures. For each test of this type, one or more motion sequence(s) or still(s) fitting the desired conditions should be selected from available material.

System specific tests

Susceptibility to random noise in video source

Reason for test   Random noise, usually unavoidable in video sources, stresses image coding and compression techniques. This test will determine the ruggedness of the compression algorithm when loaded with noisy source material.

Test procedure   *Unimpaired channel*: use the procedure described in paragraph 1.3.14 of the Objective Test Plan with the following source material:

1. Radial resolution pattern and/or zone plate generator
2. Rotating pyramids
3. Lorain Harbor

Impaired channel:

1. For Lorain Harbor set channel CNR = 20 dB. Record any impairments observed
2. Increase source noise and record any artifact. Determine POU.
3. Repeat 1 and for channel CNR's of 18 dB, 17 dB, 16 dB, 15 dB, and 14 dB.
4. Repeat 1, 2, 3 for rotating pyramid

Roaming zone plate

Use the TSG1001 to generate a static phase zone plate, which roams at approximately 16 pels/frame horizontally from left to right and then right to left. Observe any difference in quality.

Co-channel NTSC interference into ATV from single-frequency video picture material

The purpose of the test is to determine if co-channel NTSC picture material that produces a spectral line at or near the suppressed carrier frequency of the ATV system will reduce the noise margin against co-channel interference, compared to the generic co-channel interference signal.

For the test signal, use the zone-plate test generator to produce an image sequence with vertical or diagonal stripes, such that the baseband video frequency is 1.75 MHz. This corresponds to roughly 111 cycles per horizontal line.

Using the NTSC signal as the interferor, determine the Threshold of Visibility, and the Point of Acquisition or Point of Unusability. These are to be compared with the values determined for the generic NTSC co-channel interferor.

Effects on image when exciting additional DCT regions

Reason for test The CC-DigiCipher system divides the 8-X-8 DCT coefficients into 4 numbered regions of 16 coefficients. Each successive region corresponds to higher diagonal spatial frequencies and is less likely to be transmitted.

For each additional region used to encode the image, additional overhead and data bits are required. Based on the CC-DigiCipher system description, there could be a threshold effect. It might be possible that a slight change in picture content could cause the encoder to suddenly decide to send additional regions and start sending large amounts of additional overhead data bits. Of course, the additional bits that are suddenly required will be at the expense of bits used for other parts of the image. This test explores the possibility for this phenomenon and its appearance.

Description of test This test presents a consistent image on one half of the screen while varying the picture content on the other half of the screen in an attempt to cause the encoder to suddenly encode additional regions. The observers should note any drop in picture quality as the number of regions required to encode the other half is increased.

Setup Using at least the following list of complex moving images containing high diagonal frequencies, vary the amplitude of the image on only one half of the image, and observe the effect on the other half.

- noise on ½ of screen (slowly increase amplitude of noise). If no change in resolution is noted on other portions of the screen, then abandon the rest of the test.
- moving zone plate
- moving high frequency diagonal lines

Report and comment on any changes in picture quality that might be a result of a threshold effect caused by suddenly sending more DCT regions.

Oscillating panel overload test

Use the TSG1001 to generate a moving plate, create a continuous version of M16 (rotating pyramids) with no text, and generate a high detail still (e.g., Tables and Chairs) out of the Pixar. For each of the three scenes, use the video gate to replace ¼ of the picture (1 panel) with 100% random noise. Observe whether static portions of the picture contain a 3-Hz oscillation in quality. The boundary between the noise and the picture should be a vertical line 320 pels from the left or right side of the picture.

Vertical intraframe distortion variation test

With M16 (rotating pyramids preferably without text) as source video, gate 100% random noise on top 25% and 50% of picture at 0.1 and 1 Hz. Observe the bottom portion of the picture and evaluate the quality.

Slow error decay test

Use the Pixar to generate a still that is panned at a rate of 15 pels/frame (field) from right to left. Use the video gate on for 5 seconds and then off for at least 1 second in order to cause a scene change. Introduce impulse errors using the same methods as the digital specific burst error test. The impulse errors should be phased to hit the scene change from black to Pixar. The Pixar should be loaded with a scanned high-detail still, then the horizontal ramped color bar. Note that the amount of PCM refresh that takes place at the right side of the picture will be minimized using the ramped color bars. Observe the error decay time. Repeat experiment with a 16-pel/frame pan and with left to right pan.

20-microsecond echoes

Repeat the multipath tests with a longer echo, specifically one of 20 microsecond duration.

16-QAM tests

Threshold tests Using the setup described in section 19 of the objective test plan for each of the impairments listed, determine the TOV and POU for the 16-QAM mode using expert observation and commentary only (no voting). For each of the tests, the same material used for the section 19 tests of the 32-QAM mode are to be employed.

For each of these tests, the following accelerated procedure shall be used. First, set the level of impairment to that already obtained for TOV for the 32-QAM mode during the generic tests. Looking at the previously established TOV, the expert observers should become familiar with the nature and level of artifacts seen at that point. Next, switch the system to the 16-QAM mode and adjust the level of impairment until the TOV is found. Record the TOV.

Continue to adjust the level of impairment until the picture becomes unusable. Record the POU. Switch the system back to the 32-QAM mode and repeat the above process for the next type of impairment.

Unimpaired quality This test should be combined with the Free-Form Viewing. Desirably, observers should see a display of reference, 32 QAM, and 16 QAM for each image or sequence.

Source noise This could be combined with the 32-QAM source noise test.

Pull-down sequence for film mode

Reason for test Two types of tests are of value. The first (most important) is designed to examine the effect of disruption of the 3:2 pull-down sequence during a scene when the entire scene originated with 24 frame/second film material. The second type test is designed to compare the transition from 60 field per second video-originated material to 24 fps film material, with transition in the other direction, from 24 fps to 60 fields per second. Based on the proponents' answer to questions from the analysis task force, no visible artifacts would be expected in the 60-to-24 transition.

Test procedure Alternation of 3:2 pull-down sequence by editing: the test material will consist of an altered sequence of 60-Hz (59.94) field-rate video that was produced from 24 fps film scenes. After the normal 3:2 pull-down, the resulting 59.94-Hz sequence of fields will be altered by editing to include the following sequences of like frames, where each number represents the repetitions of identical fields.

3,2,3,2,3,1,2,3,2,3,2,3,2,.....

Notice that the disruption, which might occur naturally in an editing of the 3:2 pull-down video, is done in such a way that the sense of the pull-down alternation is reversed after the disruption.

The same type of disruption should be repeated at intervals convenient for observing any artifacts. The expected artifact would be a momentary loss of resolution, or slight blocking effects, for a few frames (5 to 10 frames) after the disruption. This would result from the coder using less efficient mode that codes all fields as if they contained new information, rather than the more efficient film mode.

60- to 24-fps compared with 24- to 60-fps transitions: in this test, the test material alternates, at conveniently frequent intervals (e.g., about once per 3 to 5 seconds), between 59.94-Hz video material and video derived from 24 fps film using the 3:2 pull-down. The possible artifacts include the same type of reduced resolution and blocking effects described in the sequence disruption test. The proponent had predicted there might be a difference in the visibility, depending on the direction of the transition.

Discussion: The Rotating Pyramids will provide ample detail and motion that is predictable for the video material. A film scene with substantial detail and moderate motion should be used for the 3:2 pull-down sequences. The motion should be small enough so that the sequence interruption does not result in motion exceeding the tracking capabilities of the motion estimator because it is not intended to stress the motion compensation with this test. The observers should understand that the momentary "glitch" produced by the sequence disruption is part of the test sequence, and the effect to be looked for is a change in resolution.

CATV testing

As with the system-specific ATV test procedures for CC-DigiCipher, Cable Television Laboratories and engineering V.P. Brian James have also submitted very accurate and informative information along with test procedures in one general document, the ATV Cable Test Bed Specifications, and the procedures for Cable Television Digital-specific transmission tests. Between the two, they occupy some 20-odd pages of text and accompanying diagrams, so although we would have preferred to print an additional 33 pages of the Test Procedures Manual, space simply won't permit. Yes, we could paraphrase, but much of the intent and meaning would be lost because of your author companding without the expanding. So, we'll print what appears to be most important and leave the remainder for future archivists.

However, there's not much missing since a system test bed description and diagrams will be included, much analog excised, and digital operations characterized as written.

Overview of cable test bed

Purpose and application

The cable test bed is designed for evaluating television transmission systems via coaxial and fiberoptic cable. The test bed simulates a set of critical cable television transmission impairments including random noise, intermodulation distortion, discrete carrier interference, amplitude and phase modulation, short-term transmission reflections, and high-level sweep interference. These are all sources of signal degradation present to varying degrees on typical cable systems. The test bed has the advantage of being able to develop the distortions individually for easier determination of their effect on the desired television transmission.

Description

The test bed consists of a main signal path and impairment generation sections (see Fig. 7-11) housed in an eight bay rack system. The levels and types of interference are selected by a test bed control computer. This computer also controls special test sequences conducted with panels of expert viewers.

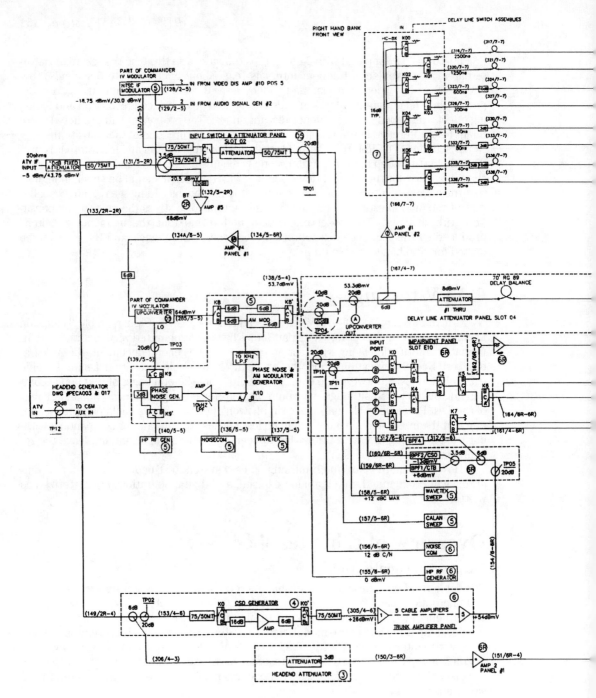

7-11 Substantive diagram of cable test bed layout.

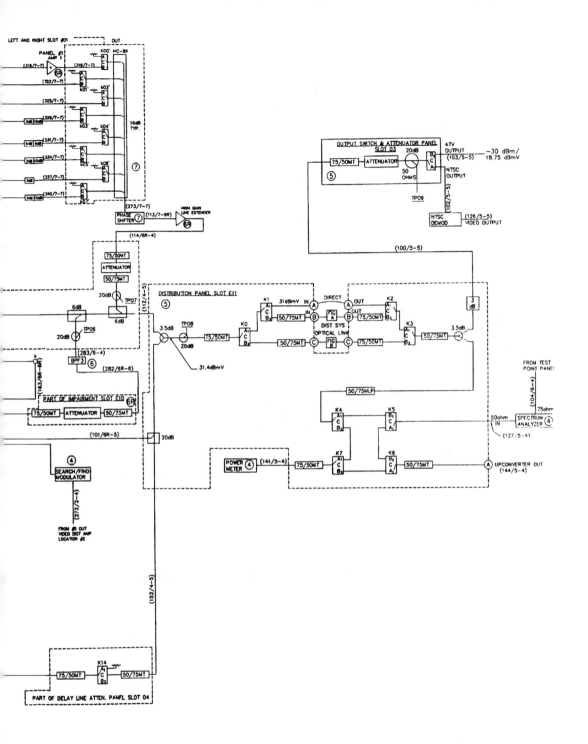

The main signal path selects either an NTSC or an ATV signal source at IF and heterodynes it to the channel 12 frequency band (204 MHz to 210 MHz), using a high-side local oscillator. The signal is amplified and passed through the test bed, where impairments are added at specified levels before being output to the ATV or NTSC receivers. If desired, the output signal can be combined with the output of a 32-channel headend to simulate the TV tuner loading found on a cable system.

The impairments can be selected individually or in a limited number of combinations and levels. Simulation of transmission path reflections can be achieved with signal delays of 20, 40, 80, 150, 300, 600, 1250, and 2500 nsec. These are created by splitting the test signal, passing a portion of the signal through delay lines and amplifiers and recombining the test signals. The level and phase of the delay signal can be varied. More than one delay can be introduced, but there is only one level and phase control.

Phase modulation of the signal under test is produced by modulating the local oscillator of the upconverter. The modulation source is a low-frequency random-noise generator. Amplitude modulation is obtained by variably attenuating the signal after the upconversion process. The modulation source is either a function generator or a low-frequency random-noise generator.

Discrete frequency interference is created by a synthesized signal generator. The level and frequency are determined by the control computer. Random noise is produced at desired levels by a computer-controlled RF random noise generator.

Two types of high-level summation sweep signals are available. One is a sweep system, which operates 10 dB above NTSC visual carrier levels and periodically sweeps through the cable frequency band. The second system periodically produces a "picket fence" of pulses throughout the cable frequency band at levels below the visual carrier level. The frequency of the individual pulses are selected, so they do not fall directly on carrier frequencies.

Second-order composite beats are created by amplifying the six video carriers that contribute to the second-order product falling in channel 12 with a single-ended amplifier and 5 post-amplifiers, then bandpass filtering the output to select the second-order product falling in channel 12. The selected product can be further amplified then attenuated, as necessary, to obtain the desired impairment level.

Third-order composite beat products are obtained by passing the combined output of 32-channel modulators through 5 trunk amplifier modules operating at elevated levels to obtain the desired third-order product. The channel 12 product can be selected in a narrow bandpass filter, then amplified and attenuated as necessary to obtain the desired impairment level. The NTSC carriers operate on an IRC frequency plan and have the option of being locked to a reference comb.

The sources for the channel modulators can be selected from CW, NTSC, or ATV modulation. The NTSC sources are laser disk players and test signal generators to randomize the sync signals. The ATV modulation is obtained by feeding the IF ATV signal into the alternate input of the modulators.

The test signal, with or without impairments, can be passed directly to the test bed output or through either the AM fiberoptic system or the distribution system. The fiber system is an AM fiber link with 20 km of fiber. The distribution system has a bridger amplifier, two line extenders and 12 taps each separated by 60 feet of cable. The taps have drops attached and the output feed is selected from the second to last tap.

Signal level and power test equipment consists of a spectrum analyzer and power meter. The input to the spectrum analyzer can be selected from numerous test points throughout the test bed or from the output of the test bed. The input to the power meter can be the test bed output or the upconverter output.

Through path description

The desired signal source is selected from either the ATV or NTSC source (see Fig. 7-12), attenuated as necessary, and fed to the upconverter. The signal is heterodyned to the channel 12 band, bandpassed, amplified, and fed through the amplitude modulator module. Next, a directional coupler feeds a portion of the signal to the delay lines while the main path is attenuated, if necessary, to obtain the correct level for impairment insertion. The delayed signal, impairments, and headend signals can be inserted into the main path after the attenuator. The signal can then be fed directly to the output attenuator and selector switch or passed through either the fiberoptic link or the distribution path. Just prior to the output attenuator, the signal is split to feed a signal to the power measurement equipment. The output attenuator sets the desired level to the signal receiver and the output select switch determines whether the signal is fed to the ATV receiver or the NTSC receiver.

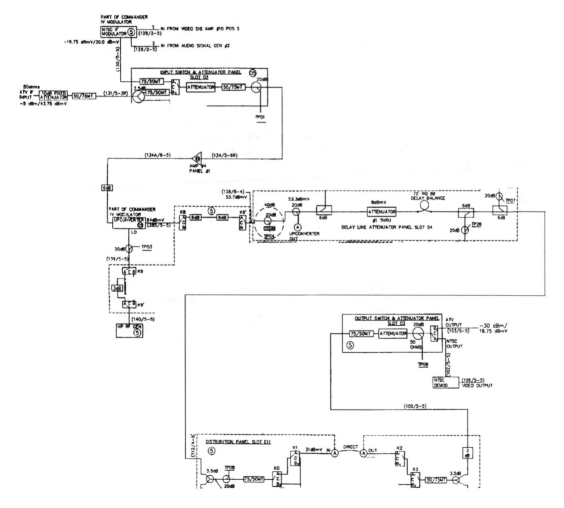

7-12 Signal through path via input/output.

Two sources of signal are available to the test bed, a proponent-supplied ATV signal or an internally generated NTSC signal. The proponent signal is to be provided at –5 dBm, then attenuated in a 10-dB input attenuator to improve input match and provide some overload protection for the test bed. The signal is split with one leg feeding the "B" port of the source selection switch and the second leg feeding the alternate IF input of the headend modulators. The IF output level of the NTSC modulator is set to provide a signal level equal to the ATV proponent signal at the "A" port of the source-selection switch. The selected signal passes through a 127-dB Wavetek variable attenuator and into the upconverter.

The IF signal, either ATV or NTSC, is heterodyned to the channel 12 band (204 to 210 MHz) in a custom-made upconverter. This unit first filters, then amplifies the signal before conversion to the channel 12 band. The mixer RF output is further amplified and band-pass filtered to provide a nominal output level of +64 dBmV. The local oscillator is an HP 8656B synthesized signal generator, which also provides a 10-MHz crystal-controlled time base for the complete test lab. The signal generator can be frequency modulated using an external source to simulate the residual frequency modulation effect of an oscillator.

The signal then passes through the AM modulator module. The signal either by-passes or passes through a custom-designed pin diode attenuator network. In the pass-through mode a controlled amount of amplitude modulation is impressed on the signal while in the bypass mode the signal is attenuated by a fixed 12 dB to maintain a constant output level. This module can simulate 120-Hz power supply modulation or low-frequency noise modulation.

The signal path next consists of a series of directional couplers and combiners and an attenuator, which splits the signal and then combines it with interference sources.

Three directional couplers follow the AM modulator. The first, a 20-dB coupler and 20-db attenuator provides a test point for the spectrum analyzer 75-ohm input. A second 20-dB coupler provides test point for the spectrum analyzer 50-ohm input. The third is a 6-dB coupler, which provides the signal to the delay line assembly.

A Wavetek programmable attenuator follows the three couplers to control the level of the test signal. The attenuator is followed by a 6-dB combiner, which combines the test signal with some of the impairments if they are selected. A second 6-dB combiner combines the test signal with the output of the delay line assembly. A 3-dB combiner combines the test signal with the combined modulator output. A final 20-dB coupler provides a test point feed for the spectrum analyzer.

The test signal and any impairments present can then be fed directly to the output splitter or pass through either a fiberoptic link or the cable distribution system. The selection is made by two series of two coaxial switches, which select the desired path. The output of this combination is split with one leg feeding the output switch and attenuator panel and the second leg feeding the spectrum analyzer or power meter.

The output signal passes through a Wavetek programmable attenuator, which sets the desired level to the receive device. The output switch routes the test signal to either the ATV receiver or the NTSC receivers.

The test bed is primarily a 75-ohm impedance system, but some switches and test equipment are 50-ohm devices. Changes from 50 to 75 ohm or 75 to 50 ohm are accomplished with matching transformers, which produce the impedance change with a minimum of insertion loss. Typically, switches in the test signal path are HP 8765A/B coaxial switches.

Specifications of through path

Input level:	–5 dBm
Maximum output level:	–30 dBm
Frequency response IF input to ch. 12 output:	+0.5 dB

C/N (1 Hz)	130 dB
Third-order distortion (2 tones, equal level):	−70 dB
Group delay:	±10 ns
Absolute delay:	approx 320 ns

Impairment path descriptions

Signal delay path

During the propagation of TV signals through the air, portions of the signal can be reflected toward a given receive site, resulting in the signal arriving via multiple paths delayed in time, relative to the time of arrival of the main signal. The result could be a ghost visible in the picture or bit errors in the case of a digital transmission system. The seriousness of these effects depend on the level, delay, and phase of the alternate path signals. The test bed has the capability of producing eight delays to determine their impairment potential on ATV systems (Fig. 7-13).

A 6-dB coupler, located in the through signal path, feeds a sample of the unimpaired test signal to an eight-way (16 dB) splitter. Each of the splitter outputs feeds a coaxial switch. One output port of each switch is terminated and the second port feeds one of eight delay lines. The delays are created in an appropriate length of RG-11 cable to provide 20, 40, 80, 150, 300, 600, 1250, or 2500 nanoseconds of delay. The 2500-nanosecond line requires amplification to maintain signal level and good signal to noise performance.

The output ends of each delay line are terminated in coaxial switches. The switches either select the delay line or a termination. The common port of each switch feeds an eight-way combining network. This splitting, switching, and recombining network allows any or all of the delay lines to be selected.

The combined output feeds a phase shifter, which can shift the phase of the signal through 360 degrees. The signal is amplified, then attenuated as required by a Wavetek programmable attenuator and recombined with the main signal in a 6-dB combiner.

Delay path specifications

C/N (1 Hz)	118 dB
Ch. 12 frequency response	±0.6 dB

Amplitude modulation

Amplitude modulation, other than that required to transmit the intelligence of the signal, can be imposed on signals transmitted through a cable system. Typical sources of amplitude modulation are "hum" from distribution system power supplies, not regulating properly, nonlinear components in the distribution path or low-frequency noise from switching power supplies and other sources. The test bed can simulate both types of amplitude modulation (see Fig. 7-14).

When the amplitude modulator is not being used it is bypassed to ensure there is no possible degradation of the test signal. A 12-dB attenuator in the bypass leg maintains a constant attenuation through the AM modulator unit.

In the AM modulation mode, the signal is passed through a PIN diode attenuator. The attenuator circuit is driven by either a waveform from a Wavetek arbitrary function generator or a NoiseCom noise generator. The amplitude of the signal from either source determines the depth of modulation imposed on the test signal. The noise is

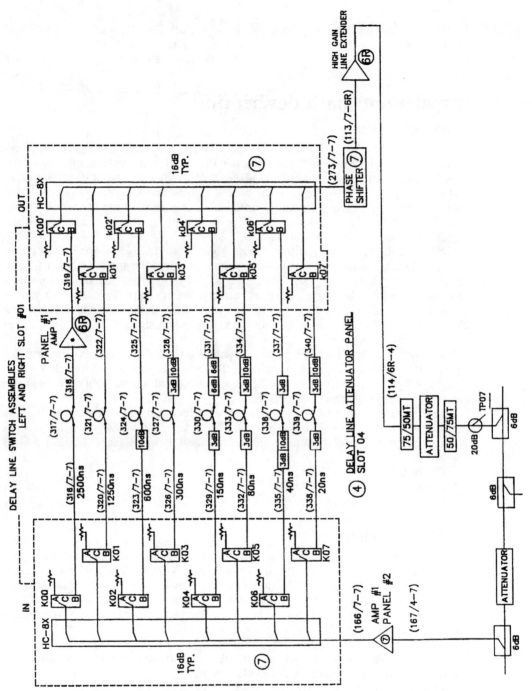

7-13   Delay line switch assembly.

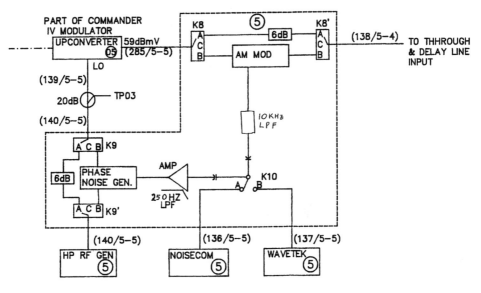

7-14 Signal cabling diagram.

band-limited to approximately 12 kHz to simulate low-frequency noise found on cable systems.

AM modulator specifications

Maximum AM modulation	10%
Residual AM sidebands (no modulation)	−58 dB

Phase and frequency modulation

Phase and residual frequency modulation can be created in cable TV systems in any of the frequency change devices. These can include heterodyne processors, demodulators, modulators, amplitude-modulated links, set-top converters/descramblers, etc. The test bed simulates phase noise found on cable systems by phase modulating the local oscillator of the upconverter. The phase modulator is a custom-built all-pass network driven by appropriately shaped noise from a NoiseCom generator. The noise has a single pole about 250 Hz, and decreases about 6 dB per octave above this frequency. The level of the noise driving the modulator determines the amount of phase noise imposed on the local oscillator.

When phase noise is not required the modulation circuit is bypassed to ensure the ATV signal does not receive any residual phase modulation. A 6-dB pad is placed in the bypass path to maintain the same nominal oscillator level when the phase modulator is bypassed.

Residual frequency modulation is simulated by frequency modulating the local oscillator signal generator with an external 120-Hz sine wave.

Phase and frequency modulator specifications

Maximum Phase modulation	±1.5 radians
Residual AM	<2.0%
Maximum frequency modulation	50 kHz

Impairment selection panel

Interference-type impairments are selected and level-controlled by the impairment selection panel (see Fig. 7-15). A set of coaxial switches selects one of the seven impair-

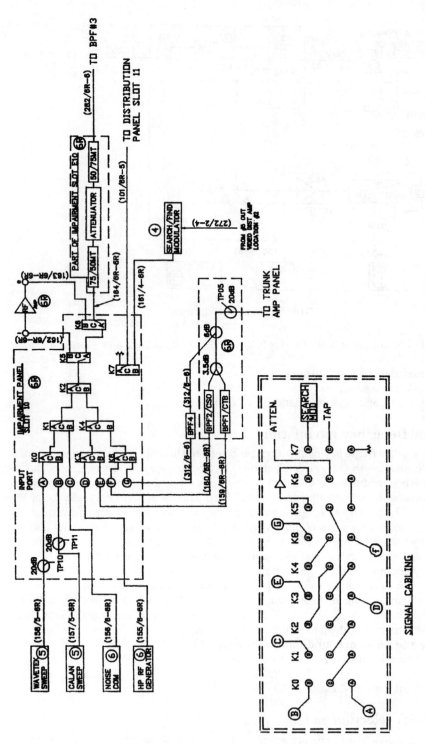

7-15 Impairment switch and attenuation panel.

ments to be combined with the test signal. A single-channel high-gain amplifier can be inserted in the impairment path if necessary to increase the level of the impairment. The inserted impairment level is controlled by a Wavetek programmable attenuator. A channel 12 bandpass filter is located after the attenuator to contain impairment products within the bandpass of channel 12.

Discrete frequency interference

Discrete frequency interference is one of a number of interference sources that can be individually selected by the impairment selection panel. The Hewlett-Packard 8656B generator's frequency and level is selected by the control computer. If desired, the signal from the generator can be internally amplitude modulated to improve its visibility on the TV screen.

Discrete interference specifications
Worst-case C/I available   0 dB

High-level sweep interference

One of two high-level sweep generators can be selected by the impairment selection panel. The Calan Model 1777 generator produces a "picket fence" type of carrier output. The carriers are equally spaced over the cable spectrum and normally operated 7 dB below the NTSC visual carrier level. The output will be set up to not transmit test carriers near critical ATV carriers and subcarriers.

The second sweep source is a Wavetek 1855B simultaneous sweep generator. This unit produces a high-level signal (typically 10 dB above the cable system NTSC visual carrier levels) and sweeps it through the cable system spectrum in a few milliseconds.

Sweep generator specifications
Frequency span   50 to 350 MHz
Output level   10 dB above NTSC Visual carrier
Sweep time   10 msec (variable)
Repetition rate   1 sec (variable)

Random noise interference

A NoiseCom random noise generator can be selected by the impairment selection panel. The output level attenuator can be controlled by the test computer. The filter in the impairment selection panel band limits the noise to the channel 12 band.

Noise generator specifications
Maximum output power   10 mW (100 Hz to 500 MHz)

Composite beat interference

In the early days of the cable industry, second-order distortion was a limiting factor if a cable operator wanted to utilize channels other than the standard VHF channels. This was overcome by the use of push-pull amplifiers, which cancelled the second-order products and left third-order products to become the limiting distortion. With the introduction of AM fiber systems, second-order products have the potential for limiting the operation of the link. The test bed has the capability of producing both second- and third-order products in various combinations.

One of four types of composite beats can be selected by the impairment selection panel, second-order only, third-order only, and unfiltered second- or third-order products. In addition, the headend can be controlled to obtain unmodulated carriers, NTSC modulated carriers, partial NTSC/partial ATV (16 channels each) and mainly (30 channel) ATV modulation.

The signal source used to create the distortion products is a set of 32-channel modulators. The modulators cover the standard cable channels from channel 2 at 55.26 MHz to cable channel 34 at 283.26 MHz with channel 12 not being used. The modulators can operate unmodulated to produce the reference CW beat product. In addition, the modulators can also produce NTSC-modulated signals or ATV-modulated signals. The ATV modulation is obtained by amplifying the ATV IF signal, splitting it, and applying it to the alternate IF inputs of the modulators. The NTSC visual carriers operate on an IRC frequency plan. The oscillators can either be locked to a reference comb or free running.

Third-order distortion products are obtained by passing the headend output signal through a cascade of 5 trunk amplifiers operating at elevated output levels. The channel 12 third-order products can either be selected by a very narrow bandpass filter centered on the channel 12 NTSC carrier frequency or a wider channel 12 bandpass filter, which might be necessary for ATV signals with non-standard carrier frequencies.

NTSC second-order products fall approximately 1.25 MHz above the visual carrier frequency. Only a small number of channels contribute to the second-order product in channel 12. The modulators that do not contribute to the channel 12 second-order products are turned off to minimize the amount of undesired third-order distortion products. These signals are first amplified by a single-ended amplifier operating at elevated output levels to produce sufficient second-order products. The signals then pass through the 5 amplifier cascade to increase their level. The second-order products can be selected by a narrow bandpass filter. A channel 12 bandpass filter can be selected if the contributing carriers are not located on standard NTSC cable frequencies.

Distortion specifications

Maximum level of second-order products	15 dB C/I
Maximum level of third-order products	5 dB C/I

Distribution system

The distribution system simulates a typical cable distribution system starting at a bridger amplifier and feeding a number of subscribers (see Fig. 7-16). As a result of the number of connectors, and passive and active devices in a distribution line, there is the potential to generate a number of very short reflections. These can contribute to a smearing of the cable picture. If time-compressed signals are transmitted in an ATV system, there is the possibility that during the time expansion in the receiver a smear might become a ghost and degrade the picture more than a slight smear or softening of the picture. If digital signals are transmitted, short-term transmission reflections can cause inter-symbol interference.

The test signal is fed to a line extender, which acts like a bridger amplifier to provide a high level output signal for the distribution system. Approximately 60 feet of RG-59 cable is used between each of the 14 two- and four-way taps to simulate typical spacing. Two line-extender amplifiers are inserted in the distribution line to maintain proper signal levels.

Each tap has one or more drops attached to the output spigots. The lengths of the drops vary from 50 to 150 feet. The drop terminations are either a 3-dB pad, a short circuit or an open circuit to simulate typical cable drop terminations.

The output of the second to last tap in the line is fed into a third amplifier to obtain a sufficiently high output level for the test bed. The result is a unity-gain distribution system simulator.

Distribution system specifications:

Frequency response (channel 12 band)	±0.5 dB
Group delay (channel 12 band)	±15 nsec

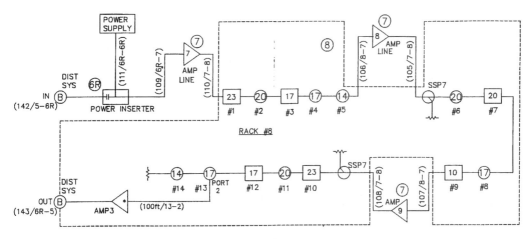

7-16 ATTC TV distribution system.

Fiberoptic system

The cable industry is rapidly moving toward AM fiber links to transport their signal from the headend to hub locations for further distribution via nominal cable. The test bed fiber system can be selected in the same manner as the distribution system simulator. The signal is applied to a Jerrold AM 550AT fiberoptic transmitter, passed through 20 km of fiber cable and received in a Jerrold fiberoptic receiver, where the signal is converted back to RF. The RF output signal level is set to yield unity gain through the fiber system.

Headend

The headend portion of the test bed consists of 32 Jerrold Commander VI modulators. These units are capable of being locked to a single reference source to simulate a coherent headend or they can be unreferenced. For the purpose of the ATV tests, they will be unreferenced because this is the typical method of operation on cable systems.

Two sources are available to the modulators, NTSC video or an ATV IF signal. The NTSC signal sources are six video disk players and two Tektronix test signal generators. Each of the video sources feeds a video distribution amplifier, which, in turn, feeds four of the modulators.

The ATV IF signal can be selected for half or 30 of the modulators through a contact closure option on the modulators. The headend output then simulates a cable headend some time after the introduction of the ATV service.

If unmodulated carriers are required, the power to the video distribution amplifier is turned off by the computer and the modulator output is only the aural and visual carriers.

Signal measurement equipment

Signal power or spectral measurements are accomplished by either an HP 8568B spectrum analyzer or an HP 438A power meter. Both of these instruments are controlled by the control computer and power levels or spectrum display printouts can be obtained by computer command.

Computer control

The test bed is controlled by a Macintosh IIfx computer operating the National Instruments Lab View software. Control software consists both of "virtual instruments" supplied with the software and others custom-written for the test bed.

The control software can "manually" operate the system or automatic test routines can be called to perform test sequences written in compliance with the Cable Test Procedure. The computer interfaces with the test equipment through the IEEE 488 bus standard. For instruments requiring contact closures for control an HP 3497A Data Acquisition/Control Unit is used.

Digital cable system testing

The advent of digital transmission techniques for ATV signals has resulted in the need to supplement the original test with procedures that will provide data on the transmission characteristics in the presence of random noise, plus other impairments. The original test required only one impairment to be present at one time. The following combines random noise and other impairments.

Intermodulation distortion

Introduction

Second- and third-order intermodulation products are one of the principal design limitations in cable TV systems. The performance of an ATV system at the end of a long cascade, where both noise and intermodulation are nearing design levels is important to the industry.

General description of method

The third-order interference level is set at 3 dB below the threshold of visibility, as determined by the Cable Television Transmission Tests procedure. The random noise power level is varied, following the standard procedure, to determine a new threshold of visibility. The test is repeated with the third-order interference set 6 and 10 dB below the threshold level. The complete procedure is completed for second-order intermodulation products.

Test and measuring equipment

Cable amplifiers
Cable channel modulators
Spectrum analyzer
IF-to-channel 12 upconverter
Narrow bandpass filters
    Bandwidth: 750 kHz
    Center frequency: 205.25 MHz (3rd order) & 206.25 MHz (2nd) two-way splitters, RF switches, and variable attenuator noise generator.

Procedures

Threshold determination

1. Connect the equipment using the narrow bandpass filter which selects the third-order intermodulation products (CTB).

2. Execute the threshold determination test with the CTB level set 3 dB below the threshold of visibility while varying the random noise power level.

3. Set the CTB level to 6 dB below the threshold level and repeat the threshold determination test.

4. Set the CTB level to 10 dB below the threshold level and repeat the threshold determination test.

5. Select the second order intermodulation products (CSO) and set the level to be 3 dB below the threshold of visibility.

6. Execute the threshold determination test by varying the random noise power level while holding the CSO level constant.

7. Repeat the procedure with the SCO level set 6 and 10 dB below the threshold of visibility.

8. If necessary repeat both measurements with CTB or CSO 15 dB below the threshold of visibility.

Record the threshold points for the noise level at each CTB and CSO level.

Phase noise modulation

Introduction

The ability of the ATV receiver to cope with phase noise is expected to be reduced when random noise is present. This test will determine the ability of the ATV receiver to operate when random noise is approaching the threshold point.

General description of method

Phase noise modulation is introduced to the ATV system by phase modulating the up-converter local oscillator with band limited noise. Random noise is added to the ATV signal at three specified phase noise levels (3, 6, and 10 dB below TOV) and the threshold of visibility of the combined interferences is determined at each of the three phase noise levels.

Test and measuring equipment

Video noise generator (such as Tektronix 1430 or equivalent)
IF-to-Channel 12 upconverter
RF generator (such as HP 8656B or equivalent)
Phase noise generator
Spectrum analyzer (such as HP 8568B or equivalent)
Plotter directional coupler and variable attenuators
Noise generator

Procedures

Threshold determination

1. Connect the equipment to test phase noise.
2. Set the phase noise level to 3 dB below the threshold of visibility.
3. Determine the random noise threshold of visibility.
4. Set the phase noise level to 6 dB below threshold of visibility and determine the threshold of visibility of the combined interferences.
5. Set the phase noise level to 10 dB below threshold of visibility and determine the threshold of visibility of the combined interferences.
6. Review the data and repeat the measurement with the phase noise 15 dB below the threshold of visibility.

Record the threshold points for the combined interferences at the specified levels of phase noise.

Residual frequency modulation

Introduction

The ability of the ATV receiver to cope with residual frequency modulation is expected to be reduced when random noise is present. This test will determine the ability of the ATV receiver to operate when random noise is approaching the threshold point.

General description of method

Residual frequency modulation is introduced to the ATV system by frequency modulating the upconverter local oscillator with a 120-Hz sine wave. Random noise is added to the ATV signal at three specified residual FM levels and the threshold of visibility of the combined interferences is determined at each of the three levels. The three residual FM levels will be 25%, 50%, and 75% of the residual FM perception threshold level.

Test and measuring equipment

Video noise generator (such as Tektronix 1430 or equivalent)
IF-to-channel 12 upconverter
RF generator (such as HP 8656B or equivalent)
Frequency modulator
Spectrum analyzer such as HP 8568B or equivalent
Plotter directional coupler and variable attenuators
Noise generator

Procedures

Threshold determination

1. Connect the equipment for the phase noise test.
2. Set the residual FM level to 75% of the threshold of visibility level.
3. Determine the threshold of visibility for the combined interferences.
4. Set the residual FM level to 50% of the threshold of visibility level and determine the threshold of visibility of the combined interferences.
5. Set the noise level to 25% of the threshold of visibility level and determine the threshold of visibility of the combined interferences.

Record the threshold points for the combined interferences at the specified levels of residual FM.

ATTC Viewing Room NTSC Television Receivers

Bank of 24 Receivers:
(Provided by manufacturers, via EIA, under FCC Advisory Committee guidelines)

Make	Model		Serial Number
JVC	AV2080S	! *	14518643
Hitachi	CT2086B		V0E014494
Magnavox	CJ4146		64390773
Toshiba	CX2047J	!	91504703
RCA	F20566AK	!	040321600
Zenith	SG2043Y	! *	022-05290362
Panasonic	CTM2043R-2		MA01710001
Goldstar	CMT2194		XC00003189
Sony	KV27XBR10	! *	7045078
Toshiba	CX2769J	!	70645621
Panasonic	CTM2775S	!	AS01490013
RCA	F27180DG	! *	930421691
Mitsubishi	CS2723R	! *	003346
Zenith	SG2795BG	!	091-42200602
Magnavox	RS5650	! *	78273259
Sharp	27RV79	!	338740
Magnavox	RK4345	!	78790383
Sony	KV20EXR10	!	8003039
Zenith	SS2021W		021-04341314
Sanyo	DS20030		V01B0600003
Emerson	TS4451A		4005A302-1207114
Samsung	TC2065S	! *	0604000590
GE	20GT425		116260975
RCA	F20536EH		040216579

Spare/Replacement Receivers (On hand):
!* Magnavox, 20 inch, Model RK4325, serial #7676316
!* Magnavox, 27 inch, Model RJ5562, serial #62644928
! RCA, 27 inch, Model F27181DG, serial #38321154
!* Sanyo, 20 inch, Model AVM222, serial #8460203056

Plus: !* Mitsubishi, 35 inch, Model CS3520R, serial #510077
("Twin" at ATEL/CRC)

Sixteen receivers are 19-20 inch; Eight receivers are 26-27 inch.
* = Baseband video output (7 of 24)   ! = Baseband stereo audio output (15 of 24)

Video Cassette Recorders (VCR)

1 each VHS - Zenith, model 2100, s/n 50620076
1 each VHS - Zenith, model 2150, s/n 41200022
2 each S-VHS - Toshiba, model SV-970, s/n 39300985 & 29301597
2 each 8-mm - Sony, model EV-S550, s/n 37754 & 37740
2 each Hi-8 - Sony, model EV-S900, s/n 37891 & 38117

Troubleshooting

After reading through both cable and TV test procedures, you may readily discover that instrument applications, parameters, and even certain readouts can be of considerable value in plain, ordinary troubleshooting. At the very least, certain system-specific tests, analytic descriptions, and apparent results can be of value in determining subsystem problems not readily apparent from reading the usual manufacturers' literature. We would suggest, therefore, that more than cursory attention be paid to various tests and their objectives when attempting to understand and evaluate generic system performance.

Regretfully, we can't supply all system-specific details, but knowing that the foregoing exists and is immediately available could be of some considerable assistance when and if the fateful hour arrives. Engineering departments might consider making such tests required reading, even if only general knowledge appears informative.

8

Commercial instrumentation and analysis

Although oscilloscopes, spectrum analyzers, multimeters, logic analyzers, and digital storage oscilloscopes will continue their days and years of durable utility, significant instrument developments are now taking place that promise to affect test and electronic laboratories throughout this country and probably many others.

Open measurement solutions

Begun by National Instruments in the 1980s, commencing with LabWINDOWS AND Lab-VIEWS, three of the nation's major electronics corporations have now formed a worldwide group to develop and sell *open measurement solutions* designed to combine engineering operations, testing and manufacturing within a single work station—all of this occurring on September 1, 1992, with the collaboration of Tektronix, Sun Microsystems Computers, and National Instruments.

Objective is to integrate test and measurement systems with "concurrent engineering," which seems to mean a combination of manufacturers pooling engineering resources for advanced instruments. Further, this group wants to offer an "open environment" for precision instrumentation, whether present, past, or future so that—based on industry standards, such as GPIB and VXI—(IEEE 488 for communications and VXI for systems, respectively, the latter an extension of VME bus), permitting a considerable number of instruments interfaces, and computers from many sources to operate on the same PC board or chassis. Because of the 1990 acquisition of Colorado Data Systems, Tektronix now claims the "industry's widest selection of card-modular instruments," while Sun Microsystems contributes UNIX®-based and SPARC® workstations, said to be relatively low-priced with exceptional operating abilities. National Instruments will supply instrument-controller hardware and highly developed software as its share, bringing together a powerful combination that could well become an integration and test-system powerhouse of considerable influence and a major market factor.

Reportedly, customers may buy individual system components from any of the companies and integrate them according to need and utility. For more sophisticated operations, Tektronix will act as vendor and integrator, combining software and hardware units from the three manufacturers. And thirdly, user software and system support can be supplied by National Instruments via service contracts. In addition, customized software or hardware is also available, offering a total solution for those engaged in extremely specific tests and measurements. Such an open approach, it's said, avoids the problem of obsolescence and any dependency on products developed by a single company, whether software or hardware, thereby avoiding entire system replacement. And by the time this information has been published, the Tektronix, National, and Sun Microsystems group should be delivering product upon order receipt.

Virtual instruments

With LabVIEW, engineers and scientists construct software modules that are dubbed as *virtual instruments.* Programs are assembled from block diagrams. Creating custom graphical interface panels so that data from many instruments a graphic compiler collects will be processed at approximately C-language speed (Fig. 8-1).

8-1 The ALLIANCE, consisting originally of Tektronix, Sun Microsystems, and National Instruments, exhibits many advanced computer-controlled for Open Measurement solutions. National Instruments

Operating on personal computers, SPARCstation, and various types of computers using Microsoft Windows, SPARCstations are, therefore, easily linked, as well as computers from other suppliers. Often, many applications can run on one screen. As an example, IC and board designers can acquire both design and tests, plus data analysis from several instruments, and project some or all on a single screen. There are also hardware additions for LabVIEW and SPARCstations using GPIB instrument controls. LabVIEW data can be supplied with combinations of plug-in data acquisition boards and GPIB, RS-232, and VXI instruments. In short, there are multiple options and add-ons available to support many or most current conditions. An example prepared by Tektronix (Fig. 8-2) illustrates Open Measurement Solutions, which includes a number of the Alliance instruments often required in research and design. Tektronix says that soon engineers can construct R & D projects "on the same platform" as the one designated for testing. Benefits are said to include better products, reduced development costs, and shorter intervals from design to market. We might suggest too, the excellent demonstration package provided by National Instrument to train personnel in using LabVIEW for WINDOWS, replete with color illustrations and step-by-step instructions. These are, indeed, very forward-looking techniques that will prove of inestimable value to designers and testers as we move from stand-alones to virtually all-inclusive instrumentation. Additional field training and instructional literature will undoubtedly be available in larger increments as the '90s progress.

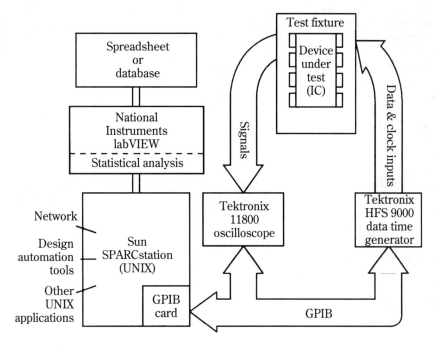

8-2 An example of Open Measurement systems in R & D. Tektronix and National Instruments

The foregoing, of course, is looking into the immediate future with test gear designed for sophisticated systems and high-accuracy tests. Conversely, hand-carried field equipment and lower-cost specialized instrumentation will always occupy a place in our industry where measurements, repairs, and service are required "on the road" and in places where space and economics are paramount. Such "suitcase" testers permit us to be even more specific in our descriptions and applications, allowing examples, illustrations, and the test procedures to become the working part of this chapter—a very satisfactory situation because further knowledge is always a useful thing and a non-chore that this author always enjoys. So let's begin with oscilloscopes and work up or down, according to recent product availability.

Oscilloscopes

Still one of the more useful items of either laboratory or field equipment in either the engineer's or technician's electronics arsenal, the oscilloscope has risen from a poor, low-grade horizontal-vertical plate cathode ray tube display to a highly useful voltage and even current monitor (with special probes) with multiple high-sensitivity channels, and remarkable accuracies from dc (0) to kilohertz (10^3), megahertz (10^6) and even gigahertz (10^9). And now, shedding its purely analog skin, the scope is rapidly entering the digital domain for super time-base accuracies, faster and faster sampling rates, and even equipment prices that were unheard of until the 1990s. The DSO, as today's digital storage oscilloscope is known, has become such a remarkable instrument that one major manufacturer doesn't even make analog scopes anymore. Another source still produces an interesting analog/digital combination, while a third, Tektronix, has now entered the "low-cost" market with a brand new 100-MHz analog unit that's sold through distributors from coast to coast.

Because many or most service agencies and smaller laboratories have little use for esoterics, we'll work with the less expensive, but utilitarian equipment that has been recently introduced to the U.S. market, especially those from Tektronix and John Fluke Manufacturing. The latter produces a scope/meter combination that should prove a wonderful accessory to field servicers who pursue problems from dc to 5 MHz (nonrecurrent) or 50 MHz (repetitive) and all sorts of current, voltage, frequency, and other related electrical phenomena. True, the price of a top-of-the-line ScopeMeter approaches $2000, but its versatility and utility in the lower and intermediate measurement ranges is remarkable.

Understand, however, that oscilloscopes display what they see in terms of digital or analog reproduction. If you want "the rest of the story," spectral analysis (a spectrum analyzer) must be enlisted to sweep and transform analog data into various component parts. As for digital, D/A/C converters, storage expanders memories, and selective readouts do the rest. If a triple-duty digital instrument is handily available, we might even try a short description of its thoroughly useful applications, although you might not really want to pay the price unless necessity requires. If you're looking at 16 to 80 channels with 1-GHz to 200-MHz timing and have $8995 handy, Tektronix' GPX might be just the thing to fill the need. Now, let's return to ordinary oscilloscopes and their interesting uses.

Analog oscilloscopes

Take your pick of two channels or four with single or dual time bases for the usual oscilloscope varieties, but be very careful of their vertical deflection factors, per-channel sensitivities, time base accuracies, and lighted or unlighted graticules. Non-lighted graticules don't photograph well and they're virtually useless in semi-illuminated areas. In addition,

4-channel scopes often have limited deflections among channels 3 and 4, allegedly because these are reserved for "digital" probing. Most modern service equipments specify sensitivities from 2 mV to 5 V/division. For the usual 8 vertical divisions, this only translates to 16 mV and 40 V, and 20 mV to 400 V with 10X low-capacitance probes. So, you can visualize what a 0.5-V channel won't do. Advise and consent suggests all four channels with 2 mV to 5 V at 2% accuracy. If these numbers don't cover your specific application, dual-trace (not dual channel) equipment is available that deflects to 20 volts, instead of 5. The 60-MHz Hameg HM 604, for instance is one of these; unfortunately, its graticule is not illuminated. Dual-trace scopes, by the way, operate from the same time base on alternate sweeps, while dual-channel units have their own separate channels and time bases and, naturally, are considerably more expensive. Fortunately, or otherwise, there aren't many of the individual-channel units still alive.

There are still many engineer/technicians who remain afraid of digital storage oscilloscopes and have never learned the real advantages of analog. It is, therefore, our avowed purpose to discuss the positive and negative aspects of each so that readers can thoroughly understand drawbacks/advantages and be able to select features that are most applicable to their particular measurements.

An analog scope is almost always faster in sweep speed than a DSO. Megasweeps for analog and lower kilosweeps or less for digital. It takes time to sample a waveform, convert the processed information to digital numbers, store, and re-convert this information to analog prior to display. Cathode ray tubes remain the same for both, but digital-to-analog and analog-to-digital conversions all take time even though sampling rates have and will increase almost dramatically as flash converters and available A/Ds become considerably faster. Some sampling rates are already in the gigahertz, and higher megahertz conversion versions are improving almost daily. As always, however, there's a price to pay, but usually only with the pocketbook.

Many do not understand, nonetheless, the one-shot capture of a waveform divides by 10 the actual frequency apparent. And the only way you can realize full DSO capability is with repetitive waveshapes. In addition, unless you have an extremely fast sampler, any high-frequency information within your selected voltage displays as a blur, rather than reproduction in detail. Technical notes don't tell you this, but any number of printouts in our lab have illustrated the point repeatedly. Remember that DSOs must calculate values—especially in risetimes, frequencies, beginning and ending data times, plus other operations, depending on instrument parameters, storage and readouts.

Some of this digital accommodation is also creeping into analog scopes through microprocessor control operations. There are programmable limit lines, pass-fail conditions, programmable volts and times per division, remote control, peak signal detection (formerly reserved for spectrum analyzers), and internal calibration from standards programmed in memory. There are more advantages (or similarities) among the analogs and DSOs, and this is why we will use a combined function oscilloscope to illustrate the discussion. Further, complex, modulated RF can be detected very well with either an analog scope or spectrum analyzer. And finally, analog oscilloscopes possess fewer setup and operating controls than do the digitals, so many technicians actually work faster and more comfortably than those who exclusively use DSOs. However, if you want a rock-steady display, high accuracy, and generally excellent printouts, a DSO is often more satisfactory for permanent records. We don't mean to over-extol the virtues of analog scopes over DSOs because both are extremely useful, but survival days for the analog instruments are far from being pegged on the calendar—furthermore, they're cheaper. So, for general portability, a considerable frequency range, single-shot or low-repetition rates, and very fast rise times, the analog versions are indispensable.

Digital oscilloscopes

Despite a few lingering shortcomings (which we all have) digital storage oscilloscopes have taken over many measuring functions of the analogs and will continue to do so as long as they can reproduce waveform displays with fidelity and reasonable control settings. Many are not nearly as large or hefty as they were formerly; therefore, portability isn't a major drawback, nor is the price because that's diminishing constantly. But to overcome *aliasing* at higher frequencies (less than two samples per period) and avoid unacceptable waveshape distortion, very fast sampling rates are necessary and such special electronics do cost money. Are DSOs now suitable for general field use? Certainly, if they're handled with care, possess auto-calibration, are not overly complex to set up, and operate on intermediate frequencies and non-complex configurations. Otherwise, carry a large checkbook and keep your DSO in the lab, along with a suitable printer and plenty of paper. And note that nonsinusoidal signals require as many as 10 samples/cycle, depending on complexity; so sampling speed is essential when something more than sine waves are examined.

Nonetheless, pretriggering of transients by capturing and storing events before actual occurrence, almost extreme measurement accuracies, real time, sequential, and random-repetitive sampling, and a considerable number of automatic functions (following setup), make DSOs most attractive for many applications. Real-time sampling, for example, fills buffer-memory in one cycle; sequential sampling allows acquisitions at frequencies higher than the analog-to-digital (A/D) rate; while random repetitive sampling shows pretrigger action and prevents aliasing. With repetitive sampling of recurrent information, reliable displays of the scope's full bandwidth are possible.

DSOs can also offer multiple independent input channels, and some even possess differential inputs. However, inputs less than a few millivolts might require external amplifiers. By the same token, high voltages can be attenuated by 10X LC probes. Other limitations are excessive noise levels, undersampling and high sampling affect resolution of marginal voltage reads. A/D converters are the electronics most affected.

Otherwise, a 50 Ms sampling grate, to avoid the Nyquist limitation (Fig. 8-3) can reliably acquire non-complex information at 25 Ms or less suitable for both lower frequency signals and single-shots. Sequential sampling needs a single sample during each cycle when the waveform is repetitive, taking considerably more time to fill the storage buffer, and random repetitive sampling operates from a timed window referenced to its trigger. Sampling, therefore, depends on trigger rates and selected delays, with samples taken, without regard to input voltages. When the DSO's buffer fills, storage and then readout occurs. A 10-kΩ buffer, for instance, with a 10-sample window, will require 1000 waveform identical repetitive signals to fill. As for an ultimate readout, it's handy for computers and other ancillaries to have a choice of RS232 (EIA) or IE[3] 488 (GPIB) from which to select, in addition to a high contrast, brightly lit cathode ray tube to view and check printout results.

Aliasing

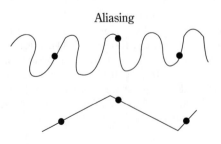

8-3 Aliasing: less than two samples per sine-wave period produces false DSO readouts.

Noise detection in analog versus digital oscilloscopes is often a very different product. The non-averaged trace of a digital scope seems to collect small noise spikes from stem to stern, whereas an analog trace appears clean and noise free. This does not mean that digital scopes are noisier than their analog brethren; rather, random noise in many signals is usually not synchronous with system trigger and, consequently, won't appear on the CRT. In digital sampling, the results show both noise and signal, but there is residual quantizing noise resulting from the A/D converters as they digitize the analog signal—especially when attempting to translate changing analog that appears between assigned digital levels. Called *quantizing*, an 8-bit digital samples analog and produces an 8-bit output, which is only one part in 264 (10^8 binary). On the other hand, one analog sweep produces a waveshape, but (because of poor phosphor retention) quickly fades past the point of display and is lost. Nonsynchronous information is completely lost because it is not retraced. Digital, of course, stores what it reads and is "ready when you are" to recall all from storage. But analog scopes with high writing speeds can "see" events that the samplers might miss. So each unto his own ability; it's yours to select, operate, and pay for. Until we begin to work with suitable equipment and individual examples, prologue remains our basic reference. Let's hope local examples bear it out.

The best of both worlds

So, analog scopes sound good, but digitals, you hear, are *great*. However, you already know a number of applications for run-of-the-mill analog scopes, and virtually nothing about digital . . .

Then, how about a 200-MHz digital and a 200-Ms DSO combined? Would a scope that can measure both voltage and power also be of interest? You know very well that current through an R load (Fig. 8-4) develops a voltage, and you should know that current through an R_1 load in series with an R_2 load of lesser value than R_1 (specifically 1 ohm), aids in evaluating this situation with channel 2. Therefore, multiplying channel 1 times channel 2, the resultant is the observed momentary power. The MATH menu and TRACK control together do the job.

Does summing and integrating signals over time stir your interest? The result in volts-seconds or, if in amperes, then your readout is coulombs. Remember $Q = CE$, where 1 coulomb equals 6.28-x-10^{18} electrons? It might sound strange at the moment, but many almost basic electron terms are returning as programmers attempt to simplify some pretty tough algorithms and equations. Here, the charge in some inductance or capacitance is the integrated waveshape of current, and measuring its dissipation becomes the "integrated curve of power," according to those who know.

Would you like to measure power losses in a switch-mode power supply? Voltage at the collector of the output transistor appears on one scope channel while R_2, the tiny sec-

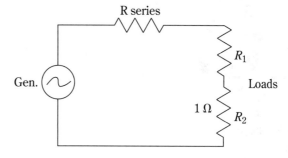

8-4   Voltage measured across the R2 load determines current flow.

ond load occupies another. Thereafter, the two signals are each displayed over four screen divisions, the MATH and TRACK operators are again activated, along with a SCALE submenu should the result require shifting in either vertical size or offset.

Power dissipation in transistors becomes proportional "to the integral of the power curve over time," says Fluke. Cursors measuring such action see the accumulated pulse power and deliver a readout in joules (or watt-seconds—a pair of equivalences). Once more, it delivers a power curve and, being finally integrated via the MATH and TRACK operations produces the integrated curve.

Fluke/Philips

What's this all about? Specifically, it's the very new and (to me) exciting PM 3394 Fluke/Philips analog and digital scope with four full-deflection channels, all sorts of interesting menus, plotting for WordPerfect® and Windows®, signal averaging, pattern and state triggering, glitch detection, tri-level sync for high-definition television, touch-and-hold probe exciter, hard copying (w/printer), system integrated tests, memory expansion to 32K samples, a Math + option, remote control operation, and more (Fig. 8-5). On the analog side, excellent displays of complex waveshapes in real time, no aliasing, AM and FM superior signal analysis, video, jitter and complex data streams, triggering for NTSC, PAL, SECAM, and HDTV, 1% accurate cursors, ADC resolution 8 bits and 16 bits wide, large memory, 32X magnification in vertical, time delay 0 to 1000 divisions adjustable, RS232-C serial processing, optional GPIB/IEEE488.2 interface, and so forth, including both European and U.S. line voltage and line-frequency operations. How about main time base and delayed time base display on the same bezel together, and 1-MΩ/50-Ω input impedances selectable.

If those specifications don't excite, then more extras to another possible source might. Here, the double performance is almost spectacular.

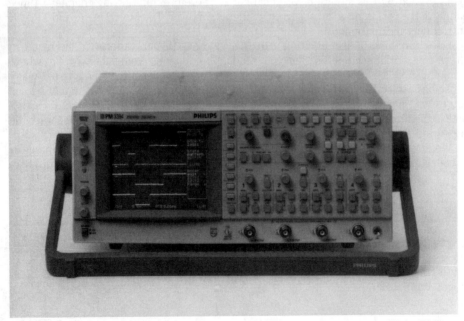

8-5 The remarkable PM3394 analog/digital 200 MHz/200M samples scope by Fluke/Philips.
John Fluke Mfg. Co., Inc.

Examples Now let's do a few waveform examples via a DS 34 Polaroid camera to support some of these excellent characteristics. In color, the trace appears blue.

No. 1 Let's observe a 70-MHz signal digitized in Autoset, with time base at 20 ns and channel 1 at 20 mV/div. Note that the trace (even at this frequency) holds perfectly still, showing a reasonable amount of modulation, which is easily examined for abnormalities or anything else that might be of interest (Fig. 8-6).

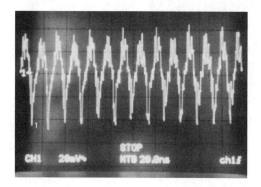

8-6 No anemic traces in this digital, even at 70 MHz.

No. 2 If the first series of waveshapes in RF (radio frequency) looks pretty good, try this one on for size. All we did was remain in Autoset, but added a time-division variation of 4X, so that the time base is now showing 5 nsec/div. Then, the Stop button was engaged plus the Status of all four channels. Channel 1, of course, is the only one that continues to be engaged. Excited about what you see? I am! And when you wish to disengage one or more functions, just push the soft-touch button and it all goes away (Fig. 8-7).

8-7 Now, a 4× expander is added plus the status condition for all four channels.

No. 3 Here you want to know the time interval between markers, as well as their difference in amplitudes. Once again, Digital and Stop modes are engaged plus markers, and the time base is reduced to 12.5 ns. Readouts show a 55.6-ns difference in times and an amplitude difference of 27.4 mV. This could be most useful in measuring any varying input voltage—especially amplitude modulation and possibly abrupt frequency changes, too (Fig. 8-8).

No. 4 This isn't the world's greatest photography because it's double exposure and we're not quite on the same graticule position and analog triggering is slightly off with a

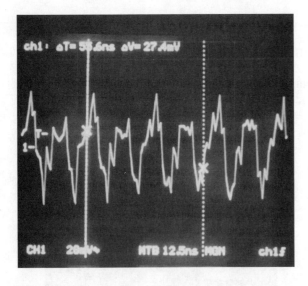

8-8 A somewhat more serious application with time and voltage between highly accurate markers.

second field superimposed. Nonetheless, here's an excellent example of why digital isn't always useful with fast modulation under these conditions, and why analog is (Fig. 8-9). We're working, of course with channel 4. If you want to see the analog color bars more clearly, simply increase channel amplitude and adjust trigger level more or less. You can also place holdoff at 47 percent for an excellent readout. Additionally, to switch from analog to digital requires only a single button that's marked DSO. Capish? And, by the way, we haven't yet read a single manual instruction! I suspect you can do the same. The above should pretty well prove exactly what has been said previously: analog and digital oscilloscopes co-exist nicely, provided they're properly used and not abused.

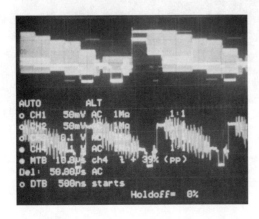

8-9 Some definite observations of why analog and digital don't mix. Fast switching (bottom) and, 2nd exposure analog (top) present very different readouts.

No. 5 This one should be entitled "what digital can do that analog can't." Here, the time base is set at 10 µs/div so that a single cycle of modulated staircase in the upper trace measures exactly 63.5 µs while the second (lower trace) originates from a function generator at a rep. rate of approximately 25 kHz. Using the analog mode, there's no way these two traces could by coordinated in sync, but digitally what's on the screen is freeze-framed and everything "stops for tea." The amplitude between the two markers, by the way, amounts to 81 millivolts (Fig. 8-10).

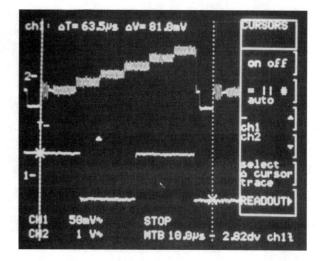

8-10 How about waveforms displayed at two different frequencies by separate signal sources? Digital, here, does it all!

No. 6 Even though we could continue ad infinitum with examples of this most satisfactory instrument, there are other instruments to describe also, although an explanation of the Compact Programming Language for oscilloscope programming done through the RS-232 serial interface would be of considerable interest. But that's described in the operating guide anyway. So, let's look at this final wave shape, which is supposed to be a triangular wave (and isn't) with the usual markers in digital format, along with the separation times and delta differences. But what makes this display unusual is that in the background there appears to be a fast Fourier transform, which is most unusual for an analog/digital scope. How useful this display becomes probably depends on the operator, but it's there, nonetheless, and can be manipulated for certain applications (Fig. 8-11).

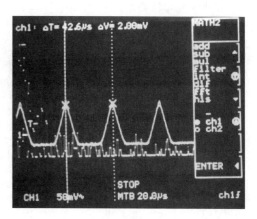

8-11 Analog + digital + FFT makes the PM3394 a most useful instrument.

Analogically, Tektronix now leads

There is often something new under the sun—in this case, it's Tektronix new line of very portable, very useful and utilitarian scopes, which are competitively priced for the lower cost market. The full line should be on the market by the time this book is published about the middle of 1993. As of now, 60 MHz and 100 MHz TAS 455 and TAS 465 models (Fig. 8-12),

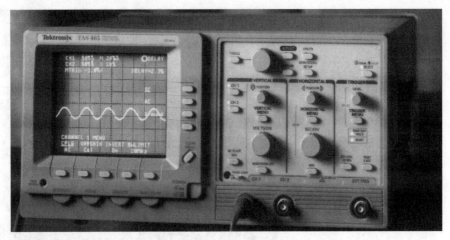

8-12 Tek's brand new line of dual trace analog scopes with many features. Tektronix

are already available and other products are expected in the meantime. The first two have announced selling prices of $1500 and $2195, respectively, and both offer major features:

1. If one of these fails within three years after purchase, you'll receive a free replacement.
2. A proprietary hybrid "circuit" contains the complete input circuitry for each of the two channels, including vertical, horizontal, and trigger operations, reducing parts counts by 75% and calibration requirements by 50%. Further, only 12 manual adjustments are needed for such calibrations.
3. There are four nonvolatile setup memories with typical retention times of five years.
4. Five 0.30-mV trigger sensitivity and filter positions.
5. Weights: just 17 lbs.
6. Respective rise times 5.8 and 3.5 ns, with deflection factors from 2 mV to 5 V per division, and dual time bases calibrated to 2 to 3%.
7. A 3-MHz X-axis bandwidth with an X-Y accuracy of ±4%.
8. Intensity, focus, readout, scale illumination are potentiometers under the front bezel, with callup and clear menu buttons on the side. To the right of the CRT are the channel 1 and 2 inputs and an external trigger connector. There are also trigger menus, manual/delay and vertical/horizontal menus. Above all this are cursor controls, utility, save/recall setups, a toggle movement control, and a special autoset used for finding the 50% level and the trigger signal's midpoint.
9. Cursors and on-screen readouts pretty well round out the features, which include delta volts, time, 1/delta time, and "absolute" volts.
10. Each of these oscilloscopes is at least 2% accurate and feature delay jitter of only 10,000 to 25,000 to 1. All meet Class 3 MIL T-28800 standards and are UL-certified. Time bases, you might also care to know, extend from 0.5 s to 20 ns – 2 ns with the 10X expander (Fig. 8-13).

If modest prices and more than considerable flexibility are attractive, then special NTSC, PAL, SECAM video triggering, cursors, and a highly integrated design should please. Analog oscilloscopes, we might add, remain very much alive!

Menu Map

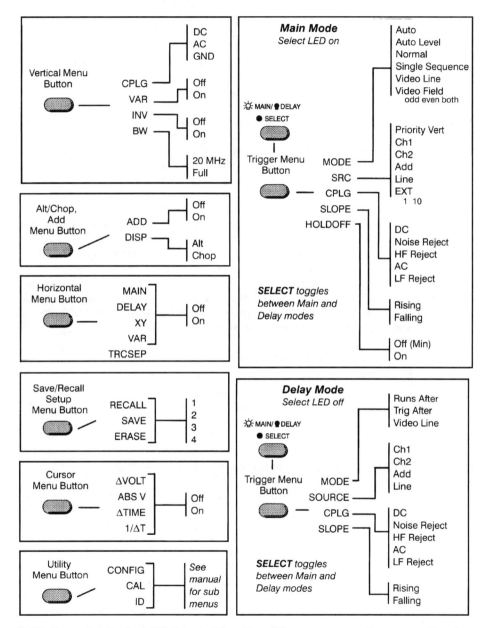

8-13 Expanded display of TAS control functions. Microprocessors offer many options for excellent, low-cost testing. Tektronix

Spectrum analyzers

Analyzing a spectrum is exactly what a spectrum analyzer does. A spectrum consists of all electronically visible phenomena within specified limits. Usual parameters are linear, dBmV, or dBmW (referenced to a millivolt or milliwatt), and detected sweeps from Hz to kilohertz, except when in the zero span mode, when the analyzer actually becomes a restricted-range oscilloscope. And now, with microprocessor controls, multiple menus, and vastly extended sensitivities and ranges into the gigahertz (10^9), the analyzer can make voltage and frequency measurements over much of the existing analog spectrum from low Hz to high GHz, store same, and repeat or delete as behooves the operator. Next to an oscilloscope and digital voltmeter, a spectrum analyzer is probably the most important piece of equipment either outside or inside the laboratory. As a specific example, satellite communications receivers and transmitters should always be setup on some particular geosynchronous spacecraft and transponder with a competent spectrum analyzer that can "see" modulation within the RF envelope whenever required, as well as transponders in each 500-MHz satellite bandspread.

Thus far, we've spoken only of analog (primarily AM/FM information), but digital bit streams are soon to be on the way, although these broadcast transmissions might appear simply as noise to the analyzer prior to detection. Ergo, a whole set of new applications are probable as the age of digital (not Aquarius) dawns on the electronics plain. Perhaps you'll have to add a logic analyzer, too, to adequately decipher the entire message. At the moment, however, let's return to the familiar world of modulated radio frequencies and gain a working understanding of what's involved. Here, it's well to begin at dc and work up to the lower gigahertz to really comprehend the vast expanse of information that can be dissected and studied within our analog world.

Analyzer varieties and how they work

Basically, there are three types of spectrum analyzers: *real time, fast Fourier transform (FFT),* and *swept tuned.* Front-end sensitivities often begin at −130 dBm and end at +30 dBm with wide-ranging resolution bandwidths, dynamic ranges, and essential frequency identification aided by internal counters that supply remarkable accuracies. There's also multiple information storage, a variety of application-specific menus, selected sweep times, expanded bandwidth settings, carrier-to-noise automatic readouts, peak waveform detection, bandwidth filtering, and automated parameter setups that are indispensable—to name a few, and there are more!

For the novice, we'll talk about Tektronix' 2700 series, which are highly useful and satisfactory instruments designed especially for CATV, video, satellite, and RF transmissions between 10 kHz and 1.8 GHz. And although satellite measurements are limited 950- to 1450-MHz block downconverter outputs, there's enough frequency and dynamic range to satisfy most routine applications. As for video, that 4.2-MHz bandspread is easily converted, whether in CATV or broadcast, between 54 and 806 MHz. For frequencies below 5 MHz, we'll enlist the aid of Tektronix' venerable, but excellent, 7L5, which also possesses digital storage and an L3 plug-in, which has terminations of 50 and 600 Ω, as well as 1 MΩ, and selectable references of dBm at 50 Ω, dBV and dBm at 600 Ω. That pretty well covers the electrical voltage/impedance measurement front. Manual calibration, however, does retard initial usage for possibly an hour, but then the input on 50 and 600 ohms will withstand a power level of +10 dBm and 100 V peak ac + dc at 1 MΩ impedance. Resolution bandwidth from 10 Hz to 30 kHz restricts input instrument noise to well over −100 dBV. The foregoing suggests that if you know your instrument's limitations, you won't be buying $330 front-end mixers and possibly a $1000 labor bill. Regretfully, spectrum analyzer repairs and special calibrations are obviously expensive.

The 7L5 A 14-control adjustment and the 7L5 plugged into a 7000 series mainframe sets up the calibration operation, which we'll exhibit, but not tediously describe. In the 10-dB and 2-dB per divisions, both wide and narrow traces must have sufficient log and amplifier calibrations to meet at the top of the graticule (Fig. 8-14). And horizontal calibration requires the 2nd and 10th vertical spikes of voltage from the calibrator to line up exactly with respective lines on the graticule. So, we're now calibrated and ready to explore a few illustrative measurements.

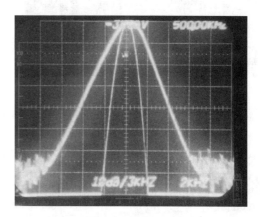

8-14 Calibrating 2-dB narrow excursion and 10-dB responses for the 7L5.

Let's examine a simple sine wave calibrated at 10 kHz on a function generator, 1 kHz resolution bandwidth on the analyzer and 2 kHz/division beginning at −6 dBV down and ending at about −78 dB on the 9th graticule. What do you see?

The center calibration dot is actually 10 kHz (Fig. 8-15). This means you're looking at a 20-kHz display with sine waves separated by 6.2-kHz intervals. Can this actually be a true measurement? If this was a true and accurate sine wave, then secondary alternations should measure 10 kHz separation. Further, even at 2 kHz/div., this isn't by any means a linear wave separation. So, how about poor symmetry on the function generator? If it won't calibrate, then you'd best do the job yourself or take it to a calibration lab and spend some $100/hour expensive bucks. These toys don't come cheap.

What do you think of the display in Fig. 8-16? These are actually a series of fairly fast oscillations because of either a reactance in the circuit or faulty setting of our signal gen-

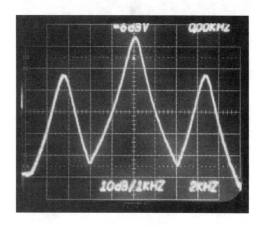

8-15 Sidelock generator's double sideband output.

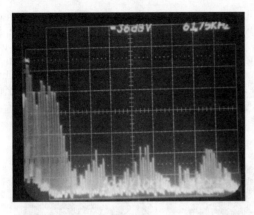

8-16 Color bars in gated rainbow generators appear spectrally as bursts of energy.

erator—usually at one end or the other of its range. Observe that the smaller oscillations are over 90 dB down, so an oscilloscope wouldn't register this problem at all. The reference with all its aberrations, however, would certainly become a big problem.

Next is the wave shape of a 10-color bar "sidelock" non-NTSC bar generator adjusted for a yellow-through-green display (Fig. 8-17). If you care to count the dipsy-doodles between sync pulses, you'll find there are exactly 10, and although they aren't perfectly linear in amplitudes, you'll find the purpose served admirably. Some of the apparent poor linearity, of course, results from the analyzer's sweep. However, if even one of these color bars was defective or a sync or termination pulse was lost, any absence would be immediately apparent.

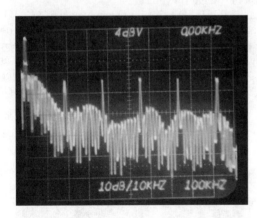

8-17 Sync pulses divide each series of 10 bars.

It's easy to see from these few examples how vitally necessary even a low-frequency spectrum analyzer can be. Were you using fast Fourier transforms (FFT) the displays would be that much more uniform and informative. But the overriding use of spectrum analysis in the RF frequencies usually takes precedence over what is normally modulation information because carriers are often just as important as the information they transport. Therefore, let's now proceed to the MHz regions and see how they appear with a very modern instrument, instead of just the 7L5.

Tektronix's 2700 series

In Fig. 8-18, we'll work with a much newer analyzer (a 2700 series Tektronix that illustrates the same pattern viewed at baseband in Fig. 8-17). This time, however, the video is modulated on double sideband channel 3. The less expensive generators don't attenuate the initial sideband at all; no vestigial here. Observe, too, top readouts for substantive information, such as marker frequency, its dBm level (at 10 dB/div.), followed by the center frequency the 0 dBm reference (top graticule), 2 MHz/div., and finally the resolution bandwidth at 500 kHz.

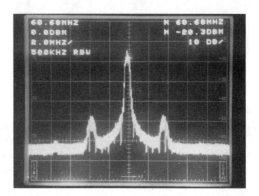

8-18 An RF picture at 60 MHz of a sidelock generator output. Sidebands are at least 30 dB down.

Measurements are not accurate, however, unless certain parameters are normalized. Therefore, we'll call up the applications menu (Fig. 8-19) to do just that. Here, signal bandwidth is measured at −3 dB, carrier-to-noise at 4.2 MHz, noise floor at 1 Hz, and Numbers 3 and 9 are checked for good measure. For Number 3, you will begin and end frequencies, start test, display results, etc. and the setup table for Number 9 pretty well repeats what we've already done for bandwidth, C/N, and noise.

With all parameters available and ready, let's do a C/N for the record and see how simple it is in the applications menu by simply pressing digit 1. In Fig. 8-20, our result is plainly evident in the upper right hand corner.

C/N reads 34.7 dB, with one marker at the top of the carrier and the reference marker some 4 divisions to the left, riding on noise. Isn't that a great deal handier than

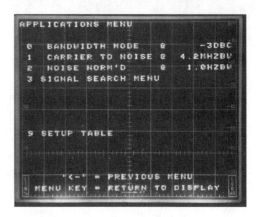

8-19 An example of modern spectrum analyzer menus carried in permanent storage and ready for immediate callup.

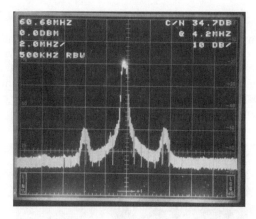

8-20 An always vital carrier-to-noise (C/N) measurement of 34.7 dB. It's a good one!

working with a messy calculation, where mistakes are easily made? Admittedly, the marker on the left isn't obviously apparent, but it's there, nonetheless.

There are also menus for input, max/zero spans, sweep, utility, scale, detector generator (AM/FM), marker frequency, and so forth. Are these difficult to learn? Not really; certainly not after a little experience with the instrument. It's just another extension of a computer, for this equipment is entirely microprocessor controlled and will operate exactly as programmed. It makes you think a little, but the results are remarkable. Combined with a worthwhile oscilloscope, you can measure almost anything in the way of time, frequency, voltage, decibels, power, amplitude, noise, etc., and even look at AM or FM pictures off the air if the proper optional detectors are installed.

Because we're looking at (Tektronix's latest spectrum analyzer is Fig. 8-21) AM video-modulated television in Fig. 8-20, would this produce a snow-free picture? To find out, just add 6 dB to C/N readout for 40.7 dB, and note that noise is only apparent at a TV receiver's cathode ray tube at 35 dB. So, there's 5.7 dB to spare, and that will certainly produce a good picture if there's no FM interference creeping in. If your antenna is amplified, all worthwhile preamps possess built-in FM traps. Use them, if needed, but examine all channels to be sure of maximum attenuation without added interference.

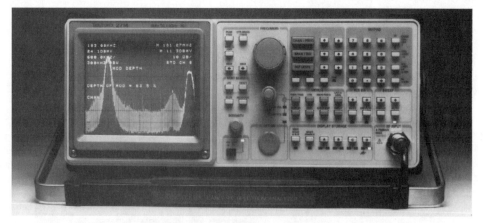

8-21   Tek's newest TV, CATV, Spectrum Analyzer, the 2714. Tektronix.

Satellite receive systems must produce a −40 dBm level for first-class pictures, but these are FM systems and 37.5 dB is added to the C/N readout, which should be a minimum of 12 dB for a good working signal-to-noise: S/N = C/N + 37.5 dB for FM satellite analog transmissions. At C band (3.7 to 4.2 GHz), there are a maximum of 24 transponders available on each satellite, and the Ku band varies between 10 and 16 for older or newer satellites (11.7 to 12.7 GHz). Following block downconversion, however, you only look at frequencies between 950 and 1450 MHz. Therefore, analyzers that operate to 1.8 GHz are entirely suitable for satellite transponder measurements following block downconversion, which delivers gains from 50 to 62 dB, depending on the manufacturer.

We could easily write several books on spectrum analyzer satellite applications, but this one deals with terrestrial television, so we'd better stick to the subject and not expand beyond channel 69 at 806 MHz. However, like HDTV, future Direct Broadcast Systems downlinked between 12.2 and 12.7 GHz will be both digitized and scrambled so that projected ordinary analog decoding there will become a thing of the past. Added to the five scrambling systems already operating in the Clarke Belt, a separate barn might become necessary to hold all the various system decoders. The Federal Communications Commission is already concerned over this proliferation and has requests for comment now in the hands of industry and other affected parties. Could there be a universal decoder for the major systems? We'll just have to wait and see. Right now, VideoCipher® 2 plus with card receives prime attention. What's next is anybody's guess.

Analyzer and digital notes

As users multiply and manufacturers suggest additional applications, considerably more uses are being discovered for both low cost and exotic spectrum analyzers. Noise/Com, for instance, suggests calibrating an analyzer with a broadband white noise source to identify its frequency response. Most noise sources have good power distribution at specific frequencies, and white noise delivers a constant spectral density over the bandwidth.

Noise sources with typical flatness responses are available between ±0.5 to ±1.5 dB, depending on frequencies between 0 and 18 GHz. If analyzer responses relative to power levels are in question, precision step attenuators are available from Noise/Com that can vary the injected noise.

Carl Matson of Tektronix has found a convenient method of measuring current harmonics from switch-mode power supplies with a digital oscilloscope having digital signal processing. Such DSOs both digitize the signal and calculate the resulting frequencies with fast Fourier transforms.

You'll need a linear current probe because one that's nonlinear will add harmonics of its own, and it must permit measurements without breaking circuits to reduce loading.

Select a usable FFT window (Hamming, Hanning, or Blackman/Harris) is suggested because sync is unnecessary, then measure amplitudes of the line current harmonics and the scope promptly displays the calculated spectrum. The cursors will measure harmonic amplitudes manually and you can then compare specified peak values. Power use and power factors are also measurable, although the scope needs RMS programming to calculate voltage and current for the same cycles.

Evaluation Engineering (EE) takes up the cause of spectrum analyzers delivering fast Fourier transforms because they have been vastly improved in recent years and reproduce all frequency components of signals simultaneously, offering better and even more accurate wave form displays. FFTs transform amplitudes, with respect to time into amplitude and phase versus frequency (or the opposite). Displacing the discrete Fourier transform procedures, the FFT does its calculations as soon as an additional sample is available. Because such sequences can take place at a certain sampling rate, real-time transforms are immediately displayed. EE notes that the highest frequency transformed is proportional to the number of samples in a time record and inversely proportional to its time. We would observe that sampling speeds are also proportional to price: and the faster FFTs are not easy on the pocketbook, even though their frequency ranges extend, at best, to the low MHz.

Terminology

GPIB spelled out is the nationally accepted General Purpose Interface Bus offering high-transfer data rates in Mbytes/sec and is also known as ANSI/IEEE 488.2 to define exactly how controllers and instruments communicate.

SCPI, another highly useful software instrument, simplifies command structures in IEEE 488.2 and develops a single-purpose command set for any SCPI-governed equipment. Together, GPIB and SCPI are the prime operating buses and commands in use for National Instruments-Sun Microsystems-Tektronix alliance, which has also recently been joined by Honeywell, DIT-MCO, and Integrated Measurement Systems (IMS). SCIP was developed jointly by Keithly Instruments, John Fluke Manufacturing, Hewlett Packard, Philips, Racal-Dana, Wavetek, Tektronix, and National Instruments.

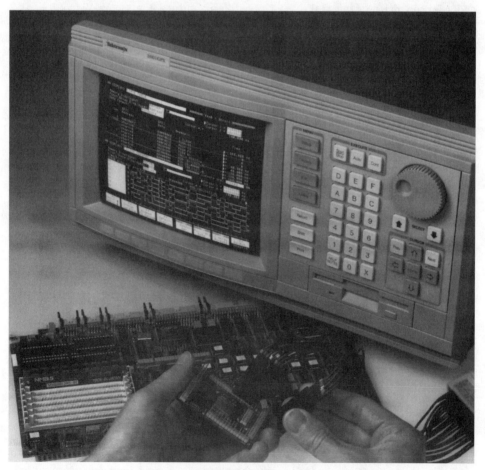

8-22   Tek's very new 3001GPX logic analyzer. Tektronix.

TIMING

1	Trigger on sample
2	Trigger on sample using duration filter
3	Trigger on Nth transition to sample
4	Trigger on Sample 0 followed by Sample 1 using duration filters
5	Trigger when Sample 0 is followed immediately by Sample 1
6	Trigger on maximum delay violation
7	Trigger on minimum delay violation
8	Measure delay from Sample 0 until Sample 1
9	Trigger on maximum pulse width violation
10	Trigger on minimum pulse width violation
11	Measure pulse width

STATE

12	Trigger on sample
13	Trigger on Nth occurence of sample
14	Trigger N cycles after sample
15	Trigger when Sample 0 is followed by Sample 1
16	Trigger when Sample 0 is followed immediately by Sample 1

STATE

17	Trigger if excessive time from Sample 0 to Sample 1
18	Measure time from Sample 0 to Sample 1, then trigger
19	Trigger on sample within range
20	Trigger on sample that occurs during subroutine
21	Store sample that occurs during subroutine

STATE+TIMING

| 22 | Store Timing data between State samples |
| 23 | Store Timing data before and after State sample |

TIMING+STATE

| 24 | Store beginning at Timing sample, trigger on Nth sample |
| 25 | Trigger on Timing sample while storing only State data |

HI-RES

| 26 | Trigger on minimum pulse width and store State data |
| 27 | Trigger on sample using duration filter |

8-23 The 27 preconfigured triggers chart for precision analysis and troubleshooting. Tektronix.

LabVIEW for Windows supplies graphical programming "on the PC" for software expansion and appropriate applications. LabWINDOWS broadens microsoft QuickBASIC and C with developments, in addition to function panels for source coding, data acquisition libraries, system control, data analysis, and display.

Tektronix's 3001GPX logic analyzer

The 3001 GPX (Fig. 8-22) delivers simultaneous state and timing logic analysis through a single 5-pF probe as it accepts synchronous and asynchronous information at 1 GHz across 16 channels, 80 channels at 200 MHz timing and 80-MHz state. All this is in either real time with graphics and, in the graph mode, your entire state buffer can be seen on the screen, solving glitches, and other problems as displayed or zoomed-in for maximum details.

Portable, too, as its high-level language through an LA-Connect links to SW development systems. The 3001GPX interconnects to an MS-DOS floppy disk, hard disk, RS-232 (series) and GPIB (parallel) COMM ports, triggers in or out on BNC connectors and a regular keyboard. There's also an external TEKLINK port-connect to an expansion mainframe for two extra PRISM-selected modules.

Triggering has been simplified, according to Tektronix, with 27 preconfigured triggers so that one of these or a programmable trigger can be selected and modified to fit the bill. If state and timing formats are not sufficient, PRISM's disassembly software is able to show your program at "five different levels of abstraction." All eight "tools" appear on a single module, and PRISM's ROM Emulator permits protype control in real time. Code and data are patched without the usual "burn and learn" procedure, speeding up the process considerably.

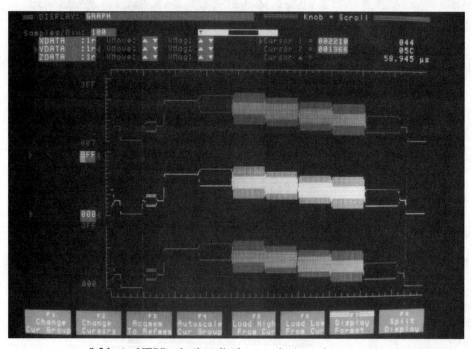

8-24 An NTSC color bar display on a logic analyzer. Tektronix.

To support these considerable claims, Tektronix has published a table on both timing and state, as well as a high-resolution chart (Fig. 8-23) illustrating all 27 triggers for rapid debugging or other system analysis. Further, PRISM automatically timestamps data, or if in two windows, then links the cursors and you have a completely time-correlated readout from any PRISM module. The CRT measures 9 inches, and floppy/hard disks can contain 720 K/40 Mbits, but the latter is optional as in GPIB for printouts and control, although series RS-232 is already installed. Total weight is 27 lbs (12 kg). A printout of an NTSC color-bar signal is illustrated in Fig. 8-24—exceptional for either a logic analyzer or run-of-the-mill DSO.

9
Antennas: propagation and reception

Considering the very small public knowledge of transmitting antennas as well as receiving antennas, we thought it propitious (and even useful) to include a chapter on transmitter/receiver characteristics that might further help explain some of the whys and wherefores of both analog and digital systems encountered in everyday operations. And we'll even begin with relatively low frequency amplitude modulation because your author has now moved to Bath Creek, North Carolina and needs every particle of gain that's feasible, amplified or otherwise.

But first, how about a little ground-wave, sky-wave propagation theory, which is as practical as wiping your chin after a crab feast? By so doing, you'll profit by more than considerable effort of our electrical forefathers, who did most of the work with either very crude or virtually no instruments at all. And this is why, for non-science folk, that even simple mathematics has become essential in this international communications world where ears, eyes, and electronics are everything—just like winning a ball game because winning is everything, according to most participants, and especially to their coaches.

Electromagnetic propagation

Like pebbles tossed into a still body of water, expanding circles or ripples are generated that eventually reach an intervening object (such as an island or the actual shore). In this scenario, the action is quite slow and readily apparent, but completely unlike radio transmissions traveling through air close to the speed of light calculated at 300,000,000 meters per second (984 feet/microsecond). That's pretty fast—even for conventional space probes. The real similarity is that water and electrical charges both propagate in ever expanding fields, becoming weaker as they depart the initial point of origin. Therefore, radio frequencies, like water ripples, fade with increasing distances making reception less likely with added separation (Fig. 9-1).

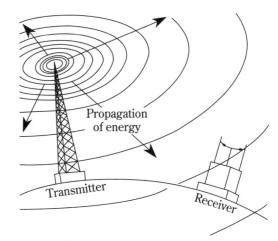

9-1 Like ripples on still water, transmitted electromagnetic waves expand in an approximate circle.

If, therefore, you wanted to know the wavelength (lambda) of some AM transmission at 1450 kHz, you'd divide this into the speed of light:

$$\lambda = 300 \times 10^6/1.45 \times 10^6 = 206.896 \text{ meters, or } 678.83 \text{ feet.}$$

Now, this is a full wavelength that would amount to an inordinately long and unwieldy antenna because the wavelength is what you're attempting to receive. But reasonable reception can be obtained with ½ lambda (or even ¼ lambda) so that 339 feet might do, or even 170 feet could offer sufficient pickup to receive many distant signals.

However, such a wire or antenna must be polarized (either vertically or horizontally) because electromagnetic waves consist of both electric and magnetic fields, which are at right angles to one another and reach maximum intensity one quarter of a 360° cycle (90° apart) and each alternately rises and falls with the passage of time so that the two are both in space and time quadrature. Therefore, the magnetic field expands in an opposite direction as the electrical field collapses, then vice versa so that at one time all energy stores in an electric field while, later, most energy stores in a magnetic field. This is why it's most important to obtain both electrical and inductive characteristics of any antenna. During RF (radio frequency) transmissions, these fields expand at nearly the velocity of light in the form of oscillations identical to current and voltage frequencies in the antennas itself. Because antennas are also called *radiators*, what one produces can also be received, although consumer antennas are not nearly as massive as transmitting arrays. If, however, they are of matching wavelengths, maximum electromagnetic energy is transferred and worthwhile sounds or pictures result.

Radio waves can be either vertically polarized or horizontally polarized (Fig. 9-2), depending on the transmitting antenna and they are so collected at the receiver. Maximum energy reception occurs only with matching wavelengths and proper polarization. However, in addition to X and Y radiation axes, there is also a Y axis, which is perpendicular to the other two. Ordinarily, this terminology of three axes applies only to properties of reflection or refraction, where beams strike a surface and are returned in an inverse direction. But here we're concerned primarily with skywaves and ground waves which might or might not reinforce one another following transmitter propagation. Therefore,

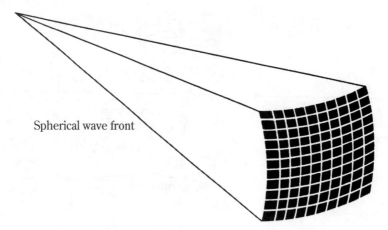

9-2   Radiated energy is usually polarized either horizontally or vertically.

we're arbitrarily going to apply the X,Y,Z rule to vertical/horizontal and earth/sky propagation to illustrate our point.

The *atmosphere* also divides into three basic parts: the *troposphere, stratosphere,* and *ionosphere.* The first extends from earth to between 6 and 12 miles; the second begins where the troposphere leaves off and extends to about 30 miles, and the ionosphere then takes over up to 250 miles. This latter atmospheric belt is the most important of the three affecting radio waves.

Radio waves can travel their electromagnetic paths along or near the earth's surface as ground waves, or by skywaves, which are reflected from the ionosphere, and even bounced back and forth until finally received. Down in Bath, NC, radio station WTOP in Washington, DC was clearly received during early mornings and evenings at a distance of some 300 miles. However, an AM station only 40 miles away in New Bern was only faintly audible on the same early morning, solidly proving that the ionosphere was our DC helper, whereas the ground wave (even with any diffractions or reflections) was pretty weak when reception depended on a built-in loop antenna.

Any solution here has a limited set of choices: string up a quarter-wave antenna; try an AM amplifier; or get a new radio with super (and expensive) characteristics. Our solution was an external antenna consisting of #20 solid telephone extension wire and a ground. As we unreeled the unshielded cable, reception became louder and louder until the volume had to be reduced to almost cutoff (Fig. 9-3). The local New Bern station came in remarkably well, but Washington, DC had completely faded for the day, thanks to daylight and the sun. Theory? Don't you believe it! Even much less than 170 ft. of available cable can usually do the job on 1.45 to 1.5 MHz every time. Don't try this at 60 Hz, however, or you'll be stringing cable for 3100 statute miles! Hertz (10^1), kilohertz (10^3), MHz (10^6), and GHz (10^9) are obviously different electronic animals and they react accordingly. Signal fading is also a multi-headed gargoyle in that it can be caused by: the arrival of more than one wave from the same source, changes in polarization because of the earth's magnetic field, variations in energy lost because of ionosphere absorption, and changes in ionosphere levels or densities producing skip distance alterations (especially prevalent at sunrise and sunset).

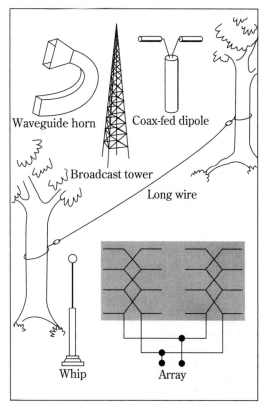

9-3 A single vinyl-clad #20 gage AM antenna made a world of difference even at 40 ft.

Waveguide horn

Coax-fed dipole

Broadcast tower

Long wire

Whip

Array

Radiating and receiving elements

A new radio appears

Perhaps to alleviate some distance, noise, reception, and traditional AM/FM problems, the National Association of Broadcasters (NAB) have announced a brand new AMAX-certified consumer tuner for best-quality AM, FM, and C-QUAM AM stereo said to produce sound quality sufficient for even studio monitoring. Called the NAB/Denon TU-680NAB tuner, it first became available in September 1992 for broadcasters at the NAB radio show in New Orleans, and later to the general public through Denon dealers around the country. In addition to 30 channel pre-sets, a special stereo decoder can produce remarkably clean FM reception.

Television characteristics

But enough of the radio wrapup, this book is about television, and so we'll drop the lower frequencies and enter the world of VHF and UHF, where broadcast TV operates between 54 to 806 MHz. It's another dimension where RF (radio frequency) carriers must allow both analog (NTSC) and digital (HDTV) modulation with totally different characteristics. Audio/video/sync processing in analog now becomes a digital bit stream in HDTV, which must contend with ghost cancellation. Ghost cancellation is now officially adopted by members of the U.S. Advanced Television Systems Committee without opposition and only four abstentions, which promptly filed a Petition for Rule Making with the Federal Communications Commission requesting use of line 19 (now set aside for VIRS, the color reference signal) in the vertical blanking interval. The system was designed and developed by Philips (U.S.) Laboratories. In addition, digital propagation during transmission has been corrected and various schemes to avoid distant-signal dropoff have now been developed that are similar to an analog fade.

Further, digital television with 5:1 compression has already been broadcast considerable distances with salutary results at UHF and will be thoroughly tested at VHF also. However, UHF should remain either the principal or only HDTV broadcast medium because UHF TV station allocations are often sparsely populated and should not interfere with NTSC.

Fortunately, it's apparent from initial tests and propagation studies that good-quality all-channel television antennas shipped today will be able to transmit or receive digital (as well as analog transmissions) equally well when simulcasting commences with the arrival of suitable transmitters. This might also bode well for the FCC's proposal to wind down all NTSC transmission 15 years from the day that an HDTV standard is fully adopted.

Will the public acquiesce? Only a few years into the future can tell the tale—especially if 150 broadcasters in the major 100 markets convert and offer HDTV to 83% of the estimated TV-viewing homes, along with price drops and performance/programming further improves. It could be a bonanza (hardly a bust), even though cost-per-set prices will tend to remain relatively high, compared with many of the less costly (but poorer quality) sets of today. For transmitters, tower space is the primary problem because full-power HDTV could cause difficulties with NTSC on the same original mast.

As for the ATTC task force on Field Testing, a Comark 60-kW transmitter has already been accepted for the tests scheduled to begin in 1994, immediately after ATSC selection of a prime system. Considerably more details on field testing follow, and the final chapters offer as many triumphs, trials, and tribulations as time will allow before final editing and publication becomes a necessity.

Meanwhile, there are some significant generalizations on home antennas and reception of which you should be aware before rushing the local discount outlet to select an el cheapo that can offer little, but frustration and chagrin because of inadequate reception. Secondly, any distance exceeding 20 miles from your TV station will usually require a preamplifier best matched to your antenna. If transmitters are widely separated or are afflicted with secondary images resulting from intervening terrain, high buildings, or towers, a 360° rotor assembly is another definite necessity. Thirdly, don't try and bury a good antenna in your attic. Usually, roof trusses prevent any significant rotation while restricting the size of your antenna, automatically produce a 3- to 6-dB power loss in dry weather (more during heavy rain and snow), and are usually poorly installed by either half-trained or untrained personnel, including the owner, who might never have heard of RG-6/U coaxial cable and long ferrule low-leakage F-connector fittings. Television antennas should always be chimney or side-house mounted for maximum strength and rigidity to prevent wind, snow, and ice from damaging or toppling them. A good TV antenna is little affected by even severe elements, although light-gauge masts will sometimes bend if chimney strap mounts are close together, loosely anchored, or cannot handle a taller-than-normal mast. Trained installers have little difficulty with any of these possible problems. Guy wires that penetrate the roof are not recommended.

Follow, if you wish, Underwriters Laboratories recommendations that all TV masts be grounded. This, however, offers a direct path to earth and can become a major attraction for even a relatively small electrostatic charge—one that can easily scorch the side of your house. As for the RF antenna and cable portion of the installation, dual grounds can often set up circulating currents that produce dark bands or wavy lines through your picture. A single RF receiver ground, along with the set plugged into a combined surge and ac filter will usually deliver excellent protection because electrical surges are much more common than a dose of lightning, which, if it does deliver a direct hit, often wipes out everything in its path. Unfortunately, nothing's perfect in our everyday world, and there is an element of chance with both lightning and surges, but with basic safeguards, the risk is minimal. If your curiosity is overwhelming, my personal television or satellite masts and kingposts are never grounded. Accept or reject, but always use a surge protector for all radio-type receivers. Never go home without one!

Another consideration often discussed concerns the television receiver. Will your present receiver pick up HDTV at all? The answer is a resounding no because of the special electronics and wide 16:9 aspect ratio versus the 4:3 (wide:tall) characteristics of today, but the old box can continue on NTSC, the other simulcast channel, for as long as your eyes and disposition can stand it. Because all HDTV telecasts will be both digitized and companded (compressed and expanded), you'll need a very wide bandpass set with probably double tuner conversion and a decoder that will expand luminance (brightness) information from a little more than 4 MHz to something like 30 MHz. Unfortunately, probably only 15 to 20% of all current U.S. receivers even have a 4.2-MHz luminance passband for today's good-to-shabby programming. A worthwhile comb filter, constant black level, and CRT (cathode ray tube) balancer/regulator does a great deal for even the late 1990s pictures, as does multi-channel (stereo) sound. A non-comb filter receiver, for your information, only supplies 2.5- to 3-MHz luminance (at best) because of the 3.58-MHz inductive color trap blocking maximum resolution and definition so that color ringing won't appear on the screen. A decent NTSC color bar generator with multi-burst from 0.5 to 4.2 MHz will identify the non-comb filter fraternity every time. Too bad that more viewers aren't trained to spot and reject these sadly restricted receivers. When purchasing, put your money in the set, not in some pressed wood cabinet. A good table-top receiver with passable external speakers is always better than high polish and fancy grain—especially for stereo and superior internal electronics, and there are a considerable number of very satisfactory speakers about for as little as $150/pair. Classical music, opera, and the Boston Pops are excellent examples of worthwhile learning and entertainment. Perhaps even a teeny-bopper rock hound might be converted, too.

We're tempted to continue with a lightning dissertation, but it would add little to what's already been generally said. Once again, the principal contribution to noiseless sound and blank screens develops from power line surges that have the unpleasant habit of wiping out operating voltage power supplies and thereby rendering consumer RF products mute. The better preamplifiers offer varying degrees of lightning protection, so endless explanations of theoretical possibilities prove nothing more than apprehensive conjecture, and that's simply a smelly mound of words.

The Cometics

Formerly tagged as Jerrold-Cometic, the great name of designer Jerrold Electronics (Pennsylvania and New York) has now been dropped and only Cometic Industries, Inc., Delhi, Ontario, Canada remains. After these superb antennas were originally designed, Jerrold sold manufacturing rights and machinery to Cometic and all U.S. supplies come directly from Canada. Shipping costs are rough unless the dealer or distributor buys a year's supply at a time. But performance and lasting qualities make up for the added price—especially if distributors can afford the necessary free-shipping units (often as many as 70 to 100 pieces). Along with these, especially for country installations, should be matching preamplifiers (needed for distant reception), as well as top-quality conductive cable and often antenna remote-controlled rotors for direct station aiming. Yes, the total bill can exceed $350 for a deluxe installation, but quality and longevity reception is always worth it. So what we'll describe are the identical antennas used by your author and the ATTC group for analog and HDTV digital field signal testing during 1993. Personal usage probably antedates this period by a full 10 years because I've never found better (Fig. 9-4).

We will, however, include Winegard's brand new UHF series as a less expensive, but effective source (Fig. 9-5), especially if coupled with their older all-channel amplifiers. If Winegard's new MATV amplifier series becomes available in time, we'll rig our entire laboratory with the main amplifier plus a half-dozen drops and give you a report on its suitability and improved operation. Math calculations come first and then actual measurements confirm or otherwise. It should be an interesting exercise with solid signal outlets for our brand new lab.

Meanwhile, let's see why these Cometic units are far superior to at least most competition and the superb construction/characteristics that makes them operate accordingly. Historically, this series of antennas began and remain as VHF log periodics, along with relatively standard UHF corner reflectors. Their multiple driven elements (sans parasitics) offer outstanding gain and broad, smooth signal pickup for VHF channels 2 to 13, with matching harness for UHF which extends from channels 14 through 69. For any distance at all, measured gain at UHF should amount to at least 10 dB over an isotropic (non-directional) dipole. If you're surprised at this single, vertical reference dipole response, think of CB and your own automobile radio's traditional lack of distant tuning. It just isn't there.

Operationally, antennas should become nearly resonant circuits. Close to series resonance, inputs approach zero impedance, while in parallel, their impedance could become infinite. If antennas result from poor design because of incorrect lengths, reactances (as well as resistances) become apparent with consequent losses. Larger-diameter units with low-resistance conductors are best within electrical limits, increasing efficiency and offering additional strength to withstand winter's ice and snow. Lower Q antennas (X_L>/R) permit broader resonances with better response over wider frequency bands.

Conventional antenna types include crossfire, end fire, and some lesser designs plus, of course, our prime log periodics. The latter were originally developed by a research group at the University of Illinois and initially marketed by the now-extinct JFD Corp. from New York just after the introduction of NTSC color in 1954–1955. Driven elements only were the prime feature, all cut within half-wave lengths of specific frequencies and spaced so that one depended on another to be resonant at calculated wavelengths and harnessed together for all-channel VHF coverage. This produced maximum gain, a fairly modest number of elements, and front-to-back phase changes of 180° for desirable backlobe and sidelobe protection. Now, late models have corner reflectors with a few UHF parasitic elements for pattern shaping and excellent gain—all harnessed and impedance-matched for a single download.

Coupled with a matching preamplifier of 18 dB gain, these antennas (in the larger group) will easily bring in stations 35 to 50 miles away and sometimes more during the May-August annual period of extended (Skip) coverage. Preamplifiers feature both anti-FM circuits, as well as some lightning protection, and will withstand considerable input signal before succumbing to obvious overload. One amplifier in the series is especially reinforced against larger-than-normal signal reception. Our preamp favorite is the 5287-H maximizer that receives VHF/UHF and even FM if that's a requirement, although an FM tunable trap is normally in the circuit to block out the herringbone effect that's especially notable on some of the lower broadcast channels. Video information usually does not take kindly to intrusions of frequency modulation between 88 and 108 MHz—especially harmonics. This particular amplifier has served well through many seasonal changes in Mid-Atlantic Maryland with neither failure nor service interruption. The many units in constant

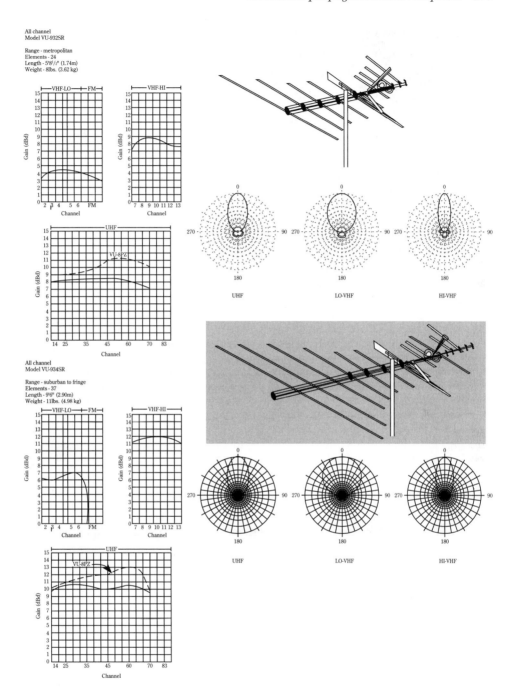

All channel
Model VU-932SR

Range - metropolitan
Elements - 24
Length - 5'8¹/₂" (1.74m)
Weight - 8lbs. (3.62 kg)

All channel
Model VU-934SR

Range - suburban to fringe
Elements - 37
Length - 9'6" (2.90m)
Weight - 11lbs. (4.98 kg)

9-4 These are the antenna types used in early HDTV field testing. Cometic Industries.

9-5 One of Winegard's new UHF antenna lines. We placed the preamplifier on the back of the corner reflector, attached to a parasitic element.

use over the past 10 years have required no replacements or been the subject of complaints. Usually, we don't offer blanket endorsements, but the record of these antennas and their preamps is outstanding.

A diagrammed chart of both the Cometics and competing antennas is illustrated in Fig. 9-6. It's been published before in a prior book entitled *Electronic Signals and Systems*; but we'll copy it because some 18 television stations were involved in Maryland and delivers a good comparison of both amplified and unamplified responses under field operating conditions. Included, are six of the better TV antennas in both amplified and unamplified situations, thereby illustrating the dramatic difference between regular and boosted reception around the Washington/Baltimore and Eastern Shore areas. All readouts among the plots originated with a Tektronix spectrum analyzer, which was carefully and accurately calibrated before the examinations began. You can trust the results with a considerable degree of confidence.

As for indoor antennas and rabbit ears, why bother? Neither type has ever been especially satisfactory even in mid-city, and certainly not in the 'burbs.

Coaxial cable

Trot down to the local "electronics" chain store and buy a hunk of any old TV cable and you'll be doubly sorry. In the first place, it's very probably RG-59/U with a #22 center conductor, flimsy single (basket weave) alleged shielding, a suspect internal dielectric (conductor-shield separator), and per-hundred-ft. losses that could even give the cable jobbers secondary hives. In any television cable that's worth its salt, you certainly want a #18 center conductor, double shielding and good moisture seal, and a jacket that won't whip itself into oblivion because of the wind. A total of 64-dB external signal or ghost rejection isn't at all unusual, and for decent reception, you're advised to require these specifications because mismatches along receiver, antenna, and cable induce all sorts of standing waves, oscillations, and even leakage that will attenuate any input signal—especially maximum analog and digital reception. Cheap in the installation business seldom translates to better. Now that you've been forewarned, please heed the voices of experience. Imagine a beautiful 16:9 aspect ratio picture emanating from a $3000 receiver with lousy video. Unfortunately, many will try, but few choose genuine quality cable.

Figure 9-7 shows what you should seek and have installed—not only as a downlead from your roof, but throughout your home or office. A lossy, poorly shielded cable is a terrible thing to contemplate. And once again, a universal warning that indoor antennas won't pass the mustard if you want quality reception. All antennas must be engineered (cut) for the electromagnetic energy wavelength intended. If not (like whip antennas on automobiles and other mobiles) both receive and transmit ranges are severely restricted. To avert deteriorating standing waves, poor impedance matches, and just plain leakage, cable, antenna, and TV inputs have to match for first-rate signal reception and transmission.

Cable lengths are also prime installation factors. At 6- to 10-dB (per 100 feet) losses, a 3-dB loss means half power, and a 6-dB loss represents half voltage. In any multiple installation beyond something like TDP's 4-way inexpensive 10G 208 4-way having an average gain of 13 dB (and a good match for the Cometic preamplifier), a prime, and somewhat expensive, main amplifier with excellent specifications is needed to serve more than this number of outlets, along with specially designed receptacles that also isolate most or all signal feedback from the source signal supply.

This, of course, is our next topic for discussion, along with the method and fundamental mathematics to substantiate the design. Once the method has been mastered and calculated several times, the degree of difficulty recedes to almost 0, but the first couple of initial attempts had better be checked at least three times for errors because you're bound to make a few along the way. System variable gain control is also desirable to avoid or cover up either interference or overload. Testing the system with dc and a signal generator is important, too, before loading with an operational input. Miscues in multiple outlet installations can cost a great deal of time and money . . . just ask anyone who's made them.

MATV

At some time or another, almost every electronics marketeer and/or installed is asked to deliver a multiple installation. Some know the ropes, others either guess or grope for answers, and inevitably lose. There are definite rules for laying out these systems and said rules had better be followed as closely as available (but not substitute) equipment permits. Watts of power signals do not make either MATV or satellite MATV. Reduced to channels 3 or 4 RF, these two are virtually the same. And further constricted to video/audio baseband, they are the same. The only real difference between them would be if several satellite receivers were set up with a 1:1 (no gain) active splitter to supply no-load information from the block downconverters. If this was the case, only one positioner would have control, and you'd invite a riot among most recipients who wanted other spacecraft selections.

So, to keep peace in the neighborhood, don't! Tactfully sell several discrete systems (on credit if need be) and keep the locals individualistic and off your back. Use a field strength meter, multimeter, oscilloscope, or whatever to positively measure the results. Signal vs noise (S/N) emerges as the prime parameter for multiple drop systems and each must be recognized and dealt with. For instance, external RF for either TV or satellite out of the block downconverter below −50 dBm or from television transmissions at about the same measure are inviting disaster. If you can look at the composite incoming analog at > −40 dBm (Fig. 9-8), you'll have an excellent video output indeed. For your television receiver, the S/N entering the cathode ray tube must be above 35 dB or the picture will decidedly exhibit noise. Notice that one measurement is dB referenced to 1 mV, while the other dB is simply a relative figure with no reference. Usually, dBm is used in terms

Chart designation	Antenna name	Channel	C/N	−3 dB bandwidth	FBR
A (★)	Jerrold/Cometic VU934-SR	2	39.5	2 × 18	17
		11	36.5	2 × 20	17
		24	42	2 × 10	14
B (◆)	TDP (Tandy) 4BG26	2	44.5	2 × 31	12
		11	34.5	2 × 30	22
		24	54.5	2 × 20	10
C (✖)	TDP (Tandy) 4BG30	2	38.5	2 × 30	12
		11	38.5	2 × 28	18
		24	51	2 × 21	26
D (●)	Winegard/Zenith 973-4002 Crossfire	2	34.5	2 × 30	16
		11	28.5	2 × 15	22
		24	34.5	2 × 20	14
E (▲)	Channel Master Ultra-Hi Crossfire 3674A	2	44.5	2 × 20	12
		11	50.5	2 × 15	20
		24	49.5	2 × 22	28
F (■)	Channel Master Quantum 1161 A	2	30.5	2 × 22	22
		11	34.5	2 × 15	22
		24	29.5	2 × 14	15

Notes

1) Amplified (heavier lines)
2) Unamplified (lighter lines)
3) Due to two couplers and one splitter, all signals are 10 dB less than actual values. Therefore, add 10 dB for real levels and values.
4) Dots indicate signal levels in dBm. Where there are no dots or other symbols, signals were below −66 dBm.
5) Distances to Washington, D.C. and Baltimore transmitters are about 35 miles.
6) Noise floor is approximately 8 dB.
7) C/N measurements reduced 5.5 dB for analyzer internal losses.

9-6 Spectrum analysis of six of the better TV antennas in the U.S., covering 18 widely separated broadcast stations in the Washington, DC and Baltimore, MD areas. Note that the heavier lines on the graph are antennas with amplification and the lighter lines are unamplified.

Channel number

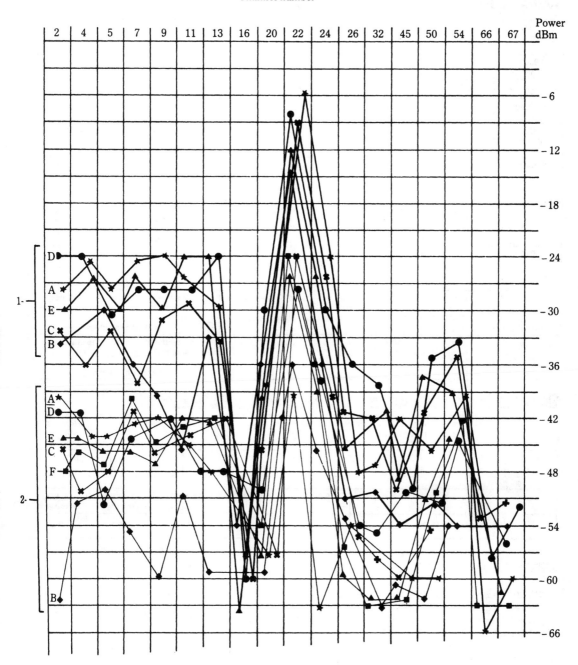

Comm/Scope TVRO Cable Specifications

Part No.	Coax Type/ Cond Dia.	Shield Coverage	Rotor # Cond/AWG Construction	Actuator # Cond/AWG Construction	Power # Cond/AWG
8502 UL listed	single RG/59 .0032"	67% alum. braid and alum. tape	3/20 stranded shielded drain wire	3/22 stranded shielded drain wire	2/14 stranded
8510 UL listed	dual RG/59 .0032"	67% alum. braid and alum. tape	3/20 stranded shielded drain wire	3/22 stranded shielded drain wire	2/14 stranded
8530 UL listed	dual RG/6 .0040"	60% alum. braid and alum. tape	3/20 stranded shielded drain wire	3/22 stranded shielded drain wire	2/14 stranded
8003	single RG/59 .0032"	67% alum. braid and alum. tape	3/20 stranded	3/22 stranded shielded drain wire (jacketed together)	2/14 stranded
8133	dual RG/6 .0040"	60% alum. braid and alum. tape	3/20 stranded	3/22 stranded shielded drain wire (jacketed together)	2/14 stranded
8123	single RG/6 .0040"	40% alum. braid and alum. tape	3/20 stranded	3/22 stranded shielded drain wire (jacketed together)	2/14 stranded
8130	dual RG/6 .0040"	40% alum. braid and alum. tape	2/20 stranded shielded drain wire	3/22 stranded shielded drain wire (jacketed together)	2/14 stranded
8136	dual RG/6 .0040"	40% alum. braid and alum. tape	3/20 stranded	3/22 stranded shielded drain wire (jacketed together)	2/16 stranded

Electrical Characteristics of Coax (measured at 68°F/20°C)

	Max. attenuation (dB/100') at these frequencies (MHz)			Return loss (to 1450 MHz)	Nom. cap. pf/ft	Nom. imp. (ohms)	Nom. vel. prop.
	450	950	1450				
RG/59	5.40	7.90	10.40	15 dB	16.2	75	82%
RG/6	4.40	6.54	8.40	15 dB	16.2	75	82%

	RG/59	RG/6	20 AWG stranded	22 AWG stranded	14 AWG stranded
DC Resistance (ohms/1000')	56.4	35.5	9.9	15.7	2.5

Comm/Scope offers a complete custom capability to manufacture TVRO cables to your specifications. Please call for details.

Both the RG/59 and RG/6 coax cables have a copper covered steel center conductor surrounded by a gas-expanded polyethylene dielectric. They have an inner shield of aluminum/polypropylene/aluminum tape bonded directly to the dielectric and an outer shield of 34 AWG bare aluminum braid.

All acutator wire configurations are shielded with aluminum polyester tape and include a copper drain wire.

All TVRO cables are jacketed in a high-grade PVC that is sunlight-resistant, totally waterproof and rated to 60°C.

Comm/Scope, Inc.

NETWORK CABLE DIVISION

PO Box 1729, 1375 Lenoir-Rhyne Blvd.
Hickory, NC 28602
(704) 324-2200
(800) 982-1708
FAX (704) 327-3577

9-7 Cable specifications and characteristics of quality cable (one of my printed sets of cable characteristics).

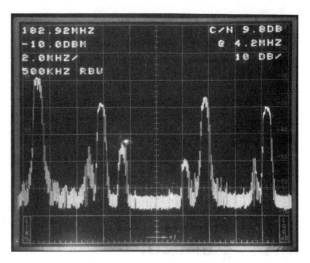

9-8 A study in large and small signal channels caused by distance and proximity. C/N for ch. 8 video equals 9.8 dB, which is totally insufficient!

of power: 1 W, for instance, is 30 dBm. Any dBV figure has to do with voltage, and sound has a common impedance of 600 Ω with ranges from about 50 Hz to 15 or 20 kHz. Video ranges will now expand from 4.2 to 30 MHz because of HDTV, and some satellite downlinks are already above 30 GHz and climbing, although consumer geosynchronous spacecraft downlinks are 3.7 to 4.2 and 11.7 to 12.2 GHz—each 500 MHz in bandwidth. The Direct Broadcast Satellite Service, however, will increase these downlinks to 12.7 GHz, but generating only ½ dB of additional space loss over Ku. Applicable polarizations for C and Ku bands are vertical and horizontal, while DBS will be circular, meaning both.

While on the satellite subject, we might also add there are already five scrambling systems in operation besides those used by the military. Whenever digital bit streams begin to descend from the heavens, there won't be room enough for all decoders to receive each system—even if you built a separate barn. And who would want to pay all that money to subscribe anyway? More advertising-sponsored programs on C band are fully expected as scrambling on Ku and DBS further clog reception for anyone but the business community.

dBV/dBW relations

As you should recall from a few paragraphs back, dBV refers to voltage and dBW to watts. So here's a few lines of remembrances to keep you on the gridiron, where we mosey into the meat of MATV. And the moment we'll consider each as one and the same, neglecting the usual CATV practice of up or downconverting, so they can place a number of programs on some set of convenient and allied channels. Otherwise, CATV would have long ago exceeded its allowable spectrum.

1 W = 1000 mW

1 dBW = 30 dBmW

dBmV (75 Ω) = dBmW (50 Ω) + 54.47 dB

dBmW (75 Ω) = dBmV (75 Ω) + 48.75 dB

dBmW (75 Ω) = dBmW (50 Ω) + 5.72 dB

In terms of logarithms:

$$\text{dBmW} = 10 \log_{10} \text{ in milliwatts}$$
$$\text{dBmV} = 20 \log_{10} \text{ in millivolts}$$

To translate just volts and watts to dBV or dBW, simply drop the "milli" from your answer. Be very careful to recall that dBW and dBmW are strictly P_2/P_1 power terms while V_2/V_1 are voltages representing ratios of inputs and outputs used to calculate gains or losses. Should a P_1 or V_1 exceed the values of P_2 or V_2, this would indicate a loss and a negative (–) sign precedes the answer. For straightforward log translations, neglect the ratios and proceed as illustrated. Any worthwhile calculator will handle logs to the base 10 very easily and anti-logs which are their inversions, plus considerably more if you invest a small amount in new equipment. Either a TI-36 solar or Sharp's EL-5200 is recommended for analog as well as binary conversions. Slide rules and their obvious inaccuracies disappeared with vacuum tubes, thank goodness!

MATV calculations

Now we come to the "rest of the story," as a well-known radio broadcaster might aptly declare. These are the calculations that are absolutely necessary in estimating the requirements of any multiple-outlet audio/video system served by a single source of amplification. Because we're not discussing cable television with its headends, trunk amplifiers, antennas, and customer drops, we'll stay with one amplifier and at least a half-dozen taps that you can exactly duplicate for your own or someone else's system. The results are accurate because this identical trunk serves my own laboratory.

In the smaller distribution systems, passive splitters will have individual losses of between 3 and 7 dB. Then, add isolation, cable, and insertion attenuation. Usually, 67% Comm/Scope double-shielded RG-6/U cable is sufficient for relatively short runs, but even less lossy wire with added amplification might be necessary for expanded systems. But, when totaling all distributed losses, the isolation loss of the final tapoff becomes significant.

You should also remember that a 0-dB level in MATV is 1 mV or 1000 μV. This is the readout suggested for adequate signal from each tapoff, or better. For extra safety, we prefer between 2 and 3 dBmV, which amounts to 1300 to 1400 microvolts (see tables at the end of the chapter). In strong co-channel areas, even an additional signal might be required for overrides. Should you have to use watts or milliwatts in examining power throughputs, remember that ac p-p must be reduced to rms (root mean square) by dividing by 2.828 ($E_{max} \times I_{max}/2$) to achieve the same resistor heating value as dc.

System layout for six taps

You can either imagine an 80 feet, two-story dwelling, a small apartment house, or my own 20-x-40 feet electronics laboratory, which will be served by the following amplification and system drops throughout (Table 9-1). Along the way, we'll take into consideration cable loss, splitter loss, insertion loss, and isolation loss. The latter is especially important because it's the difference between the available signal, the chosen isolation from the line, and the signal remaining for that tapoff's distribution. The lowest isolation value commonly used is 12 dB, and this amounts to 0.9-dB insertion loss. A 17-dB isolation equals 0.7-dB insertion loss, and 23 dB of isolation, delivers only 0.3-dB insertion loss. If you want other values, the manufacturer will furnish them provided that he has other multiple or variable taps that are suitable. Finally, cable losses between connected TV receivers and the various taps can usually be disregarded because they're usually very short.

Table 9-1. Calculated dBmV to μV conversions.

dBmV	μV	dBmV	μV	dBmV	μV
−40	10	0	1000	40	100,000
−39	11	1	1100	41	110,000
−38	13	2	1300	42	130,000
−37	14	3	1400	43	140,000
−36	16	4	1600	44	160,000
−35	18	5	1800	45	180,000
−34	20	6	2000	46	200,000
−33	22	7	2200	47	220,000
−32	25	8	2500	48	250,000
−31	28	9	2800	49	280,000
−30	32	10	3200	50	320,000
−29	36	11	3600	51	360,000
−28	40	12	4000	52	400,000
−27	45	13	4500	53	450,000
−26	50	14	5000	54	500,000
−25	56	15	5600	55	560,000
−24	63	16	6300	56	630,000
−23	70	17	7000	57	700,000
−22	80	18	8000	58	800,000
−21	90	19	9000	59	900,000
−20	100	20	10,000	60	1.0 volt
−19	110	21	11,000	61	1.1
−18	130	22	13,000	62	1.3
−17	140	23	14,000	63	1.4
−16	160	24	16,000	64	1.6
−15	180	25	18,000	65	1.8
−14	200	26	20,000	66	2.0
−13	220	27	22,000	67	2.2
−12	250	28	25,000	68	2.5
−11	280	29	28,000	69	2.8
−10	320	30	32,000	70	3.2
−9	360	31	36,000	71	3.6
−8	400	32	40,000	72	4.0
−7	450	33	45,000	73	4.5
−6	500	34	50,000	74	5.0
−5	560	35	56,000	75	5.6
−4	630	36	63,000	76	6.3
−3	700	37	70,000	77	7.0
−2	800	38	80,000	78	8.0
−1	900	39	90,000	79	9.0
−0	1000	40	100,000	80	10.0

Our system outline amounts to 52 feet of cable with a manufacturer's loss figure of 6 dB/100 ft. Therefore, using ratio and proportion:

$52{:}100 = X{:}6 = 3.16$ dB for 52 ft total

Now, let's determine	52/12 = 4.33	52/4 = 13 so	3.16/4.33 = 0.730
the individual cable	52/10 = 5.2	52/20 = 2.6	3.16/5.2 = 0.608
losses for each seg-			3.16/8.66 = 0.365
ment of the 52-ft	52/6 = 8.66	52/8 = 6.5	3.16/13 = 0.243
cable (with roundoffs)			3.16/2.6 = 1.215
			3.16/6.5 = 0.486

$$\text{total dB loss} = 3.647$$

We're well aware, of course, that dBs are not linear, but this method is quick (with a calculator) and simple enough to cover the electronic ballpark for reasonable estimates. Continuing, the various 23-, 17-, and 12-dB isolation losses are given above and you now have enough information to calculate the system.

So, combining insertion losses, cable losses, and dBmVs of amplification, let's see if we can't come up with a fairly quick and substantial (not dirty) figure that will neither confuse nor deliver misinformation. Granted, a short computer program would be considerably faster, but many of us don't have computers and calculators will have to do.

With the almighty dollar a consideration, let's see how far a +30 dBmV DA1036 Winegard amplifier can carry us (Fig. 9-9). If more is needed, a simple revision of the input and single-figure changes at each tapoff will suffice. If you wished to double the tapoffs following the same approximate dimensions, a double-ended amplifier (at extra cost, of course) will do the trick without further mental pain. These small jobbies are not nearly as difficult as one might think—just a little tedious during the first go-round, but cherry jelly thereafter. Out of the amplifier, you often have a splitter loss and that's all.

Distribution Amplifiers

Model DA-1036
(36 dB) 40-1000 Mhz

Model DA-1018
(18 dB) 40-1000 Mhz

9-9 Winegard's new +30-dB MATV amplifier.

Amp.	30 dBmV	
Split.	−3.5	
Remain	26.5	
1st Tap	26.5	
Insert'n	−0.7	Isolation 17 dB.
Cable	−0.608	
Remain	25.192	Therefore, 17 subtracted from 26.182 leaves plenty of signal for the receiver at Tap 1.

2nd tap	25.192	
Insert'n	−0.7	
Cable	−0.730	
Remain	23.762	17-dB isolation still leaves almost 7 dB for the 2nd receiver.

3rd tap	23.762	
Insert'n	−0.7	
Cable	−0.365	Again, 17-dB isolation still leaves over 5 dB for the third receiver.
Remain	22.702	

4th tap	22.702	
Insert'n	−0.7	Once more, 17-dB isolation permits more than 4 dBmV
Cable	−0.243	for the fourth receiver.

Remain	21.83	
5th Tap	21.83	
Insert'n	−0.7	Now, we're considerably closer to our isolation
Cable	−1.215	figure, with only 2.915 dB remaining.
Remain	19.915	

6th Tap	19.915	
Insert'n	−0.7	And 17 subtracted from 17.729 still leaves 0.729 dBmV,
Cable	−0.486	which remains almost 1 dBmV above 0 dBmV which, as stated, is the magic figure of 1000 microvolts.
Remain	17.729	

Observe that the 17-dB isolation tap was used throughout this exercise. It could have been calculated differently in the beginning if a 23-dB isolator had been used, but in this way, we provided uniformity throughout the entire system, and barely came out with acceptable numbers at the very end. So, you can take your pick of isolators, depending on desirable or undesirable tap locations, and work your will as long as there's enough signal propagating into the TV. If not, go back and re-calculate with no mistakes and design to suit your fancy or that of the customer. But the fancier the system, the more chance there is for several nasty problems that won't go away until they're fixed; in addition to an irate customer who can't understand why all calculations and results weren't correct in the first place. Dealing with many commercials and a number of consumers is difficult at best without a donnybrook boo-boo; that is, if you want to be paid. Camaraderie is often a wonderful thing, but empty pockets do not a stomach fill.

A little review

Please recall that any unused tapoff in the string must be terminated in 75 Ω so that standing waves do not setup on the line and cause both losses and even secondary images that you know as ghosts. Also, all cable shielding (your current return) has to make contact with system common through its various connectors. Above all, do not permit partial opens, partial shorts or loose connections. Hurried, sloppy work isn't conducive to harmonious public relations.

TV receivers without a single coaxial input require VHF/UHF band separators in all-channel systems. Connect correctly and watch for problems—especially for old dividers that were originally built in the days of Noah or one of his four-legged helpers.

A quick system estimate is always available if you have a good idea of its losses—especially one that's specified by the manufacturer. For instance, your input into the amplifier might amount to 2.0 dBmV; amplifier gain 30 dB; and system loss 20 dB

$$2.0 \text{ dBmV} + 30 \text{ dB} = 32 \text{ dB}$$
$$\underline{-20 \text{ dB}}$$

Available signal +12 dBmV

But what's 12 dBmV in terms of microvolts? If you wish, you can calculate the dBmV relationship to microvolts by the following equation. First, change microvolts to millivolts, take 20 log of the result and there's your figure: 4000 µV = 4 mV and 20 log 4 = 12.0412! Close enough? Or you can look up Table 9-1 and simply read from left to right. The answer indicated by the table is 4000 µV! In the end, how about sticking with dBs and dBmV, which is always 30 + dBV? You'll find the operation considerably easier; unless, of course, you're an impractical college engineering student or undergraduate instructor who dotes on math equations to the exclusion of almost everything else. Practical aspects do make most systems operate. For instance, would your design really need an excess of 4000 µV? Perhaps 2000, but certainly not 2X that amount! Always take care when attempting to use "examples" or engineering "trivials" when the demonstrator has no concept of the ultimate product. Do understand, also, that dB is nothing more than a relative term, but dBmV means decibels referenced to one millivolt.

You're already aware of many desirable characteristics in selecting an amplifier, but beware of the following: low-noise figures (6–9 dB) are essential and must be at least 40 dB or more compared to the signal level (40 dB S/N); in decibels, input signal plus gain specifies the amplifier's output; when broadband amplifier output is less than one or more competing carriers cross modulation is very likely and picture information of one channel will superimpose on yours; excessive darkness in any picture denotes overload and even loss of vertical/horizontal sync in severe instances; co-channel interference means the same channel will also superimpose on yours along with a probable leaky cable and finite signal delays; images to the left of the main image are identified as leading ghosts, usually caused by external pickup, and trailing ghosts resulting from reflections and can often be eliminated by carefully chosen traps or improved cable and general installation practices; wavy bands through the picture usually result from circulating currents because of different grounds, stray ac, or even motors in some peculiar instances; all passive elements (devices) in your MATV have to pass power to avoid ac shorts; and if you wish to add additional line taps, either redesign the system or try an additional line amplifier, but watch for extra noise along with further amplification.

When selecting an amplifier make sure it does exactly what you want. For instance, a SMAT (satellite) amplifier must have a bandspread of 500 MHz to accommodate even C-band signals. So, beware all passbands and S/N.

This discussion could continue ad infinitum, but the main points have already been made in enough depth to contain suitable information without loading the barnyard. We could glorify a few additional UHF-only antennas offered by both Winegard and Cometic, but only all-channel antennas will be used in the HDTV ATTC field tests, and these deserve maximum attention. We have found, however, that UHF-only antennas respond well to all-channel preamplifiers and can often handle adequate signals from channel 7 through channel 69 with excellent results. Below channel 7 their characteristics simply don't include the lower TV frequencies, so don't expect them to.

Log periodics for VHF and corner reflectors for UHF appear to respond best to the dual U/V TV bands. By now, we hope you're convinced that a few bills more makes a world of difference in television reception when there's both satisfactory cable and a better-than-average TV/monitor receiver that accepts external speakers for surprisingly good multichannel (stereo) sound—even with good old NTSC.

The Polaroid photo in Fig. 9-8 deserves a little explanation also. The broadcast stations in the Washington, NC area are channels 2, 7, 8, 9, and 12 with poorly equipped antennas. The video carriers for three of these respective stations are 175.25 MHz, 181.25 MHz, and 187.25 MHz (for channels 7, 8, and 9). Without an outside antenna, their signals measure −31 dBm, −52.7 dBm, and −39 dBm, with carrier-to-noise for weak channel 8 appearing at 5.9 dB versus 30+ dB for the other two. Such disparities make for very poor viewing and equally unhappy customers. Try and give them, if you can, a good outside antenna with a preamplifier and rotor so that three channels will suddenly have at least a half dozen more added to the family. You might find collecting something extra easier than you think!

Winegard

Another major player in the MATV/CATV systems—especially for apartment/business installations that require better-than-average equipment and setup instructions is Winegard (Fig. 9-9). In addition, Winegard, a manufacturer of television antennas (particularly low-cost UHF units) has also announced a new line of medium- and high-gain unitized power amplifiers with outputs for the DA-1018 of 6, 12, 36, and 52 channels having a gain of 18 dB and the 37-dB gain for DA-1036 with equivalent numbers, otherwise compared to the DA-1018. Outputs in dBmV for the DA-1018 range from 46-55 and those in the higher powered DA-1036 between 47-56 when fully terminated. Noise figures for this extruded aluminum-housed equipment have surface-mount components, variable gain adjustments, no external power supply, a selectable FM trap and a 3-prong grounded power cord. VSWRs measure from 1.5 max to 2.6 max, depending on frequency and power, and their passbands are specified from 40 to 1000 MHz.

We understand that signal splitters have become popular with landlords so that they can disconnect individuals who "forget" to pay their bills. If these are passive splitters, of course, additional line or trunk amplifiers are needed to overcome the 3.5- to 13-dB losses that are encountered whenever such an arrangement is required. If signal levels are kept reasonably high, noise carry along with RF doesn't seem to present a significant problem. Taps, however, with specified return loss figures would seem to be a more reasonable application, unless the landlord factor is positively necessary. As for the various types of cable needed in these systems, Winegard has a very useful table of cable attenuations that might (or should be) of interest to installers, beginning with RG-59/U and continuing all the way through RG-6/U and RG-11/U. Although Winegard recommends RG-11/U for down leads and trunk lines, RG-11/U is not used in trunk lines with tapoffs. Therefore, a good low-loss RG-6/U is always available—especially the 67-dB shielded variety, which can also be a collective part of the entire system.

The attenuation table (Table 9-2) tells a pretty good story, except that RG-6/U attenuation under 1 GHz is somewhat high—especially when compared with the one we use for both satellite and MATV frequencies. RG-11/U is better, of course, when available and suitable, but the retail cost is somewhat elevated, depending on the individual supplier.

Table 9-2.
Attenuation in dB for
various types of coaxial cable
at various television channel frequencies.

	Loss/100 ft				
Channels	**2**	**13**	**14**	**48**	**69**
RG59/U	2.6	5.4	8.4	10.5	10.3
RG59/U Foam	2.1	4.1	5.8	7.1	8.3
CL2700 (RG59)	2.2	4.4	6.5	8.0	8.7
CL2800 RG6/U	1.6	3.2	4.9	6.0	6.5
RG11/U	1.4	3.2	4.8	5.8	6.8
RG11/U Foam	1.1	2.3	3.5	4.3	4.9

Comm/Scope cable is quite useful for satellite downlinking at a loss of only 8.26 dB at 1450 MHz (per 100 ft). The Winegard system previously calculated has now undergone specific hardware testing with excellent results. Cross-modulation is Winegard-specified at 0.5%, the operating temperatures are from −30 to +140 degrees F, and the switchable FM trap can attenuate as much as 24 dB. These specifications should offer a fairly reasonable insight into such brand new products that promise to become significantly useful. Because all surface-mount active devices are normally highly reliable, you might expect extended service from both small-signal and power output devices.

10
Field testing

Field test planning and equipment approval/acquisition began during 1992 for both television and cable systems to be executed in the Charlotte, North Carolina area over VHF channel 6 and UHF channel 53. The original tower is owned by the Providence Journal Co., which has approval from the Federal Communications Commission to use the two vacant 82- to 88-MHz and 704- to 710-MHz frequencies during the entire test phase. Space on the 1335-ft Kline tower some 10 miles east of Charlotte has been donated by Lodestar Site Management, the tower's new owner. Tower load increases and upgraded standards required approximately $85,000, available because of "significant savings" of a field truck loaded by the Harris Allied Division equipped with a 15-kW generator power and air conditioners, racks, in addition to cable TV test support facilities. CableLabs equipment can be contained in the truck and will be used to test approximately 50 test locations (points) around Charlotte, with truck delivery scheduled for November 1992, allowing sufficient time for setup and preliminary testing expected to begin in 1994, depending on selection of the winning HDTV system and probably a single backup. At least that's the thinking in early 1993.

Over-the-air checks include ATV UHF and VHF and NTSC UHF and VHF in a series of four 1-minute sequences and the entire sequence repeated once, allowing a total of 12 minutes for playback. A core of trained observers were then agreed upon, that did not include system proponents, and members would be called upon as needed. Tentatively, 3 to 5 observers would be used. As for audio, sequences were to include broadcast segments with voice and music, along with decoded readings "indicating error correction, equalizer settings, and operational range during error concealment." Ghost cancelling is to be inserted at least during some test portions. Maximum tower power is to be maintained within 3 to 4 dB for the tests, and reflected power will also be monitored at the transmitter site. NTSC-only testing commences periodically when site sampling is undertaken. During this and other operations, home testing is expected with owner permission.

Current scheduling suggests tower refurbishing completion by November/December, transmitter installation later in the month, and ATV (digital HDT TV) can be aired after January. Formal ATV field testing should commence after the middle of 1994 and last for several months. VHF channel 6 will operate at 10 kW and the UHF unit will operate at 610 kW, with Andrew supplying a 3-inch VHF transmission line and Dielectric Communications supplying a 6-inch UHF unit. Larcan Communications Equipment, Canada, supplied a 30-kW solid-state VHF transmitter and Comark Communications supplied the channel 53 UHF 55-kW unit.

Other suppliers/loaners include:

Tektronix for NTSC/HDTV video and audio monitoring equipment; Sony and/or Panasonic for NTSC recorders and monitors; Coaxial Dynamics & Bird Electronics for RF wattmeters, directional couplers, and dynamic loads; Grass Valley Group for audio and video DA switching and processing; Modulation Sciences for NTSC audio processing and stereo/SAP generators; CRL for audio ATV processing ITS, the translator; Hewlett Packard for certain RF test equipment; NTIA/ITS for channel characterization equipment; JBL for speakers; Shure for audio mixers; and ATV video/audio origination equipment.

Tests and test materials

Plans were to compare NTSC and ATV signal reception at 200 selected field sites, and UHF/VHF signal-strength measurements occurring in "standard" 100-ft runs, as well as during longer-term static measurement periods. Also observed were NTSC stereo, second audio programming (SAP), captioning reception, and ATV stereo/data. Objective audio/video for NTSC/ATV were conducted and UHF/VHF channel characteristics recorded. Some 50 CATV measurements were scheduled on about 8 technically "diverse" cable systems at both cable-only sites, as well as combined cable and over-the-air combinations.

Program material consisted of audio/video test signals, selected laboratory program information pre-recorded and several minutes of ongoing real life (actual) scenes, some of which had not been previously used or recorded.

Other tests are/were separately sponsored following scheduled field tests, with Andrew Corp. providing a side-mount, high gain, directional UHF antenna for the occasion. Harris, TTC, Jampro, and Cablewave (Bogner Antenna) were also expected to participate when the format became settled. The Association for Maximum Service Television (MSTV) will aid in over-the-air testing and data analyzing. Cable tests will be funded and conducted by Cable Television Laboratories.

Further information on testing formats and proposed actions (as of the and of 1992) is in a special paper entitled "Developing the Field Test Facility for a Terrestrial Broadcast Advanced Television Service" by Edmund A. Williams, currently working for the Public Broadcasting Service in Alexandria, VA, but who is also the Manager of the Advanced Television Field Test Project, reporting to Field Testing Task Force chaired by consultant/engineer Jules Cohen with industry-wide representation. Because this paper represents a full report of the project's initial performance and objectives as of just a few months before system selection, it is included for both further information and historical perspective.

Contained also are Field Intensity U/V diagrams about the test locations, as well as block diagrams of both the transmit and field site(s) as offered by ATTC and the Field Test Project. All should substantially "speak" for themselves because they are basically art-form records of test areas and operating electronics serving them.

Some of what we've already reported will be discussed again, but the information in Mr. Williams' own words and thoughts will add immeasurably. So let's segué to Mr. Williams for his enlightened report:

Developing the field test facility for a terrestrial broadcast advanced television service

This paper presents the essential elements of the Advanced Television (ATV) field test plan developed by the Field Test Task Force of Working Party Two of the Systems Sub-Committee of the Advisory Committee on Advanced Television Service established by the Federal Communications Commission.

ATV field tests will be conducted in 1994. The ATV system employed for the tests will be the one recommended as a result of a) laboratory tests conducted by the Advanced Television Test Center and Cable Television Laboratories, b) the visual subjective tests conducted by the Advanced Television Evaluation Laboratory (ATEL) in Canada, and c) the aural subjective tests conducted by Westinghouse Research Center in Pittsburgh. The recommendation of a system for field testing will come from the ATS Standard Working Party (WP4) of the Systems Sub-Committee.

The purpose of the field test is to confirm the claimed and measured performance of the ATV system when used in a full-power, "real-world" environment.

Background

The concept of broadcasting High Definition Television (HDTV) has been advocated since the early 1980s. There have been many demonstrations of HDTV conducted at industry trade shows (NAB, SMPTE). Early in 1987, the National Association of Broadcasters and Association for Maximum Service Television conducted the world's first UHF-TV broadcast of an ATV signal. The ATV system was the NHK wide-band (9 MHz) MUSE-E system. The transmission occurred on UHF channels 58 and 59 in Washington, DC with receivers at the Federal Communications Commission, Capitol Hill, and the NAB.

In August, 1987, at the urging of the broadcast television industry, the Federal Communications Commission (FCC) issued a Notice of Inquiry on Advanced Television Systems (ATS). The FCC subsequently established an Advisory Committee on Advanced Television Service (ACATS) in November 1987, followed by the formation, in early 1988, of the Advanced Television Test Center (ATTC) by the broadcast television industry.

The Advisory Committee spent two years in a preliminary technical investigation of about 20 ATV systems and the development of test procedures that would be used by a central test facility. Laboratory tests of two analog (one Enhanced TV System) and four digital ATV systems, certified by the Committee, began in 1991 at the ATTC in Alexandria, Virginia and will continue through most of 1992.

The ATTC is sponsored and supported by CapCities/ABC, CBS, Electronic Industries Association (EIA), Association of Independent Television Stations (INTV), Association for Maximum Service Television (MSTV), the National Association of Broadcasters (NAB), the National Broadcasting Company (NBC), and the Public Broadcasting Service (PBS). Cable Television Laboratories (CableLabs) also operates a facility at the ATTC.

The results of the subjective measurement test portion of the ATTC laboratory tests will be in the form of tape recordings that will be shipped to the Advanced Television Evaluation Laboratory (ATEL) in Canada for subjective evaluation by "lay" observers.

ATEL will conduct subjective evaluation tests of the recordings made by ATTC of ATV reception under conditions of co-channel and adjacent-channel interference and noise. From these tests, and the UHF taboo, flutter, and multipath tests, will come the data for developing NTSC to ATV, ATV to NTSC, and ATV to ATV power ratios and transmitter separation distances between ATV and NTSC stations.

The analysis of these data will be conducted by the Spectrum Utilization and Alternative Working Party (WP3) of the ACATS Planning Sub-Committee. WP3 will develop the ATV to NTSC power ratios that will be used eventually in the field tests.

In addition to the work of the ATTC and ATEL will be the subjective evaluation of the program audio channels of each ATV system by the Westinghouse Research Center in Pittsburgh, Pa.

Scope of the field test project

The Field Test Task Force was formed under the Evaluation & Testing Working Party (WP2) of the ACATS Systems Sub-Committee to organize and conduct field tests at the conclusion of the laboratory tests and prior to the decision by the FCC, expected in 1993, adopting an ATV terrestrial broadcast service.

Much of the work on the development of the test plan was conducted during 1990 and 1991 by the task force. Members consisted of a dedicated group of scientists and engineers representing testing laboratories, equipment manufacturers, ATV system proponents, television broadcasters, networks, and industry associations.

The field tests are not designed to yield comparative data. Instead, the primary goals of these tests are to verify performance and operability of the selected ATV system under "real-world" conditions, and, possibly, to identify flaws that were not discovered during laboratory testing. A second important object of the tests is to provide a comparison of impairments between NTSC and ATV in the field. In addition to the over-the-air transmission tests, tests will be conducted through existing cable television systems.

The results of the field test will supplement the laboratory data that will be used to develop a recommendation to the FCC on an advanced television broadcast system.

It is the intent of the field test to verify (confirm) the performance and operability of the selected ATV system by conducting nearly simultaneous evaluations of received NTSC and ATV signals on UHF and VHF channels. Measurements and observations will be made at about 200 selected field locations, plus several cable line "drops" from each of several cable television systems within the coverage range of the transmitter.

The ATV system to be transmitted is expected to require the same or less peak power as an equivalent-coverage NTSC signal. Therefore, the transmission facility will be designed to accommodate both systems with a switching arrangement to feed either the NTSC or ATV exciter to common UHF and VHF high-power amplifiers and antennas (Fig. 10-1).

In addition to the subjective evaluation of the received ATV and NTSC signals, the task force might also incorporate a ghost canceler on the NTSC channel and make channel characterization measurements using digital or analog techniques developed by the Institute of Telecommunications Sciences (U.S. Department of Commerce).

Field test design objectives

The field test design objectives include:

- Operating the transmission facility at or near full-power on UHF and VHF.
- Simultaneous reception of UHF and VHF in the field.

- Radiation of both ATV and NTSC on the same channel.
- Means for subjectively and objectively evaluating and (if possible) recording the received ATV and NTSC signals.
- Measurement of field strength and channel characteristics.
- Measurements and evaluations at up to 200 sites along several radials and in grids (groups of sites in common environments, such as urban areas or near heavy vegetation).
- Conducting tests on several Cable Television systems.

Field test site

The selection of the field test site was contingent upon a variety of technical, logistical, terrain, and economic factors.

A site near Charlotte, North Carolina was chosen by the task force for the field test based on:

- *Site Availability* The tower near Charlotte became available late in 1991. It is over 1300 ft high and will support both top and side-mounted antennas. The owners are willing to provide tower and transmitter space for the test. The site also met most of the rest of the selection criteria.
- *Channel Selection Availability* The site meets full-power UHF NTSC separation requirements and is slightly short-spaced for a VHF channel (which actually becomes an advantage for the VHF tests).
- *Terrain Considerations* The area within a 40-mile radius of the site provides a reasonably wide variety (but without extremes) of terrain, vegetation growth, water surfaces, and populated areas of large urban (Charlotte), smaller towns and rural (farms and sparsely populated areas). There are many good roads on which to travel to the measurement sites.
- *CATV Systems* A variety of CATV systems are in the vicinity of the site, including large and small systems, those with AM and FM links, and fiberoptic systems. The variety provides an opportunity for testing ATV transmission through many typical CATV systems. CableLabs will be surveying the systems, characterizing, and selecting those that represent the technology likely to be in use during the introduction of an ATV broadcast system.
- *Metropolitan Areas* Charlotte is the most built-up city in the vicinity (5 miles west) of the site. Numerous smaller towns are within a 40-mile radius of the site.

Providence Journal Broadcasting Corporation of Rhode Island is providing the tower and transmitter building. Providence recently moved its Charlotte station, WCNC-TV channel 36, to a new site west of the city. Providence has generously permitted the old site to be used for the field test, but intends to sell it at some time in the future.

The University of North Carolina Public Television Network (UNC-PTV) also uses the Providence tower for a side-mounted antenna at the 1200 ft level for its WUNG-TV channel 58 relay, which is licensed to Concord, NC (northeast of Charlotte). UNC-PTV will be moving WUNG-TV to a new site in July 1992, after which the side-mount position and transmitter space will be used for the field test operation.

The tower itself was manufactured and erected by Kline in 1967. The tower is managed by Loadstar Tower Management, Inc., a division of LeBlanc. It has been well maintained and was recently refurbished to meet current RS-222-C standards. In addition to the two television antennas, the tower is host to the antennas for two full-power FM stations and a multitude of two-way radio and microwave antennas.

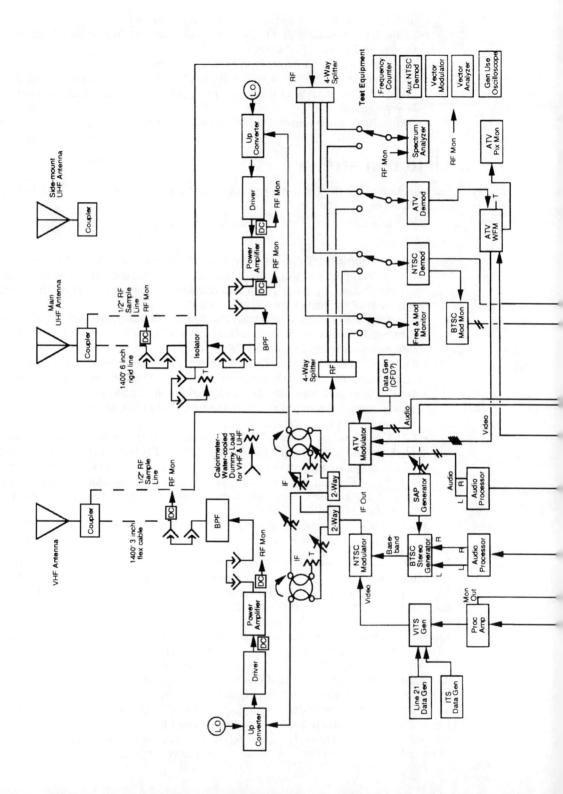

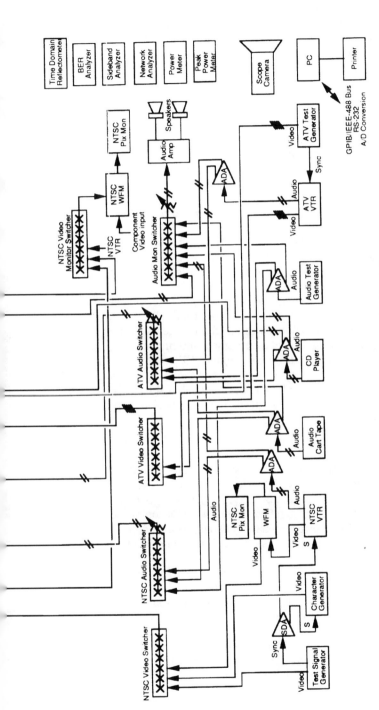

10-1 ATV field test: transmit site block diagram.

Terrain profiles developed for the proposed site show a wide, but not excessive, variety of terrain characteristics. A review of a topographic map of the Charlotte area within a 40-mile radius of the tower will show rolling and flat terrain, a wide range of covering vegetation, rivers, lakes, and urban and rural environments (Figs. 10-2 and 10-3).

Transmission facility

The building currently occupied by WUNG-TV is now vacant. After some renovation on the air conditioning, electrical, and plumbing systems, adequate space exists for two transmitters (UHF and VHF), ancillary RF hardware, and origination and control equipment.

The room for the ATV encoding equipment and digital video tape HDTV playback (and format converter), and test and monitoring equipment will be temperature and humidity controlled.

UHF Channel 53 has been selected for use in the Charlotte, North Carolina vicinity because it will meet normal NTSC separation criteria. The UHF facility is expected to operate at just under 1 MW ERP (60-kW transmitter, less line and connector losses, plus an omni-directional antenna gain of about 25 = 860 kW).

The VHF facility might have to be operated at several dB below full power as the co-channel separation requirements are not likely to be achieved. Therefore, the NTSC, as well as the ATV signal, might be transmitted at a somewhat reduced power level on the VHF channel and consideration will be given to the use of a directional antenna.

The close spacing of the proposed facility to nearby co-channel VHF stations will provide an opportunity to test the co-channel interference tolerance of the ATV system under real-world field conditions. A similar arrangement could be created to test for UHF co-channel interference by installing a translator, or modifying an existing one, at an appropriate distance for the UHF portion of the field test.

Transmission system performance

The performance specifications for the field test transmission system are substantially more stringent than would be expected for a typical NTSC facility. The complex encoding, modulation, and RF configuration schemes employed by the ATV system proponents require that the transmission system not contribute significantly to the distortion of the transmitted signal. Each ATV system employs powerful channel equalization and error correction circuits that will compensate for many of the distortions found in normal terrestrial propagation.

Therefore, it is incumbent upon the transmission system components to contribute as little as possible to these distortions so that the receiver has the best opportunity for recovering the original image and sound. In other words, the transmission system should not significantly reduce the ATV system's margin for compensating for noise and distortion imposed by the propagation path.

Determining the performance specifications for the transmission system has, at best, been difficult as several factors individually or in combination can produce various levels of degradation to the ATV signal. Moreover, the peak-to-average power ratios of the various ATV systems must be dealt with as well.

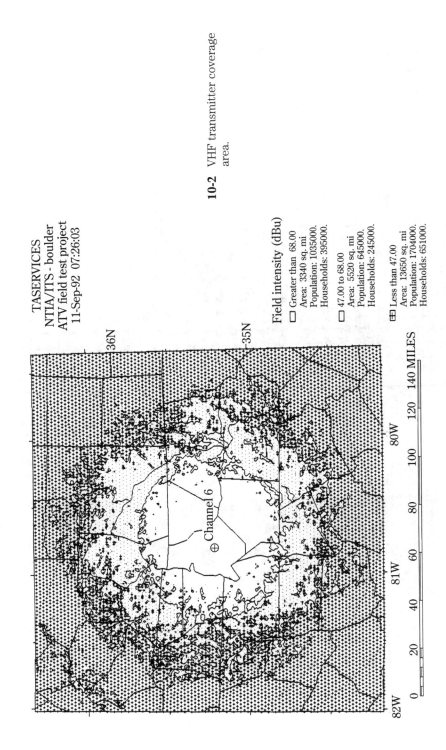

10-2 VHF transmitter coverage area.

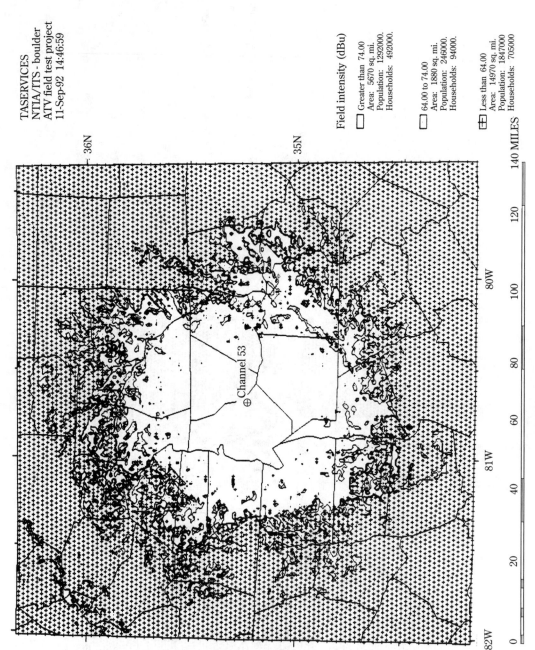

TASERVICES
NTIA/ITS - boulder
ATV field test project
11-Sep-92 14:46:59

Field intensity (dBu)

☐ Greater than 74.00
Area: 5670 sq. mi.
Population: 1292000.
Households: 492000.

☐ 64.00 to 74.00
Area: 1880 sq. mi.
Population: 246000.
Households: 94000.

⊞ Less than 64.00
Area: 14970 sq. mi.
Population: 1847000
Households: 705000

10-3 UHF transmitter coverage area.

However, the initial (and at this time tentative) objectives for the major performance characteristics of the transmission system (across 6 MHz) are shown below. These specifications appear to be a) desirable from the perspective of the ATV system proponents and b) achievable from the perspective of the manufacturers.

- Amplitude response: 0.2 dB
- Phase shift: ±10 deg.
- AM-to-PM conversion: ±0.5 deg.
  (i.e. ICPM)
- Group delay ±50 nsec
- Signal-to-noise ratio: 50 dB
- Intermodulation: −40 dB
- Non-linearity: Less than 2%
  (from 5% to 90% amplitude)
- Out-of-band emissions: 30 to 60 dB, depending upon distance from band edge.

Receiving facility

A vehicle ("field unit") that can accommodate NTSC and ATV decoders, signal measurement and recording equipment, power supply, provide comfortable operating environment, adequate space for observers, yet retain the ability to maneuver over country roads will be needed to conduct the field test. Meeting these criteria might require more than one field vehicle.

The field unit will be equipped with a 30-ft mast, appropriate antennas, field-strength and channel-characterization measuring equipment and receivers and decoders for NTSC and the selected ATV system (or systems). To evaluate NTSC and ATV reception, high-quality displays will be placed at appropriate distances from the observers. A means for recording, in some fashion, the nature of the received quality picture and sound of the NTSC and ATV signal will also be provided (Fig. 10-4).

The field unit must have its own power generator, air-conditioning, and comfortable seating for the driver and observers. A two-way radio system will be the "intercom" between field unit, the transmission site, and possibly a chase car. A cellular telephone will be available for other communications.

Several CATV systems will be included in the field test with drops installed for connection to and measurement by equipment in the field vehicle. Cable Television Laboratories (CableLabs), based in Boulder, Colorado, will be participating in the ATV field tests.

The quality of the NTSC and ATV signals will be evaluated as they pass through various CATV systems. Measurements of the signals will be made at several cable "drops," and a detailed analysis of the performance characteristics of the signal path is also expected.

Test methodology

One of the tasks of the field test task force was to develop a test plan, including the test methodology. That is, how the test is to be conducted in the field, how the measurements and observations are made and what data is to be collected. These include:

- *Test procedures* This work was substantially completed in 1990 and 1991 by the task force members.
- *Observers* Field Unit personnel will include, on a regular basis, representatives of the ATV system proponent and the FCC, and the field test staff. All will have been trained in evaluating picture quality and rating transmission impairments.

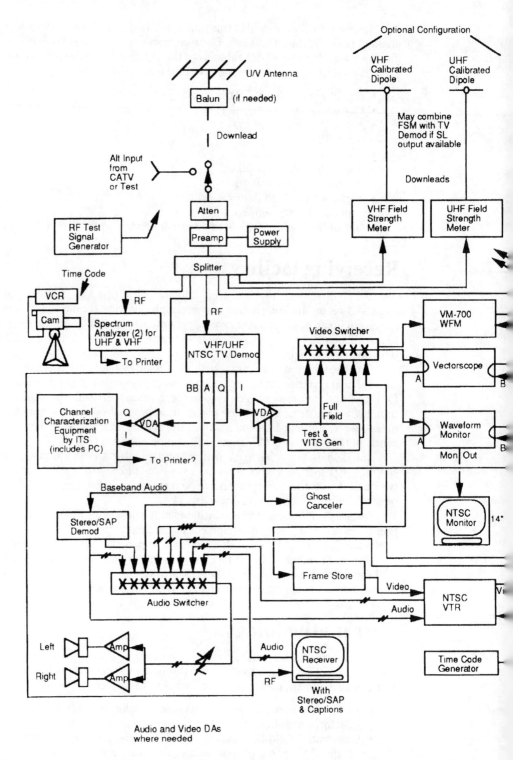

10-4 ATV field test: field unit receiving block diagram.

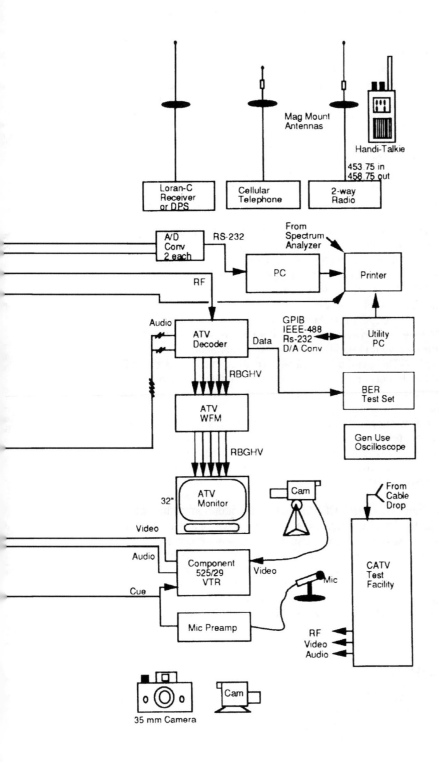

On occasion, committee officials and others could be on hand to observe the field operations.

- *Test and measurement equipment* Because the scope and nature of the field test are limited (unlike the detailed laboratory tests), the tests will be limited observation and comments on received picture and sound quality and basic signal measurements. Test equipment will include spectrum analyzers, digital transmission measurement devices, and standard video and audio measurement equipment (picture and waveform monitors). Most of the data and observation results will be recorded using personal computers (PCs). A PC with standard software or a limited amount of custom software will be used to analyze manually recorded data.

- *Field measurement sites* Approximately 200 field sites are to be visited by the field unit. Some will be along selected radials. Measurements will also be made in grids (groups) in common environments, such as urban or near heavy vegetation. A number of the sites could include a CATV "drop," as well as serve as an off-the-air site.

- *Site measurements* The NTSC UHF and VHF signal strength will be measured and recorded using standard 100-ft run procedures. Channel characterization measurements can be made based on techniques developed by ITS and the Communications Research Centre in Ottawa. Spectrum and waveform photographs will be taken of both NTSC and ATV signals. Observations will be made of the quality of received and decoded picture and sound.

- The NTSC signals will be electrically recorded. Because of the difficulty of transporting a digital ATV video recorder and format converter, another means for recording the ATV signals may be employed. This could most simply consist of a high-quality component (NTSC) video camera and recorder to record the ATV display coupled with detailed observer comments. Upon playback, the recording will show the general characteristics (and most impairments) of the ATV display, if not a real HDTV image.

- *Test signals and program materials* Test signals and a wide range of still and motion program materials (chosen from existing and approved material) will be transmitted to provide the observers in the field unit with a variety of picture and sound choices and enough time to make detailed observations and comments on the quality of the received signals.

- *Analysis of observed and recorded data* Standard methods will be used to measure NTSC and ATV signal strengths. CCIR subjective evaluation scales will be employed for the subjective observations and standard statistical analyses will be performed on the collected data. The electrical and optical recordings of the NTSC and ATV displays will serve to augment the subjective data analysis.

- *Calibration methods* A series of practice runs will be made to prove out the methodology. Specially selected reference sites can be employed to routinely verify the characteristics of the transmitted signal. An RF sample (from the input of each transmitting antenna) will be measured regularly to detect inconsistencies in the transmitted signal.

Budget and schedule

Most of the major equipment items (high-cost items), some of the personnel, the tower and building space will be donated to the project by broadcast equipment manufacturers, television broadcasters, and ATV system proponents.

The major costs for the project include; a) the installation of transmitting antenna, transmission line, transmitters and power conditioning, b) monitoring, test and origination equipment, c) project personnel, d) outside contractors, e) outfitting and operating the field unit, and f) general operating expenses (power, insurance, parts and supplies, and communications).

The field test project is expected to cost about $1,200,000 and last several months, depending upon:

- when equipment meeting the test specifications and procedures can be installed and made operational.
- when the ATV system or systems to be tested is selected by the Advisory Committee.
- weather and technical delays.

Funding is to be provided initially by remaining ATV system proponents with the bulk of the cost borne by the ATV proponent selected for field test.

The field test facility is scheduled to be ready to operate immediately after the Advisory Committee selects the ATV system or systems for testing.

Assuming four sites can be measured each working day, 50 days ($200 \div 4 = 50$) will be required to conduct the measurement portion of the field test. If the weather and equipment cooperate, the project could be completed in two and one-half months ($50 \div 20 = 2\frac{1}{2}$). It is unlikely, however, that such optimistic conditions will prevail.

Field test management

PBS, MSTV and CableLabs provides the executive management for the ATV Field Test Project. The field test manager will:

- handle scheduling, budgeting and licensing.
- coordinate the development of transmission system specifications.
- coordinate the selection of equipment.
- arrange for field test personnel.
- supervise the day-to-day operations.
- coordinate the analysis and publication of test results.

Summary

A field test of the ATV system to be selected by the FCC advisory committee as the candidate for successor to the NTSC broadcast television system will be conducted in 1994. A task force has been established to develop the test plan and oversee the field tests.

A site near Charlotte, North Carolina has been selected that permits full-power UHF and nearly full-power VHF transmission facilities, plus favorable terrain for the field tests. A 1300-ft tower is available for top-mounted UHF and side-remounted VHF antennas.

A field unit equipped with NTSC and ATV receiving equipment will visit up to 200 sites (plus a number of cable television system "drops") over a period of 4 months. The results of the field test will assist the FCC in making their decision on adopting a new terrestrial advanced television broadcast system.

The tests are made possible by the extensive participation of equipment manufacturers, television broadcasters, industry associations, and the many individuals who have generously dedicated their time and resources to this project. Stay tuned!

Acknowledgments

The author is employed by the Public Broadcasting Service as Manager of the Advanced Television Field Test Project and wishes to thank, for their input to this paper; Mr. Jules Cohen, Chair of the FCC Advisory Committee's Field Test Task Force and a broadcast engineering consultant; Mr. Mark S. Richer, Chair of the FCC Advisory Committee's Test and Evaluation Working Party and Director of Engineering for PBS; and Mr. James A. Kutzner, Secretary of the Task Force and member of the PBS Engineering Staff.

Cable

Field tests

Here are the procedures followed by the Advanced Television Field Test Project for reporting initial performance and objectives.

The cable systems planned to be used in the tests have at least 30 TV channels with spectrum available for the addition of the ATV signal. Some of the systems have AML and/or fiber links.

Receiving locations

The most optimal locations for cable tests will be the same locations as the terrestrial tests. That would allow the complete series of tests (cable and terrestrial) to be conducted at one location. The test locations will primarily be near the ends of distribution lines scattered throughout the cable systems. They will represent various depths in the trunk system and, for reference, some locations at or near the bridger outputs. Some of the test points will be after microwave or fiber links.

General

Two sources of ATV signal will be used for the cable tests: originated at the headend (or an error corrected off air signal), and received via terrestrial broadcast (both VHF and UHF). This will provide information on the quality of signals that can be carried on the system from two of the three normal cable system signal sources. The headend signal quality from the sources will be continuously monitored for bit error rate or amount of correction taking place, eye diagram, plus any other data that might be available from the receiver.

The ATV signal carried on the cable system will be inserted between two NTSC channels whenever possible. The NTSC channels will be used to test for adjacent-channel interference into both the visual and aural portions of the signal. The ATV signals from the various sources plus an NTSC reference signal will be sequentially switched onto the ATV test channel while the expert viewers are observing the ATV signal quality. That will help ensure that the cable channel characteristics are the same for all three sources. The same test channel will be used to determine system operating characteristics and NTSC quality.

The observations will be made by expert observers located in the test vehicle(s). Video tape recordings of the test signals will be made at the test locations, as well as objective test measurements to characterize the cable systems and the ATV signals.

Headend location

Receive antennas and downleads will be installed on the towers of the test cable systems. Height and type of antennas will be selected for best signal reception and will depend on tower space availability.

ATV receivers with standard IF frequency outputs will be supplied by the proponent. NTSC modulator, test signal generator, video tape machine and IF to channel converter, and remote control equipment will be installed at the headend locations. The terrestrial test vehicle will be used for the cable portion of the tests. Observers must be familiar with the impairment characteristics, both compression and transmission, of the system under test.

Site selection and tests

Test sites will be selected to encompass as many different locations in each system as possible. Sites will include headend output, hub site outputs, bridger outputs, and end of distribution line locations. Various amplifier cascade depths will be used to determine changes in operating characteristics as system depth increases.

Each test site will be characterized prior to the actual tests to ensure the plant is operating properly and to install a test drop. This will minimize setup time at the test site. A standard drop length, determined by the cable system design specification, will be used at the test sites.

Test sequence

1. Record the date and time, receiving site identification code, receiving site address, number of trunk amplifiers and line extenders, and weather conditions. Measure system test NTSC carrier level, adjacent-carrier levels, maximum and minimum system levels, carrier-to-noise, composite triple beat, composite second-order beat, inband ingress, hum, low-frequency AM noise, phase noise, frequency response, and group delay of the test channel.

2. Modulate the test channel with NTSC programming material.
   - Rate the picture impairments on the five-point scale.
   - Describe the nature of any video and audio impairments.
   - Record on videotape the video and audio test signals.
   - Record the RF spectrum.
   - Record the wave form monitor with test signals displayed.
   - Note any comments necessary to further identify signal impairments.
   - Switch to house wiring simulation and note changes in quality of picture plus BER.

3. Switch to the terrestrial VHF NTSC Signal.
   - Rate the picture impairments on the five-point scale.
   - Describe the nature of the video and audio impairments.
   - Record on videotape the video and audio test signals.
   - Record the RF spectrum.
   - Record the wave form monitor with test signals displayed.
   - Note any comments necessary to further identify signal impairments.
   - Repeat for the UHF NTSC Signal.

4. Switch to the terrestrial VHF ATV signal.
   - Measure the ATV signal level.
   - Measure the bit error rate and record the eye diagram.
   - Record the video and audio signals.
   - Describe the nature of the video and audio impairments.
   - Photograph the picture monitor during a specified still display.
   - Record the RF spectrum.
   - Record the wave form monitor with test signals displayed.
   - Switch to house wiring simulation and note changes in quality of picture, plus BER.

- Note any comments necessary to further identify signal impairments, including an identification of possible causes and, if applicable, the need for return to the site for further analysis.
- Repeat for the UHF ATV Signal.

5. Switch to the corrected/generated VHF ATV signal.
   - Measure the ATV signal level.
   - Measure the bit error rate and record the eye diagram.
   - Record the video and audio signals.
   - Rate the pictures on the five point scale.
   - Describe the nature of the video and audio impairments.
   - Photograph the picture monitor during a specified still display.
   - Record the RF spectrum.
   - Record the wave form monitor with test signals displayed.
   - Switch to house wiring simulation and note changes in quality of picture, plus BER.
   - Note any comments necessary to further identify signal impairments, including an identification of possible causes and, if applicable, the need for return to the site for further analysis.
   - If the corrected ATV signal is utilized repeat for the UHF ATV signal.

6. At a limited number of sites, connect the receive equipment to the off air receive antenna, adjust azimuth for best reception of the VHF NTSC signal. Record the received signal level and comments on the quality of the NTSC signal. Switch to an ATV signal and record the BER and scatter pattern. Analyze the scatter pattern to determine the received BER.
   - Repeat the measurements and observations with the UHF signal.

Test result analysis

Plot picture impairment ratings versus C/N, CTB, and frequency response for both NTSC and ATV signals. Repeat for the BER measurements of the ATV signal.

ATV field testing in Charlotte, NC—CableLabs

What follows is a report to Jules Cohen, Chairman of the Field Test Task force from Craig K. Tanner of CableLabs, regarding ATV field testing in Charlotte, NC.

If the ATV system selected for field testing is one that employs digital transmission, we will be faced with dealing with the threshold effect. One difficulty with viewing ATV pictures on a monitor in the test vehicle will be that there will be no indication when the signal is about to fail, and no visible evidence of why it may have failed. As part of the cable test plan, CableLabs plans to add the following tests. We believe they may be of interest for the broadcast tests, and CableLabs is willing to loan the necessary equipment and software needed so that we can all take advantage of these techniques.

ATV BER monitoring

Pseudo-random test data will replace the overall data stream (or perhaps just the video data) before forward error correction (FEC) encoding, for a period of a few minutes at each test location. Results will be recorded in the vehicle on a paper tape printer in the bit error rate (BER) test instrument. Additionally, pseudo-random data will be applied to the ancillary data stream (or second audio pair) while video testing is in process. The ancillary data test will be done primarily by monitoring the BER tester's bit error audio alarm function. At a particular site, if no digital errors are encountered in the overall bit stream, we plan to abbreviate or skip subjective viewing, since there will be no transmission impairments to conceal or judge. This will save time.

See Fig. 10-5 for a block diagram of the test setup. The proponent hardware and BER test equipment will be interfaced in a fashion similar to that done at ATTC, with the exception that we would prefer to interface with TTL levels. If the tested proponent has two data streams, they will be tested one at a time.

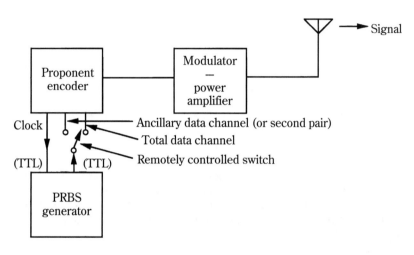

BERT at transmit site

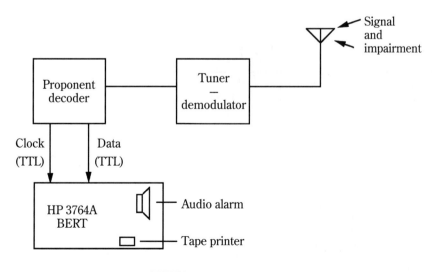

BERT in test van

10-5 BERT (bit error rate test) at transmit site and test van.

BER calculation
using constellation measurement

The purpose of this test is to calculate the selected ATV system's uncorrected BER using constellation measurement. The general steps involved in achieving this are as follows:

- For an interface at IF, the proponent will need to provide: (See Fig. 10-6)
  - ~ A data clock
  - ~ Filtered I and Q data at IF
  - ~ A coherent carrier at IF
  - ~ Baseband filters
- To interface at baseband, the proponent will need to provide: (See Fig. 10-7)
  - ~ A data clock
  - ~ I and Q baseband data that has been filtered
- Using an HP 8981A vector modulation analyzer, constellation points (i.e., scatter diagram) will be collected.
- A DOS computer with a GPIB interface board will be used to transfer constellation measurements to the PC for further analysis.
- Constellation points will be plotted immediately on the computer screen for visual inspection to compare with the received picture quality.
- Constellation measurements will be done, if possible, both before and after adaptive channel equalization to check ATV receiver capabilities.
- BER, as well as eye diagram closure, will be calculated based on the captured scatter diagram points. This will be done offline, after field measurements are completed. BER will be shown as a function of carrier-to-noise (C/N) ratio. We will, of course, fully document how these calculations are performed for the review of the Advisory Committee.
- The procedure will be fully automated and will require only a few minutes to complete. The test will need to be performed separately for each carrier in a multiple carrier system.

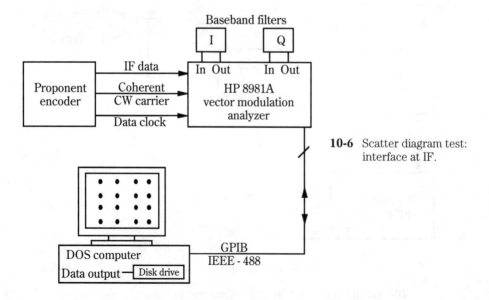

10-6 Scatter diagram test: interface at IF.

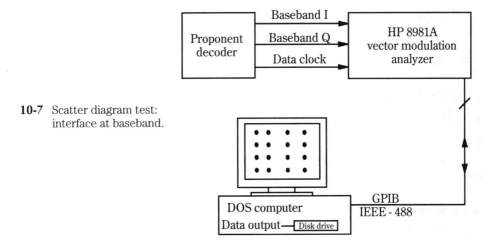

10-7 Scatter diagram test: interface at baseband.

CableLabs feels that these tests will provide valuable data, and will save time, particularly if the BER test indicates there are zero transmission errors.

On a slightly different subject, we suggest that it will be valuable for the proponent to give a data record of the coefficients being used by his adaptive equalizer at a particular test site, and software to be able to read this data to determine what the receiver evaluated the echo amplitudes and delays to be. The net result we are looking for is a channel impulse response.

Suggestion for moving ghost testing

Finally, since tower sway occurs in broadcast transmission (especially on windy days), and since sway may not be encountered during the testing period, please consider using the Hewlett Packard 11759D Transmission Channel Simulator to generate electronic tower sway. This will allow testing to be done on calm days and eliminate the chance that this important condition will not be encountered. The Transmission Channel Simulator will be located at the transmitter site. This device can coordinate the phase and delay shift for an accurate model. The field tower sway test should be done when echos are present, and no more than a couple of days should be devoted to it. We will be acquiring one of these instruments and can make it available for testing.

We look forward to discussing these suggestions with the Advisory Committee and the ATV proponents.

Note

CableLabs has studied the performance of various digital modulation schemes for high-speed data transmission over cable plant. Preliminary results of this study were published in a paper by Dr. Richard Prodan, which follows. In particular, 16QAM and 4VSB were considered for this study. Both 16-QAM and 4-VSB signals were transmitted from the cable headend and then demodulated at different locations in the cable plant. Scatter diagrams were monitored at the receive sites to see the effect of cable plant impairments. Scatter diagram data were captured on a DOS computer with proper header information for later analysis. Bit error rates versus C/N ratio were developed for both modulation schemes.

Two examples of such measurements are included for reference (see the last two pages of this document). It is important to point out that these measurements were done in absence of an adaptive channel equalizer at receiver sites. Each curve represents a different tap location in the cable system.

Performance of digital transmission techniques for cable television systems

Contained here is a report submitted by Richard S. Prodan, Ph.D., of CableLabs, Inc., evaluating CableLabs complex modulation techniques for advanced television applications.

The performance measure customarily utilized in characterizing digital modulation is the bit error rate. The bit error rate (BER) is dependent upon the carrier to noise ratio, or more precisely the bit energy to noise spectral density ratio. Either of these metrics provide the probability of error in terms of the distance between signals in energy space divided by the noise power for the additive white Gaussian noise environment.

The optimum receiver receives a waveform that is comprised of a transmitted signal corrupted by adding white Gaussian noise. The signal can be replaced by an equivalent vector form, and the noise process by a relevant noise process that can also be represented in vector form. This is done by defining a set of orthonormal time waveforms which can be used in linear combinations to represent both the signal and noise vector components (e.g., two quadature modulated carrier phases).

The vector components are derived at the receiver through a correlator or matched filter to the orthonormal time waveforms. The decision as to which signal was sent is made by comparing the distance of the received vector to all possible signal vectors. The receiver decides that a particular signal was sent if the received signal vector is closest to it. An error occurs if the received vector is closer to a signal vector that is different from the originally transmitted one.

For PAM-modulated signals with non binary symbols, a rectangular constellation and decision regions result. The constellation diagram represents the signal vectors in a two dimensional space. The rectangular nature of the signals and their resulting decision boundaries are shown for 16 QAM and 4 VSB in Figs. 10-8 and 10-9, respectively.

This Euclidean distance concept in signal energy in the presence of such noise can be reduced in the presence of additional impairments (such as channel nonlinearities, intermodulation, and intersymbol interference) caused by channel bandwidth restrictions or reflections from impedance mismatches. These impairments reduce the "effective" carrier to noise ratio of an equivalent noisy, but unimpaired channel. The bit error rate is calculated as the probability of the equivalent noisy signal erroneously crossing a decision boundary associated with the transmitted symbol (or group of bits) into another region associated with a different symbol. The effective carrier to noise with reduced implementation noise margins degraded by channel impairments has been studied to estimate the expected bit error rate of modern terminal equipment with practical performance limitations.

Transmission testing method

Two modulation formats were studied. The first format is 16 QAM double sideband pulse amplitude modulation format with quadrature carrier multiplexing and 4 levels (representing 2 bits) per carrier phase with the carrier placed symmetrically in the center of the band. The second format is 4 VSB, which is a (nearly) single sideband pulse amplitude modulation

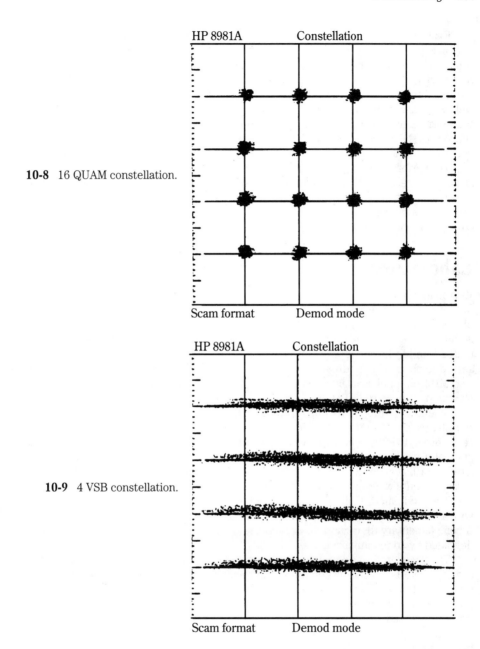

10-8 16 QUAM constellation.

10-9 4 VSB constellation.

format with a small (5 percent) vestige about the carrier at the band edge. The modulated average signal power was set approximately 10 dB below NTSC carrier level.

The approach suggested for the performance evaluation of digital modulation on the cable distribution plant is vector modulation or constellation analysis. The digital data carrier is discretely modulated in phase and amplitude to convey groups of binary digits (words) as vectors in carrier phase space. The instantaneous switching between carrier phase states requires infinite channel bandwidth. Restrictions on the modulating data signal bandwidth result in intersymbol interference in practical systems.

Evaluation of ISI is possible by examination of the baseband data modulating channel response given by an eye pattern or diagram, where overlapping data symbol periods are superimposed to determine the reduction of noise margin due to ISI. The closure of the eye results in increased bit error rate because noise in the channel is much more likely to force the signal to cross a decision boundary. The spread in the signal constellation clusters, as well as shifts in position as a result of other channel impairments, can be characterized by the constellation diagram. The constellation is a set of sampled points in carrier phase space with the carrier sampling times optimally chosen to coincide with the maximum eye openings in time of the inphase (I) and (for QAM only) the quadrature (Q) channels.

The performance of generalized digital modulation signal sets can be generated and analyzed with vector modulation equipment. Although bit error rate cannot be directly measured, it can be inferred from the constellation and eye pattern parameter measurements. These measurements can be made without constructing modems that require carrier recovery, symbol synchronization, clock recovery, data detection, differential decoding, etc.

Laboratory tests

Vector modulation equipment available from Hewlett Packard along with prototype digital Nyquist pulse shaping filters and frequency conversion equipment was employed for the digital transmission evaluations. A pseudorandom bit sequence (PRBS) generator provided the data for the digital carrier modulation. The random data modulates I and Q IF carriers in both formats. Channel filters must be designed and inserted to shape the modulation spectrum and limit the modulated carrier bandwidth. A 6-MHz channel is utilized within the 41- to 47-MHz range with an appropriate Nyquist response rolloff characteristic.

A source bit rate of 18 Mbps from the PRBS generator divided between I and Q carrier phases (for 16 QAM) or carried in the I phase only (for 4 VSB) with 10 percent rolloff (excess bandwidth) occupied a 6-MHz channel. The coherent reference from the vector generator was normally used (except for phase noise testing) to demodulate the modulated data IF carrier at the vector modulation analyzer. Constellation and eye pattern measurements were made without the need for carrier recovery.

The modulated IF signal was supplied to a Scientific Atlanta RF modulator IF input with a crystal oscillator selected for the television channel desired for data transmission. A complementary RF demodulator recovers the modulated data carrier at IF, after being degraded by added impairments.

The recovered I and Q data bitstreams can be examined for mean square eye closure, phase offsets, and dispersion in the recovered constellation samples from the vector modulation analyzer. Several hundred thousand points were downloaded via a GPIB interface to a computer for further analysis and estimation of effective carrier to noise ratio and expected error rate.

Some mean square eye closure results from the lab tests done on the CableLabs test bed in the Advanced Television Test Center in Alexandria, VA are given in Table 10-1 for various cable impairments. The "unimpaired" eye closure of 14% is because of implementation loss, analog filtering, and the modulation and frequency translation equipment. Data for a short duration reflection characteristic of cable systems is shown for –15, –20, and –25 dB. The composite triple beat level for comparable eye closure is higher than would be present for satisfactory NTSC reception. The same situation applies for composite second order interference. Phase jitter from oscillator phase noise and power supply induced residual FM show a significant degradation at levels that would be unnoticeable on NTSC.

**Table 10-1. Lab results from the
CableLabs test bed in Alexandria, VA.**

TTS	Description	QAM %	VSB %
1	Unimpaired	13.0	14.5
2	Echo @ 300 ns –15.7 dBc	35.0	33.4
2A	Echo @ 300 ns –20.7 dBc	21.5	20.5
2B	Echo @ 300 ns –25.7 dBC	15.3	15.6
3	CW Ingress at –23 dBc	30	32
4	CTB at –32.5 dBC (cw)	16.6	18.8
5	Phase noise –91.6 dBC (1 Hz) a +20 kHz from carrier	23.5	25.0
6	Composite Second Order at –32 dBc (cw carriers)	15.0	16.5
7	Hum mod. 120 Hz. 4.6%	16.5	17.5

Field tests

The laboratory tests can be repeated in the field on the TCI cable system in Boulder, CO. An additional complication arises because of the need for a recovered carrier reference and symbol timing for vector demodulation and sampling of the I and Q modulated carrier phases. This unmodulated carrier reference should be phase locked precisely to the data modulated carrier IF frequency.

During the field tests, both 4 VSB and 16 QAM signals were generated to study the effect of cable impairments. The complete test setup for the field (and the lab without the carrier and symbol timing reference recovery portions) is shown in Figure 10-10. The generation of the I and Q baseband data streams was done in the headend in the same way as in the test bed facility using a pseudo-random binary sequence generator (PRBS) and a digital filter. The digital filter generated the necessary Nyquist-shaped, bandlimited data signals which drove the external inputs of an HP8782B Vector Signal Generator. The HP Vector Signal Generator generated both a coherent pilot CW carrier at the output frequency, and a data modulated carrier with the I and Q data.

At the receive site (which was kilometers away in the field test, but less than one meter in the lab test), a coherent pilot CW carrier reference was needed by the HP8981A Vector Modulation Analyzer to demodulate its received data carrier into baseband I and Q data streams. Additionally, the Vector Modulation Analyzer needed an external input data clock to accurately determine symbol timing. This presented a design problem to the recovery of the data over the cable TV plant because the coherent pilot reference occupies the same spectral space as the data modulated carrier.

The solution implemented was not to build a modem, but to use an offset AM carrier pilot to achieve both carrier and data timing references. The AM pilot carrier was offset out of band from the modulated data carrier, and a 200-kHz AM modulation tone was put on the offset pilot. The AM pilot carrier was now 1 MHz below the 41- to 47-MHz IF band used by the modulated data carrier. Figure 10-11 shows the spectrum of the data modulated carrier and the offset AM modulated pilot tone.

The 200-kHz tone was used in the AM Pilot Receiver to both regenerate the carrier off-set, and provide a data clock to trigger the external trigger on the vector analyzer.

At RF, the spectrum is inverted from the IF. The Modulated Pilot Generator at the headend used the 18-MHz Bit Clock and the pilot CW carrier to generate the offset AM

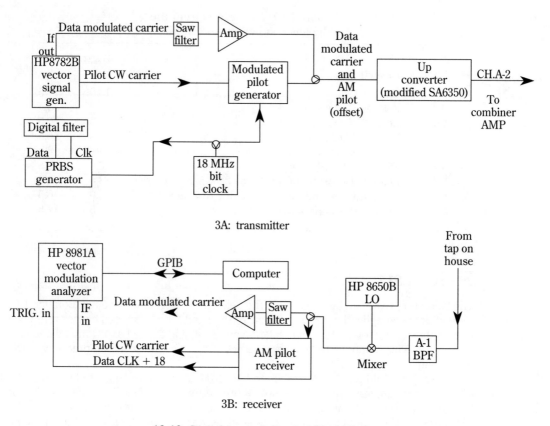

3A: transmitter

3B: receiver

10-10 Digital transmission test block diagram.

pilot, and it was summed with the data modulated carrier for an input to an upconverter. A Scientific Atlanta 6350 modulator with a frequency-agile output converter (FAOC) was used for upconversion of the pilot plus modulated carrier. Normally, the phase noise of the agile upconverter would have been troublesome, but the offset carrier recovery scheme provided immunity to phase noise, as both the out of band AM pilot and modulated carrier undergo identical phase jitter in the conversion process.

It can be shown that any frequency offset in the RF local oscillator will be present in both the modulated IF data carrier and the recovered carrier reference. Hence, carrier recovery without phase error is achieved at the remote measurement site, and all the measurements previously described for the laboratory testing can be done in the field.

At the receive site, the signal was amplified and put through a bandpass filter (BPF). Channel A-1 was used in the TCI Boulder, CO system. An HP8656B Signal Generator was used as a downconverter local oscillator (LO), and a double balanced mixer brought the data modulated carrier and the offset AM pilot to the IF frequency band. At IF, the signals were split and the data modulated carrier was bandpassed through a saw filter and presented to the input of the demodulator in the HP8981A Vector Modulation Analyzer. Off of the other split, the AM-modulated carrier was put into the AM pilot receiver. The AM pilot receiver performed two tasks. The first was to recover an unmodulated carrier reference for demodulation, and the second was to provide a data clock that the vector modulation analyzer could use for triggering, which provided the correct sampling times for the symbols.

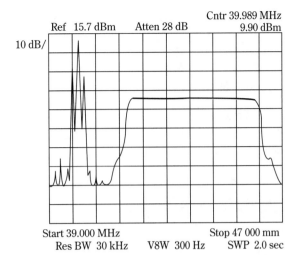

10-11 Spectrum of modulated data carrier and AM pilot tone.

The transmitter and receiver carrier and data clock reference circuitry was used for both 16 QAM and 4 VSB (Figs. 10-12 and 10-13). With both transmission methods, the AM-modulated pilot carrier remained at an IF frequency of 40 MHz. With 4 VSB, the regenerated carrier at 42 MHz was offset by 2 MHz from the 40-MHz AM carrier. In the 16 QAM case, the regenerated carrier at 44 MHz was offset by 4 MHz from the 40-MHz AM carrier. The same 41- to 47-MHz IF band was used for both VSB- and QAM- modulated data carriers.

Some mean square eye closure results from the field tests done on the TCI system in Boulder, CO are given in Table 10-2 for various tap and subscriber home locations. The signal received both at the tap and inside the house at the TV receiver input were measured. The mean square eye closure for several locations including a fiber hub are shown.

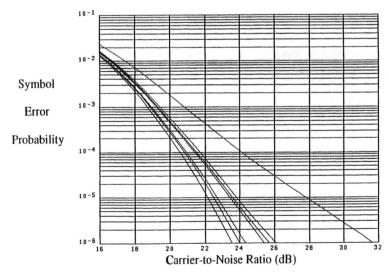

10-12 16 QUAM tap field measurements.

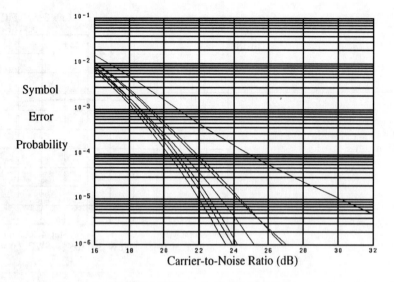

10-13 4 VSB tap field measurements.

The large variability on the resulting impairment between location in the system and between the tap and the premises wiring in this small sample is significant. The variability of performance for digital modulation within the cable plant at the subscriber drop merit additional investigation.

**Table 10-2. Field results from
the TCI System in Boulder, CO.**

Field location	QAM eye closure %	VSB eye closure %
TCI headend	13.2	14
CableLabs Lab	14.2	15.7
House 1	32	34
Tap 1	16	17.9
House 2	16	(Note 1)
Tap 2	14.7	16.2
House 3	14.7	15.9
Tap 3	14.4	17.1
House 4	19.9	23.3
Tap 4	17.2	19
House 5	22.1	22.5
Tap 5	20.9	24.4
House 6	16	15.5
Tap 6	14.8	15.2
Field fiber HUB	19.9	21.6
Lab fiber +12 amps	16.1	16.2

Note 1: Equipment out of service

Conclusion

It can be noted that rather small reflections causing intersymbol interference results in significant eye closure. This source of interference is most readily caused by cable reflections as a result of mismatches inside the house. This suggests that adaptive equalization might be required in many receive locations for a uniform level of reliable reception (suitably low error rate) at the lower signal levels that are nominally suggested (and used in this evaluation) for digital cable transmission.

The results obtained in both laboratory and field trials can be used to infer required modem performance in terms of the relative level of importance of the residual impairments at the receiver. A test of actual bit error rate requires the modem, as the carrier recovery, data, clock recovery, and symbol timing and synchronization information (and resulting equipment implementation losses) are needed to recover and evaluate the continuous baseband data stream at the destination. However, it is possible to estimate the error rate obtained using the raw data acquired in the present study. This is the subject of a future companion paper.

ATV field test project

The following observations were noted by E. Williams on October 14, 1992 in determining which antenna best suits reception of HDTV signals.

The receiving antenna proposed to be used in the field test was selected from several commercially available antennas and typical of those used in residential receiving systems.

Planning factors for receiving antennas for Advanced Television Service include the following:

Parameter	Low VHF	High VHF	UHF
Gain	4 dB	6 dB	10 dB
Front/back ratio	15 dB	15 dB	15 dB
Down lead	1 dB	2 dB	4 dB
System VSWR	2:1	2:1	2:1
RX noise figure	5 dB	5 dB	10 dB

Preliminary tests were conducted at the Carl T. Jones Corporation to determine the general performance characteristics of three antennas (compared to a standard dipole). Overall, the Delhi VU-932 comes closest to the planning parameters.

Radio Shack Model VU-110

Channel 6	2.9 dB gain	17 dB F/B
Channel 53	14.0 dB gain	26 dB F/B
Length	10'	

Delhi Model VU-932

Channel 6	3.3 dB Gain	10 dB F/B
Channel 53	9.9 dB Gain	18 dB F/B
Length	5'-8"	

Delhi Model VU-934

Channel 6	4.7 dB Gain	23 dB F/B
Channel 53	10.3 dB Gain	25 dB F/B
Length	9'-6"	

Early proponent self-testings in Washington, DC and Illinois

These were initial HDTV digital signal transmissions from regular broadcast sources to receivers at multiple points and distances during 1992 prior to system selection by either ATV or the Federal Communications Commission. Nonetheless, they are significant because of Tx/Rx conditions ordinarily encountered in commercial operations. Much of the reported results could well be repeated during ATV field tests during 1994 and even beyond. They're included in this chapter because both are the latest bonafide information available from two of the leading system proponents and will further technical understanding of the problems and advantages of both transmission and reception of the high-definition television signal. Our sincere thanks to Zenith/AT&T and to the consortium of David Sarnoff Laboratories, NBC, Thomson, and North American Philips. Both are definitive reports lightly edited to exclude some of the more tedious data and long lists of references. They were the latest technical releases available before our own editing commenced in 1993.

From this chapter, you can derive and understand the difficulties and precision with which much of this effort has been carried out. We hope the enormous, intelligent, and expensive HDTV work will be appreciated by a considerable segment of the overall electronics community.

You will note the number of Zenith figures explaining their transmitted tests. Unfortunately, we couldn't reduce quantity without removing some essential material from text, therefore, we printed most of this report to the Federal Communications Commission verbatim, including plots and charts.

Advanced digital HDTV field tests at WRC-TV in DC

To perform the tests, an application for a special experimental authorization was filed with the FCC to operate two experimental television broadcast stations on UHF channel 38. The first site was a fixed, high-power station at WRC-TV, located at 4001 Nebraska Avenue, N.W., Washington, DC. WRC-TV channel 38 alternately transmitted NTSC (visual only) as a reference signal and the digital AD-HDTV (video and audio signal) that was the primary objective of the tests. The NTSC signal had a peak visual effective radiated power (ERP) of 1040 kilowatts (55 kW peak). The AD-HDTV signal had an average effective radiated power of 130 kilowatts, based on a transmitter output power of 5 kW (average digital power).

The second site was a mobile station in the Washington vicinity, also assigned to UHF channel 38. The mobile unit transmitted a conventional NTSC television signal, in order to act as a co-channel interferor with AD-HDTV. The mobile NTSC transmitter had a peak visual ERP of 420 watts and an aural ERP of 42 watts. With these two transmitter sites and a mobile receiver located (as shown in Fig. 10-14), tests were performed under a variety of impaired transmission conditions.

Equipment

The ATRC/WRC team set up two rooms at the WRC-TV transmitter building for the tests. One room was used for the AD-HDTV encoder, and the second room was used for the transmitter and NTSC equipment. A Comark transmitter, type CTT-U-55-IC, was used for all tests. This transmitter has an NTSC peak output power rating of 55 kilowatts, and

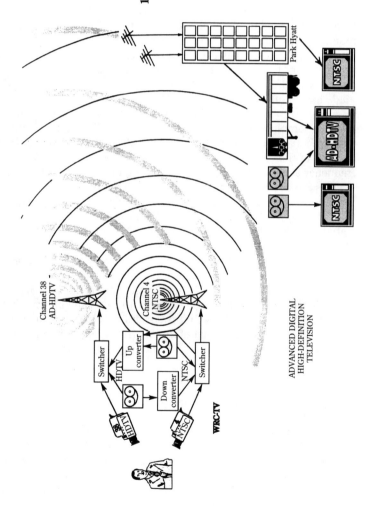

10-14 Test setup for AD-HDTV field test at WRC-TV in Washington.

is water-cooled by normal tap water. The AD-HDTV equipment is connected to the transmitter by a conventional IF interface. The encoder facility included a high-definition DVTR as test signal source, as well as a test signal generator. When AD-HDTV is being transmitted, the power output is controlled from the encoder's Spectrally-Shaped QAM modulator.

The new WRC tower is used for the test broadcasts on channel 38 and operational NTSC broadcasts on channel 4. This tower is 659 feet high, and the most feasible mount for the channel 38 antenna was at the 270-foot level. The design is a "tower in tower" approach that provides more shielding than most towers. The antenna is only 50 feet from the "old" WRC tower that is over 370 feet high, which results in enormous propagational distortions of an analog NTSC signal. However, the AD-HDTV receiver's adaptive equalizers completely remove the distortions.

The antenna is a 20-slot, 33-foot long center-fed design, with 15.3-dB gain and a cardioid pattern. The antenna is side-mounted at the 290-foot level of the WRC tower with a 0.5-degree beam tilt and a maximum power gain of 33.7 (15.28 dB), relative to a dipole. Alan Dick supplied the antenna, and LDL provided additional support in performing the rigging. Although an omnidirectional antenna is often preferred, side mounting an omni antenna results in a heavy scalloping of the coverage-area contour. Therefore, a cardioid pattern producing a 210-degree pattern, –6 dB on the sides, was selected for the tests. The transmission line is a 4-inch pressurized Andrew waveguide, type HJ11, semi-flexible, air dielectric coaxial line. For its length, the waveguide has an efficiency rating of 77%.

RF power amplifiers for digital HDTV need large and linear dynamic range. For these tests, the amplifier device chosen was the 60-kW inductive output tube (IOT) technology. IOT's have the power capability of a klystron, but with an even higher peak output because of the enlarged cathode design. Full peak power rating can be achieved at any frequency across the TV channel, a very important feature because the digital signal can have its peak energy anywhere across the channel.

The RF transmission path requires extremely linear transfer function characteristics. The amplitude and phase linearity of the RF transmission equipment and the associated power amplifiers is very important. The time and frequency domain characteristics of the digital signal closely resemble a noise signal. There is no sync pulse, black level, or white-level reference. Therefore, a digital signal is best characterized by its average power and its peak to average power ratio.

The initial testing of the channel 38 transmission of AD-HDTV was performed at low power in the middle of the night, in order to avoid any intermodulation or frequency selection problems. One of the first transmission tasks accomplished was a precise power calibration of the power output of the AD-HDTV signal, in relation to NTSC. A calibration chart was developed using NTSC and HDTV transmission through the high-power dummy load (Fig. 10-15).

Test procedures

NTSC was always sent as a reference signal for set-up purposes. The field intensity (measured in dBμ) was determined at each site, with initial site survey measures over 100 feet. The field strength measurements were made transmitting NTSC over UHF channel 38 transmission system. When the receiver truck received the AD-HDTV signal, bit error rate measurements were performed to determine the optimum receive point within the predetermined areas. A Loran C measuring unit was used to determine exact coordinates and distance from the transmitter.

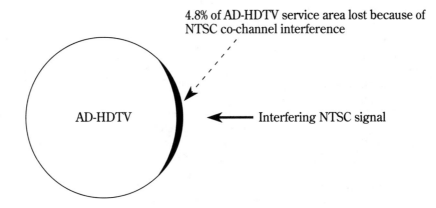

4.8% of AD-HDTV service area lost because of NTSC co-channel interference

AD-HDTV

Interfering NTSC signal

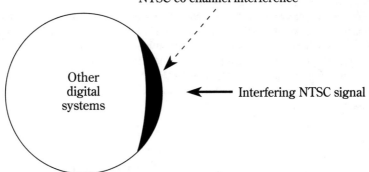

12.6% of other system's service area lost because of NTSC co-channel interference

Other digital systems

Interfering NTSC signal

10-15 In both diagrams, the large circle indicates the ATV noise-limited coverage in the absence of NTSC interference. The shaded region shows where ATV reception is lost because of interference from a co-channel NTSC station. The remaining area is the ATV service area. AD-HDTV provides a significantly larger service area than other digital systems because of its outstanding immunity to NTSC co-channel interference.

Broadcast television systems are subject to many transmission impairments, such as noise, multipath distortion, and co-channel interference. In NTSC transmissions, noise manifests itself as "snow," multipath distortion manifests itself as "ghosts," and co-channel interference manifests itself as an interfering sync bar or picture superimposed on the desired picture. The field tests confirmed the performance of AD-HDTV when subjected to the transmission impairments of an actual broadcasting environment.

Performance in the presence of noise was tested by receiving at many sites. The primary receive sites were Annapolis (30 miles), Port Republic, (40 miles), Easton (55 miles), and Point Lookout (70 miles). All tests and measurements were made with standard consumer antennas (Radio Shack U-120 and U-100 antennas), using antennas no more than 30 feet above the ground. Each transmission on channel 38 was monitored. For the NTSC, a spectrum analyzer, waveform analyzer, vectorscope, professional demodulator, off-air receivers, and field strength meters were used to monitor channel 38 NTSC, as well as the out-of-band products. For AD-HDTV, monitoring of channel 38 was performed by using a spectrum analyzer to determine power level and frequency. Both NTSC and AD-HDTV received pictures were gathered at each receive site. While NTSC exhibited a familiar increase in noise level as the distance from the transmitter was increased, the AD-HDTV pictures remained completely free from picture degradation until the noise level approached the threshold of SS-QAM's standard priority carrier.

The effects of multipath distortion were also experienced at each of the receive sites. The NTSC transmissions exhibited typical ghosting artifacts, while the AD-HDTV remained unaffected by multipath distortion under the identical propagation conditions. Airplane flutter was noted in certain locations in close proximity to Washington National Airport. Flutter was noted with NTSC transmissions on VHF channel 4, as well as on UHF channel 38. Under the same conditions, no noticeable effect was observed or recorded on AD-HDTV.

In order to test co-channel interference, a low-power mobile UHF transmitter was used as a channel 38 interferor. To simulate a wide range of co-channel scenarios, a limited number of interfering transmitter locations were used, with transmissions performed at various power levels. A calibration curve was developed for distance versus signal strength of the co-channel interferor. Adjusting the power of the co-channel interferer thus replicates co-channel interference condition at varied distances from the receiver. The co-channel tests were conducted primarily at Annapolis, using moderate and weak signals. The NTSC receiving antenna and the AD-HDTV receiving antenna were mounted on the same mast, 180 degrees apart. NTSC exhibited typical visible artifacts at low levels of desired-to-undesired (D/U) signal ratios. AD-HDTV continued to perform perfectly up to 0 dB D/U ratio, where the interfering NTSC signal power was identical to the power of the desired AD-HDTV signal. Zero dB D/U ratio was measured with an antenna front-to-back ratio of 17 dB.

Conclusions

The Washington, DC field tests demonstrated that AD-HDTV can be transmitted by normal broadcasting facilities to practical consumer receive and antenna systems. AD-HDTV easily survived the nonlinearities associated with high-power broadcast transmission. In addition, the system performed extremely well in the presence of noise, multipath distortion, and co-channel interference, conditions that severely impaired NTSC transmissions. These performance advantages translate into a larger service area than can be achieved by the competing systems. These results show that AD-HDTV is well-suited to serve as the simulcast digital HDTV the best system possible standard for America.

Proponent examination of the Zenith HDTV digital system broadcast during May 1992

The following is a report to the Federal Communications Commission on the experimental broadcasts of the AT&T and the Zenith Electronics Corporation's proposed digital spectrum compatible high-definition television system (DSC-HDTV) over the facilities of television station WMVT, UHF channel 36, Milwaukee, Wisconsin, authorization expiring October 1, 1992.

Transmission equipment developed for the Zenith DSC-HDTV broadcast system evaluated by the FCC Advisory Committee on Advanced Television System at the facilities of the Advanced Television Test Center was installed at the television transmitting facilities of UHF Station WMVT, Milwaukee, Wisconsin. The broadcast signal was received approximately 70 miles away at the facilities of Zenith Electronics Corporation in Glenview, Illinois. A mobile test vehicle was used to receive the signal closer to the transmitter.

The experimental transmissions took place on:

5/2/92	2:30 AM to 5:30 AM	
5/3/92	12:45 AM to 5:30 AM	
5/23/92	2:15 AM to 5:30 AM	
5/27/92	1:10 AM to 7:30 AM	
5/27/92	10:00 PM to 7:30 AM	5/28/92
5/28/92	10:00 PM to 7:30 AM	5/29/92
5/28/92	3:30 PM to 5:45 PM	

Except for very infrequent intervals of fading prior to 5/27/92, the digital signal was reproduced in Glenview without error, even though the receiving location was well over the horizon and beyond the equivalent Grade-B NTSC distance of 48 miles.

There was no reported interference to other services. However, a local Milwaukee cable system experienced some difficulty. Some cable systems that carry Channel 36 experienced crosstalk interference to adjacent channels during the tests. It is thought this was caused by the AGC circuits in their receivers not seeing NTSC sync, going to maximum gain, and amplifying the HDTV signal in the retransmission process at a relatively high level. After being aware of this, an effort was made to contact them, before testing, to avoid the problem. When HDTV broadcasts become standard, cable systems will use the appropriate receivers and the problem will be eliminated.

Initial experiments

On May 2 and 3, 1992, after the normal broadcast hours of the previous day of UHF channel 36, Milwaukee, Wisconsin television station WMVT, the transmission hardware of the Zenith/AT&T DSC-HDTV system was installed. The initial tests were on dummy load in order to determine linearity correction, drive level for the desired power output, and frequency-response equalization of the transmitter. Block diagrams of the setups are shown in Figs. 10-16 and 10-17.

Transmitter modifications

The transmitting plant of WMVT includes an RCA TTU-60D transmitter, which uses as power amplifiers (PA) integral cavity Klystrons in pulsed mode, driven by intermediate power amplifier (IPA) stages, fed by an NTSC exciter on-channel, at a level of approximately 2 watts at peak of sync. Because the output signal of the DSC-HDTV transmission processing equipment is a 6-MHz modulated digital spectrum at an IF center frequency of 44 MHz in accordance with the Zenith/AT&T proposal, a separate exciter was installed consisting of a linearity corrector, upconverter from IF to Channel 36, and output amplification providing approximately 6 watts. The interface location of the WMVT transmitter was at the input of the motor-driven attenuator preceding the IPA and Klystron stages. The linearity corrector and up-converter exciter were supplied by Television Technology Corporation (TTC), Louisville, Colorado.

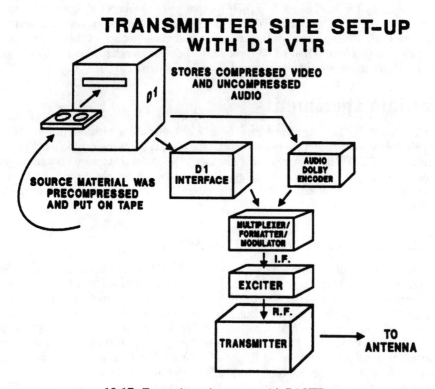

10-16 DSC-HDTV equipment at WMVT channel 36, Milwaukee.

TRANSMITTER SITE SET-UP
WITH D1 VTR

10-17 Transmitter site set-up with D1 VTR.

The aural transmitter was turned off and the notch diplexer was bypassed by a specially fabricated 6⅛" coaxial patch. This action was necessary to avoid distorting the frequency components of the digital signal which span the full 6-MHz television channel. In the DSC-HDTV system, the digitized audio is time-multiplexed with the digitized video.

Pulsing

The Klystron pulser was turned off because there is no consistent peak in the noise-like DSC-HDTV signal, such as the sync in NTSC transmissions. Although normally the Klystrons in the pulsed-mode could provide 60 kW at NTSC sync, only 50 kW could be provided in the nonpulsed mode.

Linearity correction

Some months prior to the actual over-the-air Milwaukee experiments, computer simulation showed that it was feasible to correct the non-linearity of Klystrons using 4-point correction (pre-distortion) for both magnitude and incidental carrier phase modulation (ICPM). The items of interest were data waveform eye-height reduction (crushing) and the accompanying out-of-band generated components.

The Klystrons were linearized initially using an NTSC stairstep signal provided by a 41- to 47-MHz NTSC IF source, with the intention of additional adjustment improvement when applying the digital signal. It was discovered that the linearity corrector, being designed for NTSC signals, did not operate properly on the digital signal because of back-porch NTSC clamping. The clamp circuits were disabled and, consequently, the average value of the digital signal was used as a gain reference in the corrector.

System frequency response equalization

The DSC-HDTV hardware has the unique capability to pre-equalize for linear distortions in the transmitter components (i.e., bandpass cavity responses, interstage tuned-circuits, and transmission line reflections). The equalizer, which is in the form of a multi-tap transversal filter, is adjusted by using a reference receiver being fed with a channel 36 sample from the transmitting antenna transmission line. The receiver has a post-equalizer, also in the form of a multi-tap transversal filter, which is effective in correcting the linear response distortions (i.e., magnitude and group delay ripple, etc.) in the signal path up to the input of the post-equalizer. If the receiver has no linear distortions of its own, the tap weights determined for the post-equalizer are those needed to correct for the transmitter components. Under control of a microcomputer, the tap-weights of the post-equalizer in the receiver are transferred to the transmitter pre-equalizer, thus equalizing the transmitter up to the antenna transmission line sample point. With the receiver hardware used for this experiment, there was some equalization needed for the receiver's own distortions, which were not separately corrected. The consequence was a slight upward frequency response tilt in the transmitted signal. Future reference receiver hardware implementation will include a properly calibrated demodulator.

Transmitter power measurements

The average power output of the visual transmitter is measured with a Bird ThruLine/Wattmeter terminated in a dummy load, which absorbs all the power. The power dissipated in the dummy load is determined by the calorimetric method. The rectified voltage provided by the rectifier/coupler element of the Bird ThruLine/Wattmeter is measured by a voltmeter/indicator calibrated in kilowatts. A calibration procedure reconciles the calorimetric true (heating) power with the average reading of the voltage. The average power indicated by the voltmeter is correct for constant value sinusoidal carrier signals but is probably in some error when a noise-like digitally modulated DSC-HDTV signal is measured. Nevertheless, the average power level was established by the ThruLine/Wattmeter indicator during the experimental digital broadcasts.

Initial experimental broadcasts used a pseudo-random digital sequence having a mix of 4-level and 2-level data in the approximate ratios of 60% to 40%, respectively, in order to measure the characteristics of the transmission path to Glenview, Illinois from Milwaukee, Wisconsin and thus to determine feasibility of the 70-mile broadcast.

WMVT NTSC/HDTV coverage parameters

The predicted coverage for HDTV in comparison to NTSC from WMVT, Channel 36 is shown in Chart I. HDTV coverage is based on 16 dB S/N ratio and the ATV Planning Factors proposed by PS-WP3. The Grade B NTSC contour and the noise-limited HDTV contour are seen to be similar at 48 miles and 51 miles, respectively. The actual transmitting antenna pattern, however, is not circular, but has maximum gain in the westerly direction, minimum gain in the easterly direction over Lake Michigan with less than maximum gain in the southerly direction toward Glenview, Illinois.

The 51-mile coverage is predicted from an ERP of 25 dBk for HDTV, which is minus 12 dB (relative to 37 dBk), a maximum facility power. Taking into account transmission line loss and antenna gain in the southerly direction, the average HDTV transmitter power is 12.55 kW. The actual power used was varied up and down from that value.

Initial Zenith, Glenview, Illinois receiving site parameters

The Zenith, Glenview, IL, receiving site is located at 42 degrees, 4 minutes, 30 seconds North and 87 degrees, 51 minutes, 53 seconds West. The initial digital broadcasts made use of a receiving antenna height above ground of 126 feet. Chart II shows the pertinent receiving site parameters. The initial receiving antenna was an array of 4 Yagi antennas arranged in a diamond configuration. Some experimenting with the spacing of the horizontal Yagi antennas of the diamond array was done in order to create a pattern null in the direction of west-northwest or about 77° from due north. This was done to reject as much as possible a low-power co-channel 36 at Palatine, Illinois, approximately 8 miles away from the Glenview site. Prior to the digital broadcasts commencing May 23, 1992 at 2:15 AM, several hours of (D) desired (Milwaukee) to (U) undesired (Palatine) signal-level measurements were made. The typical received D/U ratio (NTSC to NTSC) was 15 dB, sometimes much better, sometimes worse. Of course, the Milwaukee signal was far more variable than the Palatine signal with deep fades as the afternoon sun would go down—even though the D/U ratio at night would be higher. It was this experience at the critical late afternoon hours [see Chart V(c) and accompanying Plots 1(a)-1(l)], which resulted in the decision to substantially alter the receiving antenna height and configuration. After all, many people were invited from other parts of the country, including FCC members and staff, to experience these digital broadcasts so better assurance of adequate received signal was required to have a successful event.

Final Zenith Glenview site parameters

The receiving site parameters used for the public experimental digital broadcasts are shown in Chart III (Compare with Chart II). The major changes in receiving parameters are in antenna height (190 feet versus 126 feet) and in down-lead loss (11 dB versus 7.5 dB), resulting in a few dB increase in received signal level, but the most important result is a more consistent signal with less frequent fading. The co-channel interference ratio was also modestly improved.

The increased height receiving antenna installation was complete by May 26, 1992 and measurements were made of desired signal levels, as well as D/U co-channel 36 ratios over a period of a few hours. Measurement data is shown in Chart V(d) and Plots 3(a) – 3(d). The measurements from 6:02 AM 5/27/92 to 6:22 AM were ranging tests for the purpose of establishing threshold. The antenna was reconfigured from the diamond arrangement mentioned earlier to a vertically stacked array of four Yagi antennas. The increased vertical gain of this modification may have been partly responsible for the reduced fading phenomena.

Co-channel interference

The receiving environment (as mentioned above) included interference from another channel 36 station approximately 8 miles from the Glenview site. That other Channel 36 is a low-power TV station located in Palatine, Illinois. An agreement with that station allowed for the possibility of shutting down the transmitter to illustrate performance with and without co-channel interference. That agreement was exercised several times (Fig. 10-18).

Adjacent-channel interference

A channel-35 signal was noted during the digital broadcasts. We have identified it as located in LaSalle, Illinois, received off the back side of the receiving antenna. No problems were experienced from that interference. See spectrum Plot 2 (Gurnee) and spectrum Plots 3(a) - 3(d) (Glenview).

Program material
used for the public demonstrations

Although the pseudo-random data stream referred to earlier was useful for measurement purposes, it was appropriate to broadcast some high-definition sequences during the public demonstrations on 5/27/92, 5/28/92, and 5/29/92.

The high-definition video sequences were previously recorded in compressed form (approximately 17 Mb/s) on a D-1 digital component video tape recorder. The accompanying audio was recorded on the D-1 digital audio tracks. During the D-1 playback process at

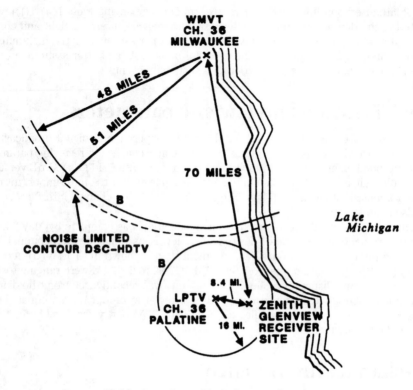

10-18 A co-channel interference situation.

channel 36, WMVT, the audio was encoded using the Dolby AC-2 compression algorithm. The playback compressed video, data and Dolby compressed audio data was added to other DSC-HDTV format components and the resulting digital stream was appropriately configured, modulated, and broadcast.

It is important to note that the D-1 VTR used in this fashion did not correct for tape dropouts; thus some errors caused by the video source resulted in perceived video decompression errors. During the public broadcast demonstrations, the number of errors observed as a result of D-1 VTR dropouts was small.

The sequences used were:

1. Opening station identification with the "10/36" slide. Introduction by David Felland, Director of Engineering, Station WMVT. The video was upconverted from a wide aspect ratio NTSC component camera to the 787.5 progressive format. This was followed by the following video and audio test sequences.
2. Computer generated scene with motion called "Pots."
3. These sequences were repeated three times:
   - Moving toy train, from the BTS KCH 1000 studio camera operating at 787.5 progressive scan;
   - Jeep trip to biplane and biplane ride, from Showscan 60 fps, 70-mm film;
   - Computer-animated graphic "Eggflow," from the AT&T pixel engine.
4. Slides to demonstrate resolution of fine detail.
5. The following sequences from a demonstration tape made for the 1992 NAB (11 minutes):

- Rafting, horse rider, helicopter, biplane scenes from a Showscan film, 60 fps 70 mm;
- "War of Roses" film excerpt, 24 fps, 35 mm;
- Jack Benny Kinescope, upconverted NTSC;
- Robots, eggs, computer-animated scenes;
- Tour of ATTC Laboratory, Upconverted NTSC;
- Graphics, text and animation windows, computer-animation display; Biplane scene, downconverted Showscan, NTSC ghosts added, Upconverted;
- Panned tulips displayed split screen, one side from a 1125 interlaced source upconverted to 787.5, the other side from a direct 787.5 source;
- New York City streets and parks, upconverted from 1125 source; fashion models, from a Kodak 24 fps film, Telecine, upconverted; basketball game Chicago Bulls versus New York Knicks, NTSC 4:3, upconverted;
- Bulls versus Knicks, wide NTSC 16:9, upconverted;
- Bulls versus Knicks, BTS KCH-1000 camera scenes;
- Computer animation, 1125 upconverted to progressive scan.
- Chicago Bulls versus New York Knicks basketball game scenes (approximately 8 minutes). Four cameras were used, two BTS KCH-1000 cameras, a JVC 210 NTSC component camera modified for 16:9 aspect ratio, and a standard NTSC camera. The KCH-1000 camera signals were recorded on a Sony HDD-1000 recorder after formatting by a Tektronix FC-500. The NTSC camera signals were upconverted to the 787.5 progressive format.

Notes

NTSC upconversion was performed in two steps. First, a Faroudja LD-1 converted the signal to 525-line progressive scan. Then, a Zenith designed upconverter generated the 787.5-line progressive-scan signal from the 525-line progressive input.

1125 interlace upconversion was performed on Sun workstations. Intrafield filtering and processing were used to provide transparent conversion including reproduction of 1125 interlace artifacts.

Measurements and observations made at Glenview

The receiving parameters of the Glenview site were identified and discussed in several of the previous sections of this report. The Glenview receiver site setup is shown in Fig. 10-19. Data for both the early experiments using the initial receiving site parameters (including antenna height) and the later experiments, including the public showings, are shown in several charts beginning with V(a) and ending with V(g). The charts are identified by date and they can be cross-compared with the Field Test Vehicle data for the same date and time. Transmitter power (not ERP) is shown on all charts; therefore, there is no separate chart for the transmitter site. Included with each chart is a plot of signal-to-noise ratio after equalization. Each chart shows: (1) Time, (2) Transmitter Power, (3) Received RF Signal Level at the receiver RF input, and (4) Signal-to-Noise Ratio after equalization. The data was taken manually and the plots were based on data taken automatically by computer. Each "—" indicates No Data.

The public tests took place on Wednesday evening through Thursday morning (5/27/92, 5/28/92), Thursday evening through Friday morning (5/28/92, 5/29/92) and Friday afternoon (5/29/92). Attendance was by invitation.

The attendees for the Wednesday evening through Thursday morning transmissions were principally from the Milwaukee and Chicago television broadcast stations.

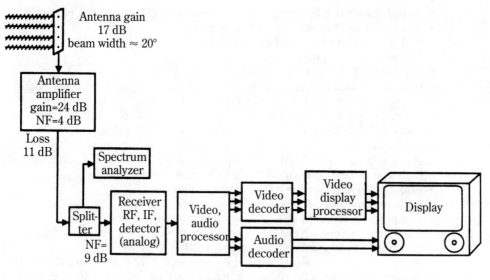

10-19 Glenview receiver site setup.

The attendees for the Thursday evening through Friday morning transmissions were primarily from the press and networks for the early demonstrations and from the technical community for the later demonstrations, which included optional visits to the Field Test Vehicle in Gurnee, Illinois.

The attendees from the Friday afternoon demonstrations were from the technical community, particularly from manufacturer organizations.

The typical agenda for each demonstration was as follows:

- Description of what's being done
- Viewing of received and decompressed DSC-HDTV signal
- Demonstration of co-channel interference rejection
- Overview of Zenith/AT&T DSC-HDTV system
- Transmission/reception of fast-motion sports
- Questions/discussion
- Receiving/decompression equipment demonstration
- Refreshments
- Technical, hands-on opportunity

Measurements and observations made in the mobile field test vehicle

The two locations used for reception in the mobile field test vehicle were Lake Geneva, Wisconsin and Gurnee, Illinois. Figure 10-20 shows the locations, with respect to Milwaukee and Glenview.

The equipment arrangement in the field test vehicle is shown in Fig. 10-21. The Yagi antenna was mounted on-top of a 30' mast. A pre-amplifier was used at the end of a 52-foot downlead in order to supply signals to a spectrum analyzer, as well as the receiver portion of the DSC-HDTV transmission system. With the aid of a personal computer, such parameters as signal-to-noise ratios before and after equalization for frequency domain distortions, such as multipath or antenna response tilt, block error rate after error

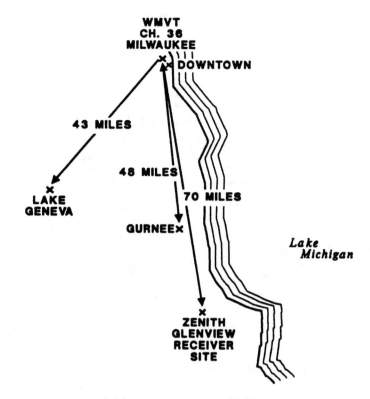

10-20 Zenith field test vehicle sites.

correction, received signal strength, and identification of co-channel interference conditions could be objectively determined.

The Lake Geneva, Wisconsin observations took place between the hours of 4:30 AM and 7:30 AM on the morning of May 27, 1992. The receiving equipment in the field test vehicle served a dual role initially as a transmitter demodulator for transmitter set-up purposes fed by the channel 36 antenna transmission-line sample—then, after traveling from Milwaukee to Lake Geneva, as a Field Test Receiver.

Some measurements are shown in Chart V(h) of the received signal at Lake Geneva. The chart shows: (1) time, (2) transmitter power, (3) received RF signal level, and (4) signal-to-noise (or interference) ratio after equalization, and (5) the "error" column in the charts is for the number of uncorrected bit errors read out from a counter on the receiver. This data was taken manually. Plot 7 shows data taken automatically by computer of received S/N after equalization as a function of time for the Lake Geneva test.

The Gurnee, Illinois observations took place on two days. The receiver was again used as the transmitter demodulator placed in the field test vehicle outside the transmitter building. Subsequently, it was used as the field test receiver: (1) on the morning of May 28, 1992, between the hours of 1:00 AM and 7:30 AM, and (2) on the morning of May 29, 1992, between the hours of 2:25 AM and 7:30 AM.

The field test site was the Gurnee Mills Shopping Center (S.C.). The data for 5/28/92 is shown in Chart V(i), while the data for 5/29/92 is shown in Chart V(j)2. These charts show data taken manually. Plots 8 and 9 show data taken automatically by computer of received SIN ratio after equalization as a function of time for the same tests at Gurnee.

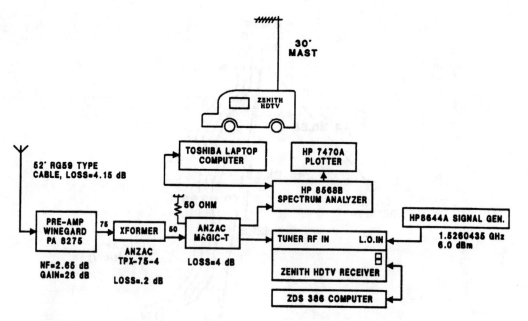

10-21 Channel 36 HDTV and NTSC signal-monitoring setup in the field test vehicle.

Special note should be taken of an experiment conducted between 4:05 AM and 4:20 AM during the morning of May 28, 1992 for the purpose of checking for fading conditions. The field test vehicle, which was originally facing east (but with antenna pointing north) was moved to face north. The receiving antenna was rotated in direction to maximize signal level, which turned out to be north. The truck was moved slowly for a total distance of 210 feet toward the north. No change in signal level in excess of 0.5 dB was observed. The transmitter power for this experiment was 1 kilowatt.

Conclusions

What we have shown with this long-distance experiment in digital high-definition television broadcasting is that:

- True high-definition picture and sound can be transmitted through a single 6-MHz terrestrial channel.
- Reception at the NTSC Grade-B distance for two radials is stable, with little fading, for the terrain involved, with a 30-foot-high receiving antenna.
- Reception well beyond the NTSC Grade-B equivalent is subject to substantial time fading varying rapidly, particularly in late afternoon. However, the usual approach to far fringe reception by using an adequately elevated antenna will substantially decrease the time fading and provide satisfactory reception.
- Conventional transmitter devices with their normal electrical characteristics are usable for digital HDTV.
- There needs to be a study of transmitter linearizing techniques applicable to digital signaling waveforms.
- The rectifier-type wattmeters used at transmitters (and at manufacturing plants) need a change in calibration in order to measure the noise-like transmitted signal.
- Co-channel interference can be rejected at the extreme far fringe of the service area.

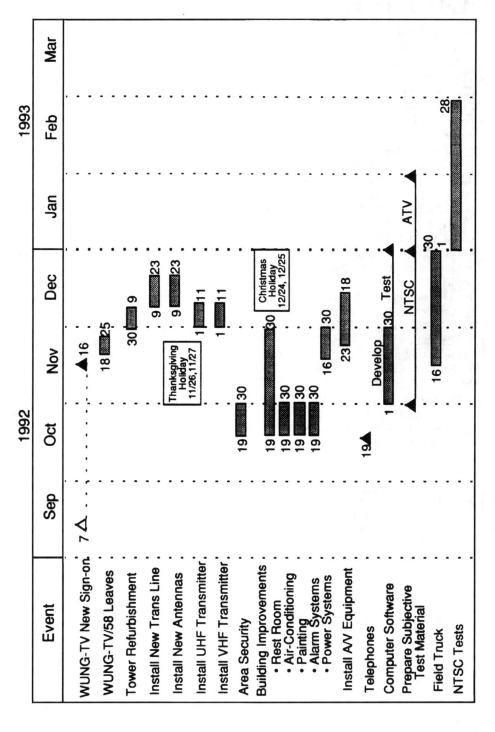

ATV Field Test Construction Schedule

WMVT transmission system

The WMVT transmission plant used by Zenith for the tests of the "Digital Spectrum Compatible" high-definition television system consisted of the following equipment.

The transmitter is an RCA TTU-60D, using two VA 891H klystrons to produce visual NTSC power of 60 kW peak, 35.4 kW average, on channel 36 (602–608 MHz). An RCA TTUE 44 exciter with two solid-state 10 dB IPA's is used, as well as an RCA pulser to drive the klystrons. The pulser was bypassed and the exciter replaced with a slightly modified TTC exciter. The TTC exciter was fed into the transmitter on the motorized power control input. This attenuator was never changed during tests. All power changes were made with external calibrated pads.

The output of the aural klystron was not used and beam current to this tube was disabled. The diplexer, with deep sound notch, was bypassed at the 6⅛" transmission-line patch panel, with a patch fabricated by Dielectric Corporation. The special long patch was needed as the combiner output and antenna input were not adjacent to each other on our panel.

The output of the visual combiner was applied directly to the antenna, or 50-kW dummy load, as desired. When feeding the dummy load, "power" could be read on the Bird ThruLine Wattmeter. When using the antenna, only relative power could be read on the transmitter reflectometers. Accurate power changes were measured with the spectrum analyzer.

The changeover between normal NTSC operation and HDTV involved exchanging the exciter outputs, bypassing the pulser, removing beam current from the aural klystron, changing the transmission line patch, and moving the tap for the monitoring feeds. These changes took about five minutes for two people to accomplish.

The antenna is an RCA TFU-28 UHF Pylon, mounted on the west side of the tower at the 914-foot level. This is 890 feet above average terrain. There is 1077 feet of line feeding the antenna with a loss of 1.3 dB. The antenna has a power gain of 17.26 dB in the main direction, which is west, and has 64% of maximum power to the south. The effective radiated power is 1230 kW horizontal and 2340 kW at 0.5 degrees beam tilt.

The tower is located at 43 degrees, 5 minutes, 48 seconds North; and 87 degrees, 54 minutes, 19 seconds West. It is owned by Gaylord Broadcasting and also supports the antennas of WVTV, WMVS, three FM stations, and communications and microwave systems.

Chart I

WMVT-NTSC Channel 36 Milwaukee		WMVT-DSC-HDTV Channel 36 Milwaukee	
Frequency	602 - 608 MHz	Frequency	602 - 608 MHz
ERP	33.7 dBK	ERP	25 dBK
HAAT	889 feet	HAAT	889 feet
Grade B contour	48 miles	Noise-limited contour	51 miles
Theoretical horizon	42 miles	Theoretical horizon	42 miles

Chart II
Zenith receiver site
(initial parameters)

Distance from ch. 36 Milwaukee	70 miles
Receiving antenna height	126 feet above terrain
Antenna gain	17 dB
Down lead loss	7.5 dB
Antenna amplifier NF	4 dB
Antenna amplifier gain	24 dB
Receiver NF	9 dB
Receiver antenna horizon	16 miles
Sum of horizons (+ receiver)	58 miles

Chart III
Zenith receiver site
(final parameters)

Distance from ch. 36 Milwaukee	70 miles
Receiving antenna height	190 feet above terrain
Antenna gain	17 dB
Down lead loss	11 dB
Antenna amplifier NF	4 dB
Antenna amplifier gain	24 dB
Receiver NF	9 dB
Receiver antenna horizon	19.5 miles
Sum of horizons (+ receiver)	61.5 miles

Chart IV
LPTV channel 36
Palatine, IL

Frequency	602 - 608 MHz
Visual carrier frequency offset	−10 kHz
ERP	12.7 dBK
HAAT	200 feet
Grade B contour	16 miles
Distance to Zenith receiver site	8 miles

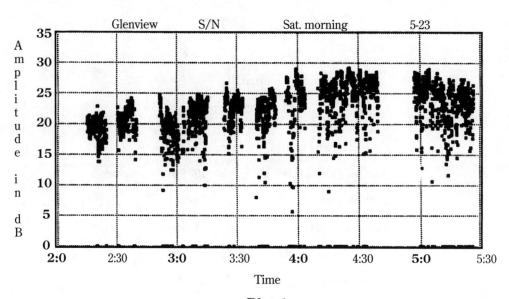

Plot 1

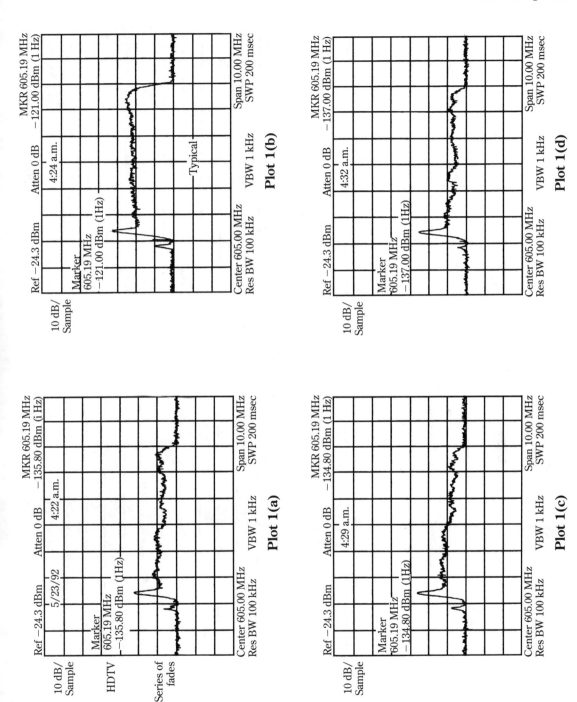

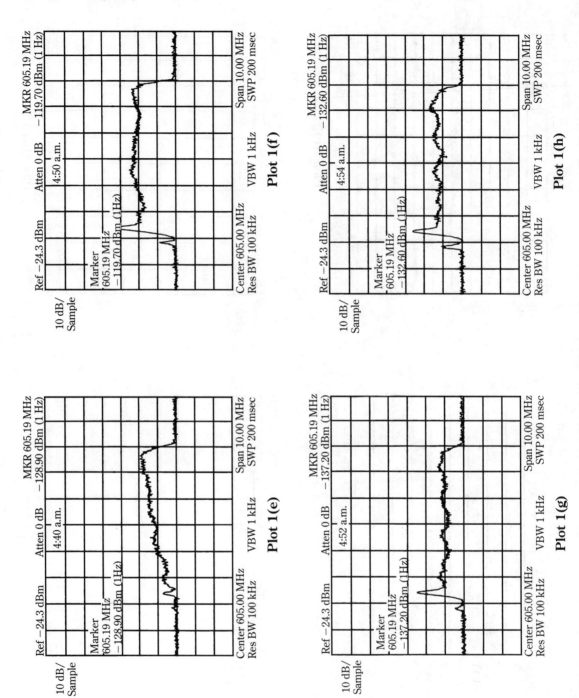

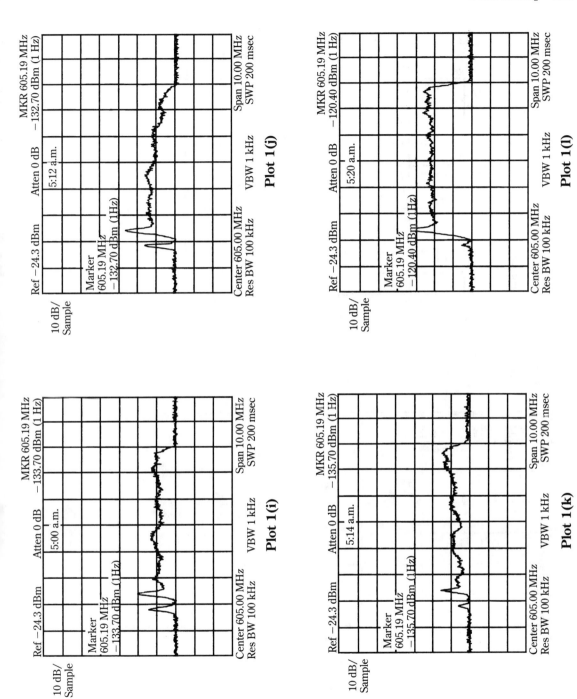

Plot 1(i)

Plot 1(j)

Plot 1(k)

Plot 1(l)

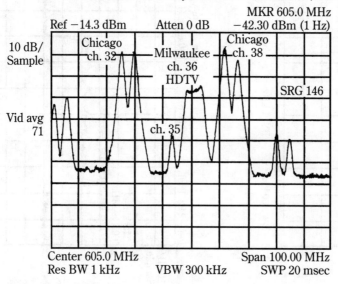

5:12 a.m. 5/29/92 Ch. 36 Adj channels at Gurnee Mill, S.C.

Plot 2

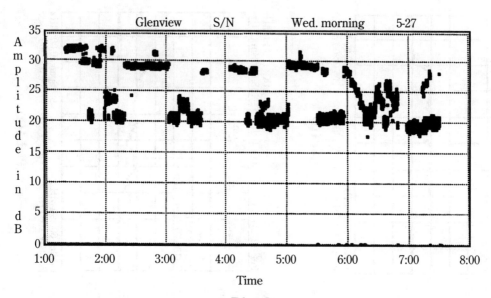

Time

Plot 3

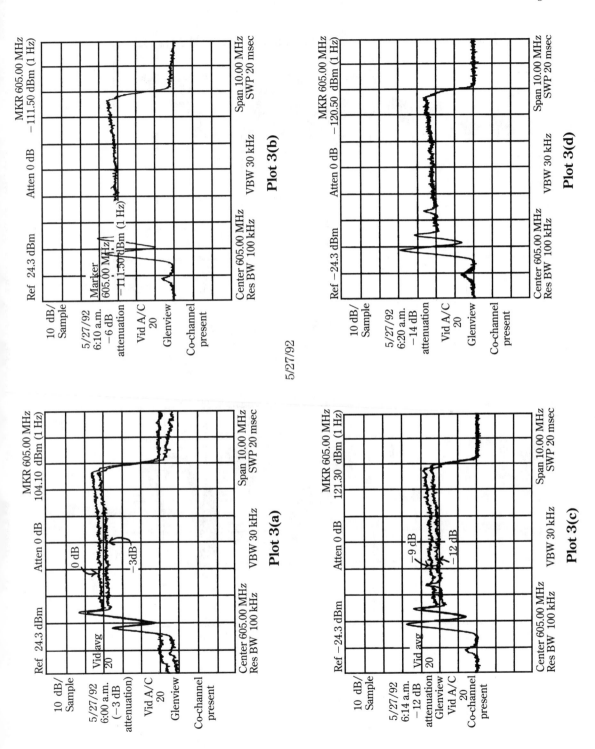

Plot 3(a)

Plot 3(b)

Plot 3(c)

Plot 3(d)

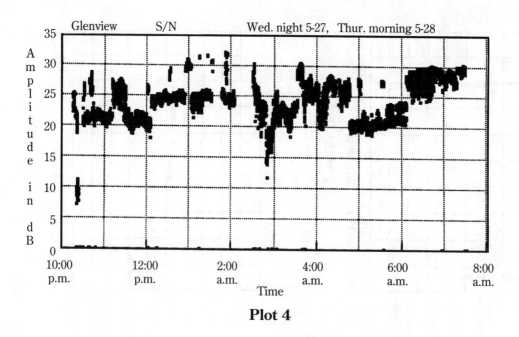

Plot 4

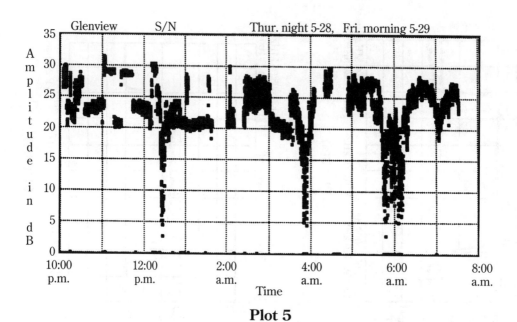

Plot 5

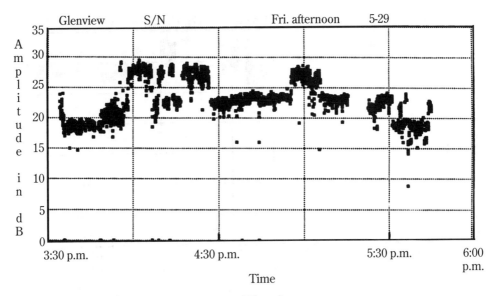

Plot 6

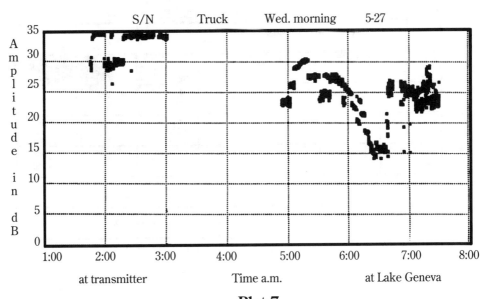

Plot 7

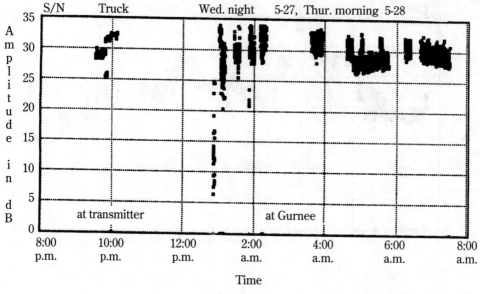

Plot 8

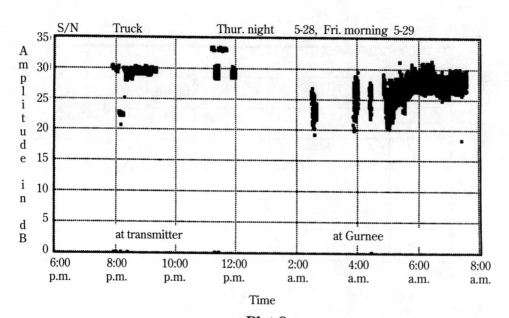

Plot 9

Chart V(a)

Glenview reception - May 2, 1992

Time	Transmitter power (KW)	Received signal (dBm)	S/N (dB)	Errors	Remarks
2:30 a.m.	10.2	−52.1	--	--	First transmission. No HDTV receiver yet.
2:55 a.m.	10.2	−54.8	--	--	Co-channel on/ post comb in
4:53 a.m.	10.2	−54.8	18 to 20	0-10	
5:02 a.m.	10.2	--	21.5	0	Co-channel off/ post comb off
5:07 a.m.	20.4	--	22.5	--	"
5:10 a.m.	Decrease power to threshold (binary data)		13.0	--	"
5:18 a.m.	12.8		23.1	--	"
5:22 a.m.	16.1		23.4	--	"
5:25 a.m.	− − − − − − − Transmitter off − − − − − − −				

Chart V(b)

Glenview reception - May 3, 1992

Time	Transmitter power (KW)		Received signal (dBm)	S/N (dB)	Errors	Remarks
12:45 a.m.	23.9		−32.9	26-27	--	Co-channel on/ post comb out
1:00 a.m.	23.9		--	--	--	" "
1:19 a.m.	23.9		--	--	--	" "
1:25 a.m.	23.9		--	--	--	" "
1:30 a.m.	23.9		--	--	--	Co-channel on/ post comb in
1:33 a.m.	23.9		--	--	--	" "
1:35 a.m.	23.9		--	--	--	" "
1:39 a.m.	23.9		--	--	--	" "
1:43 a.m.	23.9		--	--	--	" "
1:45 a.m.	23.9		--	--	--	" "
1:47 a.m.	23.9		--	--	--	" "
1:50 a.m.	23.9		--	--	--	" "
1:53 a.m.	23.9		--	--	--	" "
1:55 a.m.	29.9		--	--	--	" "
2:18 a.m.	29.9		--	20	--	" "
2:22 a.m.	29.9		--	20	--	" "
2:36 a.m.	29.9		--	20	--	" "
3:12 a.m.	29.9		--	21	--	" "
3:22 a.m.	29.9		--	--	--	" "
3:45 a.m.	0		--	--	--	Co-channel on/ co-channel interference measurement
3:55 a.m.	29.9		--	--	--	Co-channel on
3:56 a.m.	29.9		--	24 (steady)	--	Co-channel off post comb out
4:12 a.m.	29.9		--	--	--	" "
4:13 a.m.	29.9		--	24	--	" "
4:16 a.m.	29.9		−50.5	24	--	Power ranging
4:24 a.m.	24		−52.1	26.5	0	" "
4:27 a.m.	19		−53	27	0	" "
4:29 a.m.	15		−53.9	27.5	0	" "
4:30 a.m.	12		−55	26.8	0	" "
4:32 a.m.	9.5		−55.9	25.5	0	" "
4:34 a.m.	4.8		−58.8	23.5	0	" "
4:36 a.m.	2.4		−60.9	21.5	0	" "
4:37 a.m.	1.2		−64.2	19	0	" "
4:39 a.m.	0.95		−65	18.5	0	" "
4:41 a.m.	0.76		−66.1	16.8-17.6	0	" "
4:43 a.m.	0.6	(0)	−67.1	16.5	0-2000	Co-channel off/ post comb out (automatic transmitter shutdown)

Time	Transmitter power (KW)	Received signal (dBm)	S/N (dB)	Errors	Remarks
5:00 a.m.	24		26.5	0	
5:05 a.m.	24	--	22.3	0	Co-channel on/ post comb in
5:08 a.m.	24	--	21.3	0	" "
5:09 a.m.	24	--	--	0	" "
5:17 a.m.	24	--	22	--	Power ranging
5:20 a.m.	12	--	22	0	" "
5:21 a.m.	6	--	20.4	0	" "
5:24 a.m.	7.6	--	21	0	" "
5:25 a.m.	9.5	--	20.5	0	" "
					Some errors Variable with co-channel video content
5:27 a.m.	12	−55.4	22	0	co-channel on/ post comb in
5:30 a.m.	--------- Transmitter off ---------				

Chart V(c)

Glenview reception - May 23, 1992

Time	Transmitter power (KW)	Received signal (dBm)	S/N (dB)	Errors	Remarks
2:15 a.m.	16.0	−54.8	19.9	--	Lower diamond antenna. Post comb in
2:45 a.m.	16.0	--	23-25		Post comb in
4:22 a.m.	16.0	−67.7	--	--	Series of fades
4:24 a.m.	16.0	−52.9	--	--	" "
4:29 a.m.	16.0	−66.7	--	--	" "
4:32 a.m.	16.0	−68.9	--	--	" "
4:40 a.m.	16.0	−60.8	--	--	" "
4:50 a.m.	16.0	−51.6	--	--	" "
4:52 a.m.	16.0	−69.1	--	--	" "
4:54 a.m.	16.0	−64.5	--	--	" "
5:00 a.m.	16.0	−65.6	--	--	" "
5:12 a.m.	16.0	−64.6	--	--	" "
5:14 a.m.	16.0	−67.6	--	--	" "
5:20 a.m.	16.0	−52.3	--	--	" "
5:30 a.m.	---------------- Transmitter off ----------------				

Chart V(d)

Glenview reception - May 27, 1992

Time	Transmitter power (KW)	Received signal (dBm)	S/N (dB)	Errors	Remarks
1:10 a.m.	14.5	−34.9	31.0	0	Co-channel on
6:02 a.m.	14.5	−33.1	28.1	0	" "
6:04 a.m.	7.25	−36.0	26.7	0	" "
6:08 a.m.	3.6	−43.4	25.2	0	" "
6:13 a.m.	1.8	−48.3	23.3	0	" "
6:17 a.m.	0.9	−53.2	20.8	0	" "
6:20 a.m.	0.71	−52.9	19.7	0	" "
6:22 a.m.	0.57	−52.9	21.4	0	" "
7:30 a.m.	-------------- Transmitter off --------------				
10:12 p.m.	16.0	−47.9	30.0	0	Co-channel off/ post comb out
10:30 p.m.	16.0	−46.9	21.0	0	Co-channel on/ D/U 14-25 dB
11:44 p.m.	16.0	−37.7	21.0	0	Co-channel on

Chart V(e)

Glenview reception - May 28, 1992

Time	Transmitter power (KW)	Received signal (dBm)	S/N (dB)	Errors	Remarks
2:29 a.m.	16.0	−40.4	28.0	0	Power ranging with co-channel
2:30 a.m.	8.0	−41.9	26.1	0	" "
	4.0	−44.6	23.8	0	" "
	2.0	−48.3	26.7	0	" "
2:44 a.m.	1.6	−51.2	21.4	0	" "
2:42 a.m.	1.3	−52.4	21.4	0	" "
2:37 a.m.	1.0	−51.6	23.2	0	" "
2:41 a.m.	0.8	−53.9	18.5	0	" "
2:39 a.m.	0.6	−54.1	24.5	0	" "
2:40 a.m.	0.5	−55.0	24.4	0	" "
10:03 p.m.	16.0	−40.2	28.3	0	" "
12:00 midnite	16.0	−37.7	23.0	0	" "

Chart V(f)

Glenview reception - May 29, 1992

Time	Transmitter power (KW)	Received signal (dBm)	S/N (dB)	Errors	Remarks
12:03 a.m.	16.0	−42.5	- -	0	No co-channel
12:14 a.m.	16.0	−45.4	30		" "
	8.0	−48.1	29.5	0	" "
	4.0	−50.0	29.5	0	" "
	2.0	−52.6	29.2	0	" "
	1.0	−56.1	29.1	0	" "
	0.5	−58.4	28.4	0	" "
12:23 a.m.	16.0	−48.1	23.0	0	Co-channel
	8.0	−50.5	24.4	0	" "
	4.0	−52.0	23.3	0	" "
	2.0	−54.0	22.2	0	" "
	1.0	−59.7	17.1	20	D/U = 6-7 dB
	0.5	−63.0	13.8	9000	
3:53 a.m.	16.0	−66.9	- -	- -	
3:57 a.m.	16.0	−69.7	- -	- -	
4:48-7:30 a.m.	1.0	- -	- -	- -	
7:30 a.m.	- - - - - - - - - - - - - - Transmitter off - - - - - - - - - - - - - - -				

Chart V(g)

Glenview reception - May 29, 1992

Time	Transmitter power (KW)	Received signal (dBm)	S/N (dB)	Errors	Remarks
3:45 a.m.	16.0	−51.9	18.5	Bursts	Co-channel
4:07 a.m.	16.0	−55.8	28.0	- -	No co-channel
4:08 a.m.	1.0	−64.9	21.0	0	" "
4:10 a.m.	16.0	−55.8	28.0	0	" "
4:45 a.m.	16.0	- -	22-23	Bursts	Helicopters
5:46 a.m.	- - - - - - - - - - - - - - Transmitter off - - - - - - - - - - - - - - -				

Chart V(h)

Lake Geneva reception - May 27, 1992

Time	Transmitter power (KW)	Received signal (dBm)	S/N (dB)	Errors	Remarks
5:03 a.m.	16.0	−59.9	26	0	No preamp
6:35 a.m.	1.0	−73.9	16.2	420	No preamp
6:48 a.m.	1.0	−46.6	25.1	0	With preamp
7:30 a.m.	-------------- Transmitter off --------------				

Chart V(i)

Gurnee reception - May 28, 1992

Time	Transmitter power (KW)	Received signal (dBm)	S/N (dB)	Errors	Remarks
1:00 a.m.	- -	- -	33.3	0	
3:38 a.m.	16.0	−16.1	32.1	0	
3:42 a.m.	1.0	−28.4	29.5	0	
3:45 a.m.	0.5	−31.9	30.0	0	
4:05 a.m./ 4:20 a.m.	1.0	−26.4	31.0	0	Experiment to check fading conditions. Only 0.5 dB change over 210 feet in shopping center parking lot.
7:30 a.m.	-------------- Transmitter off --------------				

Chart V(j)

Glenview reception - May 29, 1992

Time	Transmitter power (KW)	Received signal (dBm)	S/N (dB)	Errors	Remarks
2:25 a.m.	1.0	−46.4	23.0	--	
2:36 a.m.	1.0	--	24.0	--	
3:36 a.m.	1.0	−41.5	--	--	
3:45 a.m.	16.0	−31.8	--	--	
3:53 a.m.	16.0	−30.9	--	--	
4:00 a.m.	16.0	−30.9	26.5	--	
4:15 a.m.	1.0	−37.9	25.0	--	Post comb in
4:24 a.m.	1.0	--	22.2	--	
4:31 a.m.	--	--	--	--	Transmitter off
4:48 a.m.	16.0	−27.9	29.2		
4:50 a.m.	--	--	26.8	--	Post comb in
4:57 a.m.	Lower	−34.9	21.6	--	
5:01 a.m.	Lower	−36.9	22.0	--	
5:05 a.m.	16.0	−30.9	28.0	--	
6:19 a.m.	16.0	−29.9	28.0	--	
7:30 a.m.	16.0	−22.9	29.6	--	
7:31 a.m.	-------------- Transmitter off --------------				

11

System audio improvements and the impending decision

Laboratory testing of all initial systems (except audio) was completed at the Advanced Television Test Center during August 1992 and plans were immediately made to wrap up the entire undertaking with system selection during the second week of February, 1993. Immediately thereafter field testing of the chosen system and backup would commence and be completed before the Federal Communications Commission announces the final HDTV system winner on or about July of the same year.

In the interim, two important actions have taken place: ATV Chairman Richard Wiley requested that all ATV system proponents declare their proposed methods of including 5-channel (with surround sound) audio to the Technical Subgroup of the Special Panel by November 2, 1992; and has further appointed a Technical Subgroup of the Special Panel to consider "improvements" to the various systems, but avoiding any major changes or new systems. All submissions must include "a complete and detailed technical description of any proposed improvements and the expected effect that these changes will have on all performance parameters of the system . . ." Patent related information must also be disclosed, as well as any other intelligence needed to evaluate these improvements. The deadline for such written submissions was set for Nov. 2, 1992, with no extensions "contemplated." Proponent meetings with the Technical Subgroup are also scheduled for mid-November to review these submissions for one day of explanations and also to "underwrite costs associated with this effort." Technical Subgroup Panel chairmen and members are listed at the end of the chapter.

A draft outline of the 5-channel composite coded or independent coded audio systems described in ATSC document T3/186 as originated and with little editing follows:

Investigation for analysis of the characteristics of five-channel composite-coded or five-channel independent-coded audio systems described in document ATSC T3/186

General

Chairman Wiley has requested that the ATV system proponents submit a description of their method of incorporating the HDTV audio features described in the ATSC T3/186 to the Technical Subgroup of the Special Panel by November 2, 1992 (see Chairman Wiley's letter to the proponents of August 21, 1992). This document outlines a proposal for testing five-channel audio systems. The Audio Task Force and SSWP2 will modify this proposal according to the proponents' responses to Chairman Wiley's letter and subsequent actions by the Advisory Committee.

Proposed schedule

By the end of November, a month after the proponents' proposals are received, the SS/WP-2 Audio Task Force will finalize the draft test plan for submission to SS/WP-2. During this same time period, it will assist the Advisory Committee in locating and outfitting a test facility/laboratory in which to conduct the multi-channel audio listening tests and will obtain the required test material. The five-channel (5.01) audio listening test material, with video, will be selected and prepared by the end of November so that the months of December and January can be spent preparing and editing recordings through the proponent audio systems. The ATV multi-channel audio test laboratory facility will be constructed to meet the requirements of the Audio Task Force and must be operational by mid-January 1993, which is the earliest starting date for audio system listening tests. The Task Force will review the performance of the laboratory procedures prior to the start of formal testing.

The time required for testing a single proponent is estimated at five weeks. Time savings could be realized with each additional proponent. Upon completion of the tests, the laboratory, with the support of the Task Force, will write a final ATV audio laboratory test report for submission to the Advisory Committee. It will show test results, but will not make a recommendation.

Subjective tests

The purpose of the tests is to certify the performance and measure the quality of the proposed multi-channel audio systems by subjectively comparing the performance of the encoded signal with the audio source. The tests will evaluate the proponents' ability to comply with the recommendations of the ATSC T3/186 document. Because the proponents' full ATV systems are not available for laboratory five-channel audio testing, the subjective tests will be conducted with audio encoder and decoder connected directly together. Complete system certification tests will be conducted during field tests.

List of subjective test types and descriptions

- Five-channel system performance, both quality and failure characteristics, of composite or independent coded systems.
- Compatible performance operating with fewer than five audio channels: 5-channel reproduction from 3/0 and 2/0 source material and 2-channel reproduction from 5 channel and surround-sound source material.
- System coder's loudness performance versus established loudness reference, such as that of CBS or Zwicker; (see ATSC T3/186 $ 1.5.7, Uniform Loudness).

- System quality performance after dynamic range control (see ATSC T3/186 $ 1.5.8, dynamic range control).
- System quality performance after receiver-type equalizers.
- System-specific tests.

Laboratory environment and configuration

The listening conditions for HDTV multi-channel sound system evaluation will include:

- Listening distance: 3H and 4H or 5H; for 50" displays or larger, up to 5 assessors can be used laterally (thereby ensuring a high percentage of off-axis listening).
- Test material: at least 10 critical test sequences will be used. They should cover a range of different types of program material and at least one should have a noisy audio source. Sequences for evaluation should include items critical for localization (including on- and off-axis listening), image stability and loudspeaker placement.
- The test material will be obtained from film (cinema) and video (MTV) sources in Hollywood in order to get meaningfully related picture and sound images. The material should be critical to the specific type of coding under test.
- Expert assessors: the assessors should all be experts because of the complexity of these listening tasks and judgments.
- Multi-assessor organization: presentations are arranged in pairs, which are termed "A" and "B." Each presentation consists of a sequence 5–60 seconds in length (depending on content) of a particular program-material item. The first presentation can be either the reference or the test condition, and if the reference is suitable, the assessor is not told which is which. A random order is used.
- The assessor is asked to give an opinion of the quality of both A and B. The pairs of presentations need to be repeated a sufficient number of times for the assessor to gain a mental measure of the qualities of each. This might typically involve three repetitions, during the third of which, the assessor is asked to vote on the quality of A and B.
- For voting, the assessor uses two continuous lines (like thermometers), on which is marked the opinion of audio quality. The lines are subdivided into five intervals, and associated with each is one of the quality scale descriptors.
- Single assessor organization: presentations are available in pairs, and the assessor can switch between A and B, until the mental measure of the qualities of each are established. Then a continuous quality scale is used as previously.
- The reference for assessments of multi-channel sound system quality will be a discrete 5.01 channel source signal with no bit-rate reduction; reproduction will be by loudspeakers.
- The reference for assessments of multi-channel sound system failure will be the unimpaired audio system itself.
- CCIR Rec.s 562 and 797 outline further properties and conditions for listening studios and control rooms.

Subjective test methods

- Double stimulus continuous quality method: this is a test of the
  - ~ transparency of each channel,
  - ~ sense of reality and
  - ~ compatible signal quality.

- Double stimulus impairment method: this is a test of the system failure characteristics.

Field certification

The Advisory Committee's Special Panel will select the ATV video and audio system for field testing. The field tests will be used to certify the audio performance experienced in the subjective tests. The multi-channel audio output of the proponent decoder will be recorded with the ATV video in the field test truck. The performance of the video tapes will be evaluated by experts in a controlled listening and viewing environment. At selected field test sites the RF signal level will be lowered until the video or audio signal fails. The performance of the audio and video will be recorded by the expert observers.

Advisory Committee on Advanced Television Service (ACATS) Technical Subgroup of the Special Panel

Mr. Joseph A. Flaherty
Co-Chairman, Technical Subgroup
Chairman, Planning Subcommittee, ACATS
Senior Vice President, Technology
CBS Inc.
51 West 52nd Street
New York, NY 10019

Dr. Irwin Dorros
Co-Chairman, Technical Subgroup
Chairman, Systems Subcommittee, ACATS
Executive Vice President, Technical Services Bellcore
290 West Mt. Pleasant Avenue, Room 1E309
Livingston, NJ 07039

Mr. Birney D. Dayton
Chairman, SS/WP-1, ACATS
President
NVision, Inc.
P.O. Box 1658
Nevada City, CA 95959

Dr. Robert Hopkins
Chairman, SS/WP-4, ACATS
Executive Director
Advanced Television Systems Committee
1776 K Street, N.W., Suite 300
Washington, DC 20006

Mr. Renville H. McMann
Chairman, PS/WP-1, ACATS
Consultant
963 Oenoke Ridge
New Canaan, CT 06840

Mr. Mark Richer
Chairman, SS/WP-2, ACATS
Vice President, Engineering & Computer Services
Public Broadcasting Service
1320 Braddock Place
Alexandria, VA 22314

Mr. Victor Tawil
Member, PS/WP-3, ACATS
Vice President
Association for Maximum Service Television
1400 16th Street, N.W., Suite 610
Washington, DC 20036

Mr. Craig K. Tanner
Chairman, PS/WP-6, ACATS
Vice President, Advanced Television Projects
Cable Television Laboratories, Inc.
1050 Walnut Street, Suite 500
Boulder, CO 80302

Ex officio

(FCC)
Mr. Robert Bromery, Deputy Chief,
Authorization & Evaluation Division
Office of Science & Technology
Federal Communications Commission
2025 M Street N.W., Room 7118
Washington, DC 20554

(ATTC)
Mr. Peter M. Fannon, Executive Director
Mr. Charles W. Rhodes, Chief Scientist
Advanced Television Test Center
1330 Braddock Place, Suite 200
Alexandria, VA 22314

(ATEL)
Dr. Paul J. Hearty, Director
Advanced Television Evaluation Laboratory
600 Terry Fox Drive, Suite 109
Kanata, ON K2L 4B6
Canada

(CableLabs)
Mr. R. Brian James, Director, ATV Testing
Cable Television Laboratories, Inc.
c/o ATTC
1330 Braddock Place, Suite 200
Alexandria, VA 22314

Dr. Richard Prodan, Director, ATV Laboratory
Cable Television Laboratories, Inc.
1050 Walnut Street, Suite 500
Boulder, CO 80302

System (Proponent) Contacts:

AD-HDTV (ATRC)

Dr. James E. Carnes
President & Chief Operating Officer
David Sarnoff Research Center
201 Washington Road
Princeton, NJ 08540-6449

Mr. Amihai Miron
Director, Television Systems Research
North American Philips Corporation
345 Scarborough Road
Briarcliff Manor, NY 10510

Channel Compatible DigiCipher (ATVA)

Professor Jae S. Lim
Director, Advanced Television Research Program
Massachusetts Institute of Technology
50 Vassar Street, Room 36-653
Cambridge, MA 02139

Mr. Robert Rast
Vice President, Advanced Television
General Instrument Corporation
6262 Lusk Boulevard
San Diego, CA 92121

DSC-HDTV (Zenith/AT&T)

Mr. Wayne C. Luplow
Division Vice President, R&D
Advanced Television Systems
Zenith Electronics Corporation
1000 Milwaukee Avenue
Glenview, IL 60025-2493

Mr. Ralph L. Cerbone
Advanced Television Project Manager
AT&T Microelectronics
2 Oak Way
Berkeley Heights, NJ 07922

Mr. Robert K. Graves
Government Affairs Vice President
AT&T
295 North Maple Avenue
Basking Ridge, NJ 07920

Narrow-MUSE (NHK)

Dr. Keiichi Kubota
Senior Scientist
NHK (Japan Broadcasting Corporation)
1 Rockefeller Plaza, Room 1420
New York, NY 10020

12

Reported improvements to the four remaining digital systems in 1993

The final four months of auxiliary examinations has now ended and includes various improvements supplied by the proponents themselves during early and mid-1993. All will be reported in exact detail wherever practical so that you will have a working knowledge of necessary changes accompanied by available and supporting engineering data. In so doing, we are making you privy to a number of ultimate changes that will probably determine who finally receives the FCC's supremely important approval. Conversely, the FCC might see several advantages in two or more systems and request or order a special combination. Early fall should reveal the selection, although we already know that a single, well-conceived HDTV system would please the Federal gentry on M St., N.W. immensely.

We'll begin with the General Instrument/M.I.T. CCDC system, which includes data rate, chroma resolution, tuner filter, error reduction, audio, SAW filter, peak clipping, and packetized transmission, followed by a similar report on DigiCipher.

Other systems render their own disclosures in comparable detail—all with comprehensive changes discovered during the various stages of laboratory and observer testing. Although this book does not include the actual field tests scheduled for Charlotte, NC, full system details have been covered and the final free-air examinations will simply constitute "proof-of-the-pudding" trials to confirm quality reception and transmission of the single system selected by the HDTV committee.

Packetized transmission of CCDC HDTV G.I.

Introduction

The CCDC system currently has fixed data multiplex format supporting three pairs of stereo audio (755 kbps total), one 126 kbps of data channel for ancillary data services, and one 126 kbps of control data channel for subscriber authorization. To fully support the ATSC T3/186 requirements, packetized transmission is being implemented at the transport layer. The proposed change simply rearranges the location of the audio and the data preserving the current data line structure and the overall transmission characteristics while it provides enhanced flexibility, interoperability, and extensibility.

As the impact on the hardware is minimal, the packetized transmission of the CCDC system will be available by February 1, 1993. The proposed change affects only one circuit board in the encoder and one circuit board in the decoder. The following sections describe data structure, effects on error performance and video quality.

Data structure

Figure 12-1 shows the CCDC packet format. Each packet consists of one packet header byte, 157 bytes (115 bytes in 16-QAM mode) of video, audio, ancillary data or other services, and 10 Reed-Solomon (RS) check bytes for forward error correction. The packet header contains three sync bits and five bits of service type that can support up to 32 different services, including video, audio 1, audio 2, program guide, teletext, conditional access control, closed caption, special audio services for visually impaired (VI) and hearing impaired (HI), and other services. The use of the service type enables flexible allocations of various ATV services and full extensibility while the overhead required to support the packet format has less than 1% of impact on the available data capacity for video transmission.

During line 1, the packet contains 3 bytes of frame sync, 110 bytes (68 bytes in 16-QAM mode) of system control and service identification data (contains descriptions among other things), 44 bytes of closed caption data, and 10 RS bytes. The descriptors identify the digital services that are available. The locations of the digital services within the overall data multiplex need not be specified by the service identification data because of the use of the service-type header in each packet. The data capacity will be high enough to fully implement headers and descriptors proposed by SMPTE.

Audio and data packets contain a subheader in addition to the packet header as shown in Fig. 12-1C. The subheader contains a 3-bit continuity counter and a 5-bit subservice type. The continuity counter is used to control lost and/or out-of-sequence packets caused by errors in the packet header. The subservice type can be used to further expand the service type, thus allowing further extensibility. The system, therefore, can support over 500 different services.

Effects on error performance

The packetization of the CCDC data will have essentially no effect on the video performance in the presence of uncorrectable errors because the video data performance will be dominated by already existing packetization at the macroblock level. The audio and ancillary data, however, can be subject to packet header errors that can cause lost or out-of-sequence packets. Use of the continuity counter allows the detection of such conditions so that proper error concealment can be performed. Furthermore, the probability of having packet header errors is considerably small. Also, occasional loss of line 1 packets does not have any impact on the error performance because the locations of the digital services within the overall data multiplex are not specified by the service identification data and

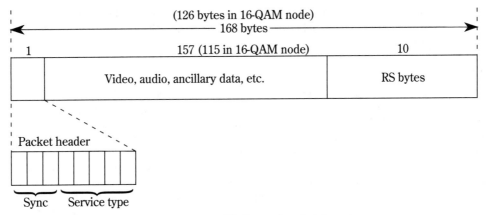

(A) General packet format

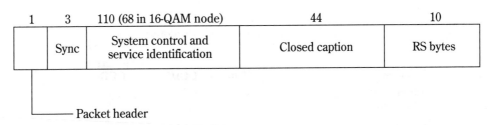

(B) Line 1 packet format

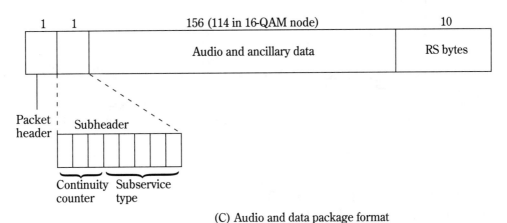

(C) Audio and data package format

12-1 CCDC packet format.

enough redundancy will be used in transmitting the system control and the service identification data. Therefore, the overall error performance of the CCDC system will remain essentially the same.

Effects on video quality

Because each packet has only one overhead byte (packet header), the impact on the available data capacity for video transmission due to the packetization is less than 1%. To fully support the ATSC T3/186 requirements, the CCDC system will be configured to support the services shown in Table 12-1. Two ancillary data services at 126 kbps are provided to support the BER measurement during the field testing and to allow enough capacity for anticipated data services, such as teletext, program guide, and conditional access control. The ancillary data services can be individually enabled or disabled. When disabled, the unused data capacity is automatically used for video transmission to optimize the video quality. As can be seen in the table, the impact on the video data when all ancillary data services are enabled together with six-channel audio services is less than 0.8%, which will cause negligible effect on the overall video quality.

**Table 12-1. Bit allocation of CCDC
system in 32-QAM mode (bits/second).**

Services	Current CCDC	Packetized CCDC
System control and service identification	13,426	23,256
24-bit sync	719	719
Closed caption	—	10,549
Audio services 6 channels	775,245	777,245
Ancillary Data Services for teletext, program guide, conditional access control, etc.		
Allocated	251,748	—
2 × 126 kbps (can be individually enabled)	—	251,748
Packet header	—	125,874
Video data	18,866,975	18,717,605
Total	19,888,113	19,888,113

Packetized transmission
of DigiCipher HDTV G.I.

Introduction

The DigiCipher system currently has fixed data multiplex format supporting two pairs of stereo audio (503 kbps total), one 126 kbps of data channel for ancillary data services, and one 126 kbps of control data channel for subscriber authorization. To fully support the ATSC T3/186 requirements, packetized transmission is being implemented at the transport layer. The proposed change simply rearranges the location of the audio and the data preserving the current data line structure and the overall transmission characteristics while it provides enhanced flexibility, interoperability, and extensibility.

As the impact on the hardware is minimal, the packetized transmission of the DigiCipher system will be available by February 1, 1993. The proposed change affects only one circuit board in the encoder and one circuit board in the decoder. The following sections describe data structure, and effects on error performance and video quality.

Data structure

Figure 12-2 shows the DigiCipher packet format. Each packet consists of one packet header byte, 144 bytes (105 bytes in 16-QAM mode) of video, audio, ancillary data or other services, and 10 Reed-Solomon (RS) check bytes for forward error correction. The packet header contains three sync bits and five bits of service type that can support up to 32 different services, including video, audio 1, audio 2, program guide, teletext, conditional access control, closed caption, special audio services for visually impaired (VI) and hearing impaired (HI), and other services. The use of the service type enables flexible allocations of various ATV services and full extensibility while the overhead required to support the packet format has less than 1% of impact on the available data capacity for video transmission.

During line 1, the packet contains 3 bytes of frame sync, 97 bytes (58 bytes in 16-QAM mode) of system control and service identification data (contains descriptions among other things), 44 bytes of closed caption data, and 10 RS bytes. The descriptors identify the digital services that are available. The locations of the digital services within the overall data multiplex need not be specified by the service identification data due to the use of the service type header in each packet. The data capacity will be high enough to fully implement headers and descriptors proposed by SMPTE.

Audio and data packets contain a subheader in addition to the packet header as shown in Fig. 12-1C. The subheader contains a 3-bit continuity counter and a 5-bit subservice type. The continuity counter is used to control lost and/or out-of-sequence packets because of errors in the packet header. The subservice type can be used to further expand the service type, thus allowing further extensibility. The system, therefore, can support over 500 different services.

Effects on error performance

The packetization of the DigiCipher data will have essentially no effect on the video performance in the presence of uncorrectable errors since the video data performance will be dominated by already existing packetization at the macroblock level. The audio and ancillary data, however, can be subject to packet header errors that can cause lost or out-of-sequence packets. Use of the continuity counter allows the detection of such conditions so that proper error concealment can be performed. Appendix C of the November 2 submission further describes the error concealment techniques employed in Dolby AC-3 decoder. As described in the Appendix, packetized transmission is preferred for audio error concealment purposes. Furthermore, the probability of having packet header errors is considerably small. Also, occasional loss of line 1 packets does not have any impact on the error performance because the locations of the digital services within the overall data multiplex are not specified by the service identification data and enough redundancy will be used in transmitting the system control and the service identification data. Therefore, the overall error performance of the DigiCipher system will remain essentially the same.

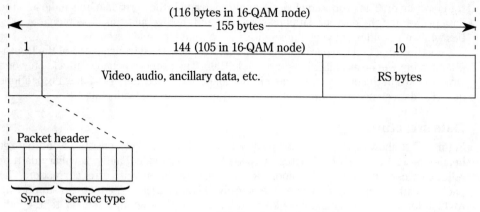

(A) General packet format

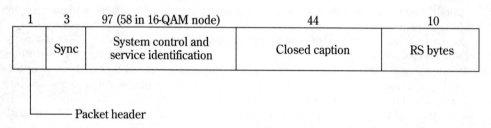

(B) Line 1 packet format

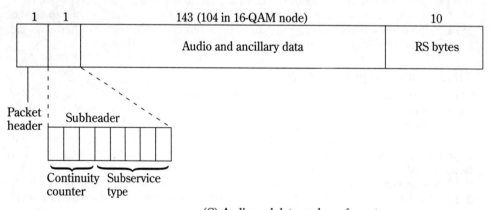

(C) Audio and data package format

12-2 DigiCipher packet format.

Effects on video quality

Because each packet has only one overhead byte (packet header), the impact on the available data capacity for video transmission due to the packetization is less than 1%. To fully support the ATSC T3/186 requirements, the DigiCipher system will be configured to support the services shown in Table 12-2. Two AC-3 audio services will be implemented to allow five channel (3/2) surround audio in two languages. Two ancillary data services at 126 kbps are provided to support the BER measurement during the field testing and to allow enough capacity for anticipated data services, such as teletext, program guide, and conditional access control. The ancillary data services can be individually enabled or disabled. When disabled, the unused data capacity is automatically used for video transmission to optimize the video quality. As can be seen in the table, the impact on the video data when all ancillary data services are enabled together with two Dolby AC-3, five-channel audio services is less than 2.3%, which will cause negligible effect on the overall video quality.

**Table 12-2. Bit allocation of DigiCipher
system in 32-QAM mode (bits/second).**

Services	Current DigiCipher	Packetized DigiCipher
System control and service identification	13,426	23,256
24-bit sync	719	719
Closed caption	—	10,549
Audio services		
2 × AC-2	503,496	—
2 × AC-3	—	755,245
Ancillary Data Services for teletext, program guide, conditional access control, etc.		
Allocated	251,748	—
2 × 126 kbps (can be individually enabled)	—	251,748
Packet header	—	125,874
Video data	17,482,361	17,084,359
Total	18,251,750	18,251,750

Sarnoff and Zenith

The two final competing units are offered by the Sarnoff Consortium (AD-HDTV) and Zenith/AT&T (DSC-HDTV). Although no diagrams are included, each report is detailed—especially the one emanating from Zenith, which also states that compressed data can be recorded and played back via Super-VHS technology accompanied by several modifications. Single-channel QUAM is undergoing further development for transmission over cable in the AD-HDTV system, as well as an improved current motion search range for pixel motion compensation. Zenith notes over 14 changes scheduled for updates.

Sarnoff AD-HDTV improvements

Trellis coding

A hardware implementation of trellis coding, which will provide a coding gain of 3 dB, is currently in bench test, and will replace the set-partition coding circuits in the AD-HDTV prototype. We expect these circuits to be fully integrated prior to March 15th.

Receiver carrier recovery pull-in range

The AD-HDTV prototype hardware has been improved to include second-order carrier recovery loops. These circuits have been integrated and tested in our lab. The prototype hardware can now demonstrate a pull-in range in excess of 30 kHz.

Quality of the high-priority safety net

The two-tier packetization and transmission capabilities of AD-HDTV provide a safety net that would take effect under severely impaired transmission conditions. The MPEG++ prioritization algorithm divides the MPEG codeword stream after compression, into High Priority (HP) and Standard Priority (SP) streams. This unique feature of AD-HDTV allows improvements to be made to the encoder prioritization algorithm without affecting overall picture quality.

Progress in improving the picture quality of the high-priority safety net continues, and improvements can be anticipated even after an HDTV standard has been established. Because the quality of the HP safety net is highly dependent on program content, the refinement process is very time consuming. Some improvement will be demonstrable should additional testing commence on March 15th; however, it should be understood that this will be an area of ongoing improvement.

Adjustment of the HP/SP power ratio

Because AD-HDTV has two separate 32-QAM carriers, the amount of power in each can easily be varied. This unique feature of the AD-HDTV system can be exploited by broadcasters to address some difficult interference problems. Although we believe this optimization is best addressed in a field test environment, the prototype hardware will provide for the adjustment of HP/SP power ratios for any additional testing required.

Upper and lower adjacent-channel rejection

Although the ATTC test results of adjacent-channel performance appear quite adequate to allow an AD-HDTV transmitter to be co-sited with transmitters for adjacent NTSC channels, we believe improvements in adjacent-channel immunity can be demonstrated. A custom SAW filter, with greater stop-band attenuation, will replace the existing, "off-the-shelf" SAW filter in our tuner. Although this SAW filter improvement will be integrated by March 15th, we expect further refinements of the tuner to be an on-going process beyond that date.

Receiver adaptive equalizer range

The AD-HDTV prototype hardware has been upgraded with an adaptive equalizer with a range of ±8 μsec.

QAM for cable

Because cable transmission does not have the co-channel requirements that are essential for terrestrial simulcast, AD-HDTV was designed to provide a conventional, single-carrier QAM transmission over cable. We will not be able to demonstrate this feature should additional testing of AD-HDTV commence on March 15th. However, we are diligently working on the required hardware, and we expect it to be available by June 15th.

Encoder motion search range

Although the AD-HDTV system supports a [–1024,+1023] pixel motion compensation range under the MPEG standard, the prototype hardware delivered for testing had a relatively small search range of [–32, +31] pixels. The limits of our current motion search range have been adequately documented in the motion compensation overload test. While work is in progress on hardware to provide a wider search range, we will not be able to demonstrate the extended search range in hardware, should additional testing of AD-HDTV commence on March 15th.

Multi-channel audio

AD-HDTV will also be able to demonstrate a capability to deliver 5 channel audio prior to March 15th.

Summary of DSC-HDTV improvements—Zenith

Improvements accepted by the technical subgroup

Implemented now

Vertical noise coring in video source

This improvement adds vertical source noise coring in addition to the existing horizontal source noise coring. The improvement increases overall coder efficiency by reducing the number of bits wasted on coding noise, and improves picture quality. The improvement only affects the encoder and is implemented in hardware and ready for testing now. The Subgroup approved the improvement, with lab testing before field testing.

Improved quantizer vector selection codebook

This improvement adds entries to tables contained in the encoder and decoder and requires no hardware changes. The improvement reduces twinkle in still pictures and visible artifacts in noisy or complex pictures. The improvement is implemented in hardware and ready for testing now. The Subgroup approved the improvement with lab testing before field testing.

Modified quantizers, perceptual weights, scale factors, and VLCs

These improvements modify the entries in a variety of tables in the encoder and decoder and require no hardware changes. The improvements reduce artifacts in saturated color regions, in complex or noisy pictures, and for iso-luminance patterns. The improvements are implemented in hardware and ready for testing now. The Subgroup approved these improvements with lab testing before field testing.

Improved leak calculation

This improvement replaces a suboptimal way of fixing "limit cycles" associated with leak with a superior method. The improvement removes temporal breathing, reduces buffer oscillations and improves overall coding efficiency by 50%. The improvement is implemented in hardware and ready for testing now. The Subgroup approved the improvement with lab testing before field testing.

Improved error concealment via unity leak

This improvement replaces errored blocks with unity leak, and only affects the decoder. The improvement provides effective concealment of errors in still pictures and in motion pictures, where accurate motion vectors are available. Picture quality in the presence of heavy errors is improved and better soft coding is obtained. The improvement is implemented in hardware and ready for testing now. The Subgroup approved the improvement with lab testing before field testing.

Modified buffer control, increased decoder efficiency and controlled audio/video delay

This improvement involves parameter changes in the encoder to provide faster scene changes and a better distribution of 2-level and 4-level segments. It also involves modifications in the encoder and decoder to control the relative delay between the audio and video display. These improvements are implemented in hardware and ready for testing now. The Subgroup approved the improvements with lab testing before field testing.

Reduction of pilot level

The pilot level as tested at the ATTC was conservatively high. This improvement reduces the pilot level for both 2-level and 4-level data by 3 dB. Improvements are expected in upper-adjacent ATV-into-NTSC interference as well as from lower transmitted signal power. The improvement is implemented in hardware and ready for testing now. The Subgroup approved the improvement with lab testing before field testing.

Changes in offset frequency and dispersion

An additional 30-Hz offset in the transmitter carrier frequency is proposed, which eliminates a color stripe observed in ATV-into-NTSC co-channel interference tests. A change in the dispersion is also used to lower the peak-to-average power ratio by 1.5 dB. This latter improvement is implemented in hardware and both improvements are ready for testing now. The Subgroup approved these improvements with lab testing before field testing.

Correction of slice error problem

This improvement corrects a hardware problem in the decoder that caused a timing fault in the compressed video data deformatter, giving occasional undetected errors in a given slice (64 H-x-48 V pixel block). The improvement is implemented in hardware and ready for testing now. The Subgroup approved the improvement with lab testing before field testing.

Filtering of input to motion estimator

This improvement overcomes a "half-pel" flashing block problem that occurs when an accumulator overflow condition causes erroneous motion vectors to be computed for several 32H-x-16V blocks in a scene. The improvement is implemented in hardware and ready for testing now. The Subgroup approved the improvement with lab testing before field testing.

Adaptive two-dimensional source filtering

This improvement affects the encoder only and involves performing a slight spatial two-dimensional frequency roll-off in the input to the encoder, based on an estimate of picture complexity. The change improves picture quality—especially for complex pictures. The improvement is implemented in hardware and is ready for testing now. The Subgroup approved the improvement with lab testing before field testing.

Optimization of decimation filter for coarse motion estimation

This improvement involves only the encoder and provides better coarse motion estimators by relaxing the decimation filter. The improvement reduces "swarming" artifacts in high-frequency regions (e.g., high-frequency zone plates). The improvement is implemented in hardware and ready for testing now. The Subgroup approved the improvement with lab testing before field testing.

Optimized selection of segments for 2-level transmission

This improvement affects the encoder only and involves parameter adjustments to provide a more optimal selection of segments to be sent as 2-level data. The improvement provides better picture quality when only 2-level data can be received. The improvement is implemented in hardware and ready for testing now. The Subgroup approved the improvement with lab testing before field testing.

Two DSC-HDTV programs in one 6-MHz cable channel

This improvement involves the use of a 16-VSB transmission format to achieve a 43-Mb/s data rate, which can provide two DSC-HDTV programs over a single cable channel without any perceptible increase in the cost of terrestrial broadcast receivers. The improvement is implemented in hardware and ready for testing now. The Subgroup approved the improvement for the purposes of lab and field testing, and requested the proponent to transmit its position on the benefits of this option to PS/WP-3, PS/WP-4, and any other appropriate working parties.

To be implemented time for field testing

Spatially adaptive leak

This improvement involves changes to the encoder and decoder to permit the encoder to vary the leak value on a block-by-block basis. Significant improvements are expected in the coding of pictures that contain partial scene changes, extreme amounts of uncovered background, or very high amplitude source noise. This improvement is not yet implemented, but it will be available in time for field testing. The Subgroup approved the improvement, recommending lab testing after system selection, but before field testing.

Faster adaptive equalizer that adapts on data

This improvement involves a faster adaptive equalizer for use in the ATV receiver. The new equalizer will adapt on data, resulting in better tracking of time-varying multipath signals. This improvement is not yet implemented, but it will be available before field testing. The Subgroup approved the improvement, recommending lab testing after system selection, but before field testing.

ATSC T3/186 audio and flexible assignment of audio, video, ancillary and conditional access/encryption data

A multichannel sound system to fulfill the audio requirements of T3/186 will be implemented in hardware and should be ready for lab testing by 12/26/92. The system will utilize the Dolby AC-3 5.1-channel system, plus the Dolby AC-2A system for an additional two independent audio channels. This choice might be revisited if another audio sub-system becomes available before testing begins. The Subgroup approved this improvement subject to appropriate testing.

The inclusion of headers to allow flexible allocation of data will be accomplished in time for testing prior to field testing. This flexible allocation capability will be implemented to the extent the interfaces to the various services to be carried are adequately specified before testing. The Subgroup approved this improvement, with lab testing recommended after system selection, but before field testing.

Future improvements to be implemented after field testing

Video encoding parameter optimization

- Perceptual thresholds
- Coefficient scaling for quantization
- Buffer control
- Motion estimation
- Adaptive motion vector budget
- Quantizer vector selector
- Leak adaptation
- Adaptive source filtering
- Robust segment selection algorithm

Other improvements underway

DSC-HDTV consumer VCR

The certification document for DSC-HDTV noted that the compressed data signal could be recorded and played back using Super-VHS technology. Experimental units have now been developed using S-VHS tape and S-VHS heads with modified transport, demonstrating the viability of VCR recording and playback of DSC-HDTV.

Canada's evaluation for digital

This portion of the chapter could be entitled "Canada speaks," for it contains evaluations from our northern neighbor and their various Canadian college non-expert observers.

These observers serve a very useful purpose of how the educated general public might view the remaining systems as members when undergoing a general review of taped sequences provided by our Advanced Television Test Committee, generated under the strictest laboratory conditions.

Under direct auspices of the ATEL Advanced Television Evaluation Laboratory, Department of Communications, Government of Canada, such assessments were supported by the Canadian Broadcasting Corp., the Communications Research Centre, Leitch Video International, Rogers Engineering, Tektronix (of Canada), Telesat Canada, and Advanced Broadcasting Systems of Canada. You can see there's considerably more involved than a handful of undergraduates. Also note that although Japan's NHK Narrow MUSE was evaluated along with the others, it has never been anything but an analog system and the FCC wanted only digital, so that signal processor was declared ineligible. At this juncture, Chairman Wiley and probably many at the FCC would happily welcome an amalgamation of the remaining four systems, so the prime features of each could be combined into a single system. But there are many electronic, business, patent rights, U.S.-European personalities, and other considerations with which to contend and satisfy, so the FCC might have to make an arbitrary and binding decision after all.

Admittedly, these are not final results of all system evaluations because another four months of further testing have taken place, but the following charts do represent all the digital systems remaining plus the NHK offering, which has dropped out. Therefore, they at least represent the basics of digital, which will become the U.S. high-definition television system for now and into the 21st century.

Here are certain acronyms with which you should become thoroughly familiar:

TOV	Threshold of Visibility
POU	Points of Unusability
POA	Point of Acquisition
ATVA	American Television Alliance
ATRC	Advanced Television Research Consortium
NHK	Japan Broadcasting Corp.
D/U	Desired/Undesired Ratio for "perceptible but not annoying" for digital *D/U* becomes "slightly annoying" when describing NTSC action
DSC-HDTV	Zenith & AT&T
AD-HDTV	Sarnoff, Thomson, Philips, NBC *DigiCipher* and *General Instrument Corp.*
CCDC	Gen. Instrument & Mass. Inst. Technology

These abbreviations and NHK appear throughout the chart studies and ratings to follow. We will, however, select the more pertinent and instructive examples for inclusion because there simply isn't space to publish them all. A single page of CATV information appears at chapter's end.

Interoperability/suitable for cable

The Advisory Committee considers performance in a cable transmission environment under two selection criteria: transmission robustness and interoperability. Performance in a number of analyses and tests, some of which are reported here, are used in these determinations.

The results of assessments of Cable Received Quality are summarized in the Table 12-3.

For Cable Received Quality, the table shows that none of the ATV systems was affected by transmission through the cable distribution plant and that, in consequence, there were no differences among systems. For Fiber Received Quality, no subjective assessments by non-expert viewers were carried out. Expert observers at Cable Television Laboratories determined that none of the ATV systems was affected by transmission through the fiber distribution plant and that this test was unnecessary as it would add no information beyond that available from tests of Cable Received Quality.

Table 12-3. ATV cable received quality.

D: distribution quality minus ideal reception quality (if positive, distribution quality exceeds ideal quality); R: statistical ranking of systems (lower values are better)

	Stills	**Camera**	**Film**	**Graphic**	**Graphic**
	[S01-S10]	**[M01-M10]**	**[M17-M20]**	**[S14]**	**[M16]**
N-MUSE	D: −0.24	D: −0.58	D: −0.45	D: +0.14	D: −0.37
	R: *3.0*	R: *3.0*	R: *3.0*	R: *3.0*	R: *3.0*
DigiCipher	D: +0.35	D: −0.42	D: −0.78	D: −0.43	D: +2.06
	R: *3.0*	R: *3.0*	R: *3.0*	R: *3.0*	R: *3.0*
DSC-HDTV	D: −0.18	D: +0.16	D: −0.98	D: −2.31	D: −0.62
	R: *3.0*	R: *3.0*	R: *3.0*	R: *3.0*	R: *3.0*
AD-HDTV	D: +0.15	D: +0.06	D: −0.18	D: +0.84	D: −0.20
	R: *3.0*	R: *3.0*	R: *3.0*	R: *3.0*	R: *3.0*
CCDC	D: +0.27	D: −0.22	D: −0.49	D: +0.83	D: −0.90
	R: *3.0*	R: *3.0*	R: *3.0*	R: *3.0*	R: *3.0*

Note:

1—In accordance with standard statistical practice, ties share the average of the ranks they otherwise would be assigned (e.g., 2 cases tied for first place would be assigned ranks of 1.5, the average of ranks 1 and 2).

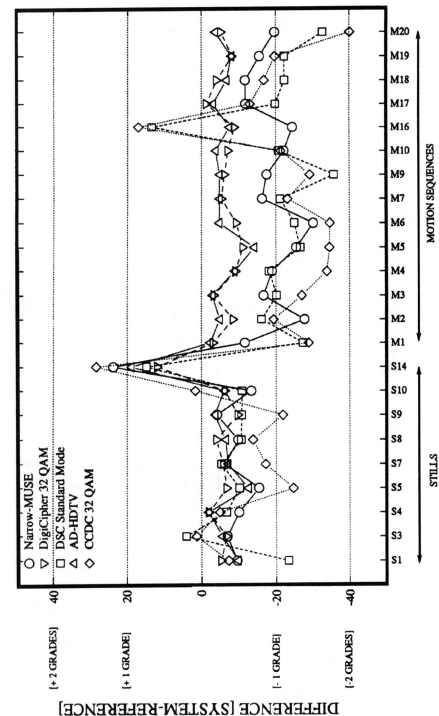

FIGURE 1: ATV BASIC RECEIVED QUALITY DIFFERENCE SCORES

○ Narrow-MUSE
▽ DigiCipher 32 QAM
□ DSC Standard Mode
◁ AD-HDTV
◇ CCDC 32 QAM

DIFFERENCE [SYSTEM-REFERENCE]

[+ 2 GRADES] [+ 1 GRADE] [- 1 GRADE] [-2 GRADES]

TEST MATERIAL

[S1-S10 SCANNED FROM STILLS; M1-M10 TAKEN FROM CAMERA ; M17-M20 TRANSFERRED FROM FILM VIA CAMERA;
S14, M16 CONVERTED FROM GRAPHIC SOURCES]

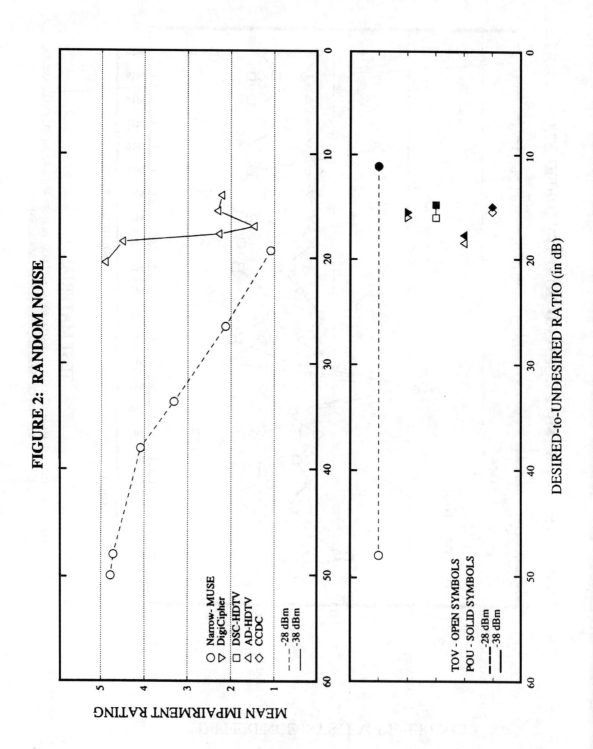

FIGURE 2: RANDOM NOISE

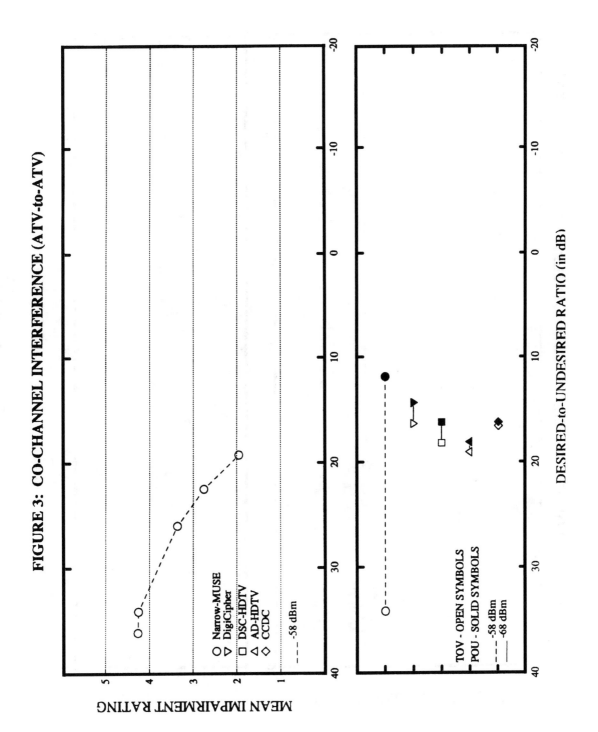

FIGURE 3: CO-CHANNEL INTERFERENCE (ATV-to-ATV)

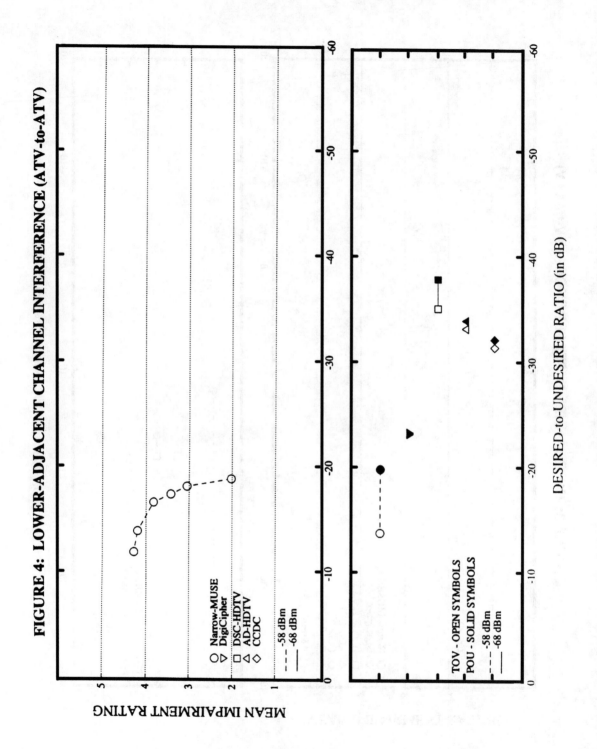

FIGURE 4: LOWER-ADJACENT CHANNEL INTERFERENCE (ATV-to-ATV)

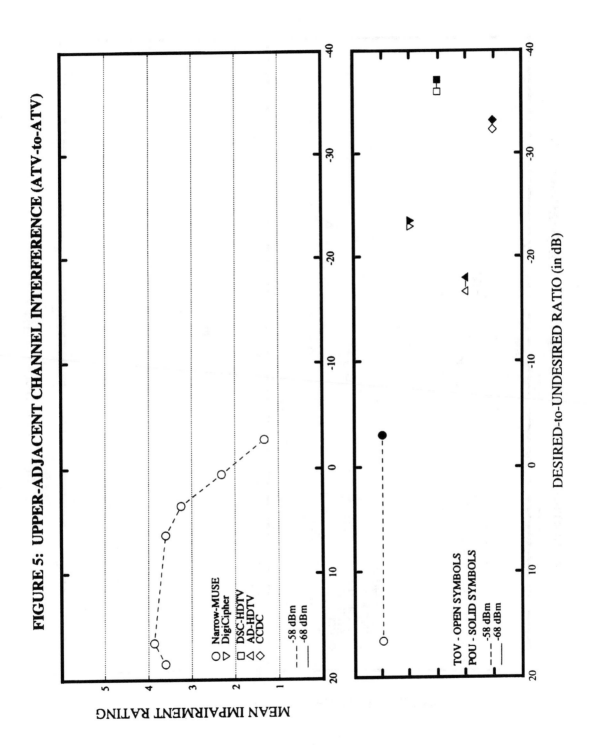

FIGURE 5: UPPER-ADJACENT CHANNEL INTERFERENCE (ATV-to-ATV)

MEAN IMPAIRMENT RATING

DESIRED-to-UNDESIRED RATIO (in dB)

○ Narrow-MUSE
▽ DigiCipher
□ DSC-HDTV
◁ AD-HDTV
◇ CCDC

--- -58 dBm
— -68 dBm

TOV - OPEN SYMBOLS
POU - SOLID SYMBOLS

--- -58 dBm
— -68 dBm

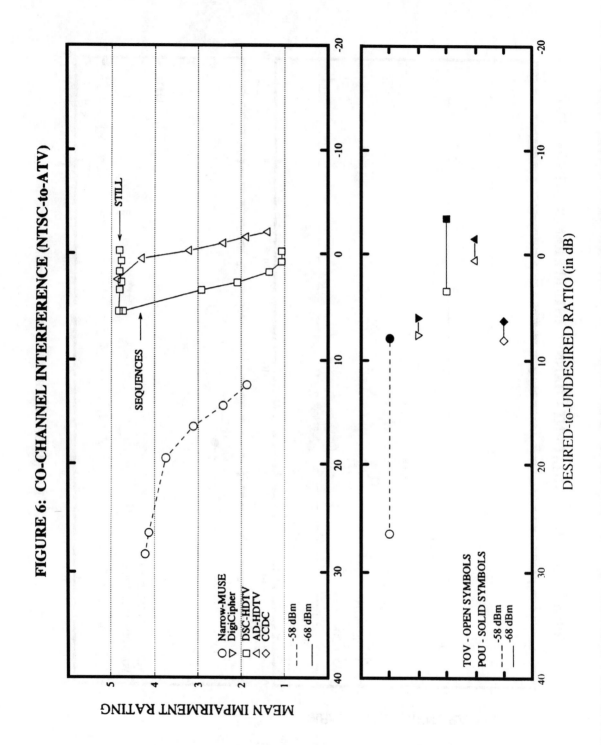

FIGURE 6: CO-CHANNEL INTERFERENCE (NTSC-to-ATV)

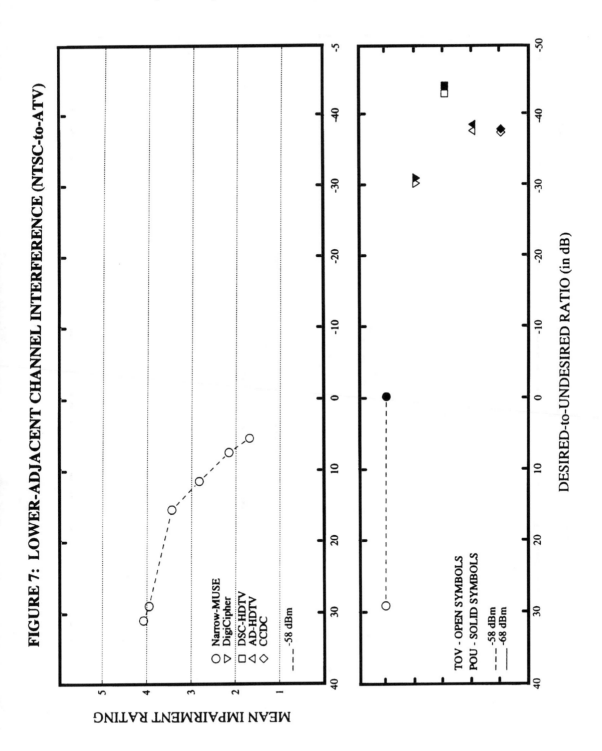

FIGURE 7: LOWER-ADJACENT CHANNEL INTERFERENCE (NTSC-to-ATV)

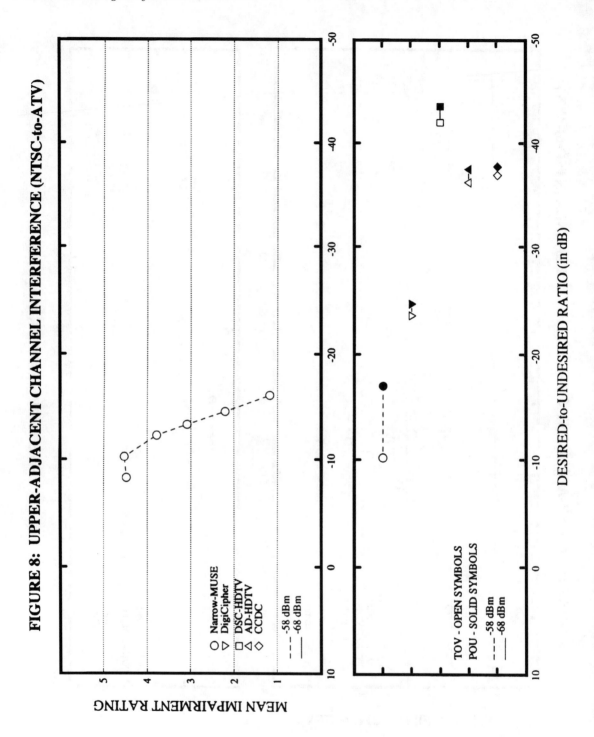

FIGURE 8: UPPER-ADJACENT CHANNEL INTERFERENCE (NTSC-to-ATV)

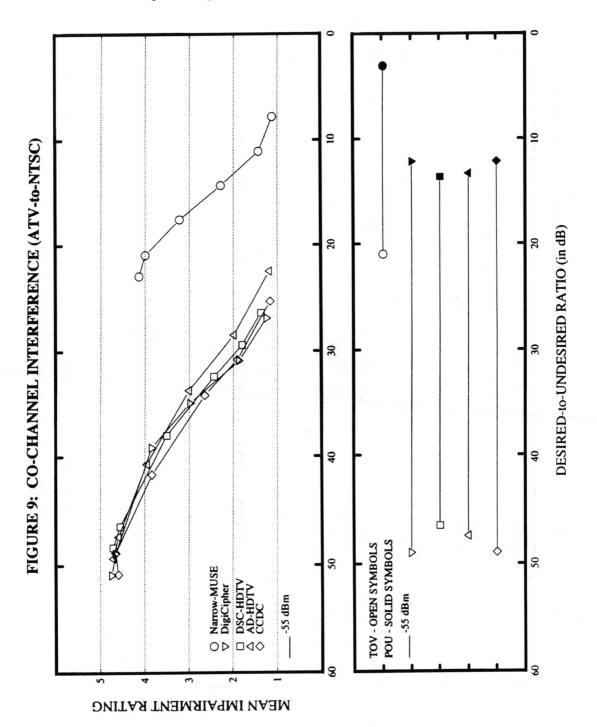

FIGURE 9: CO-CHANNEL INTERFERENCE (ATV-to-NTSC)

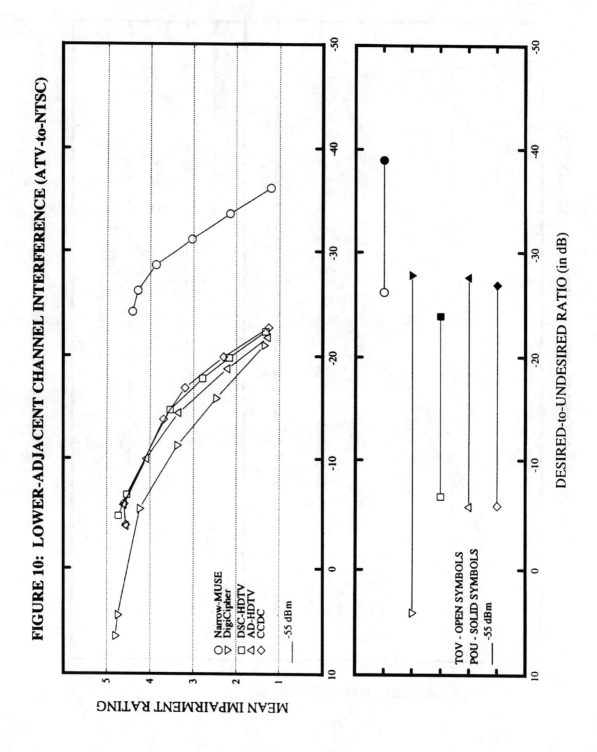

FIGURE 10: LOWER-ADJACENT CHANNEL INTERFERENCE (ATV-to-NTSC)

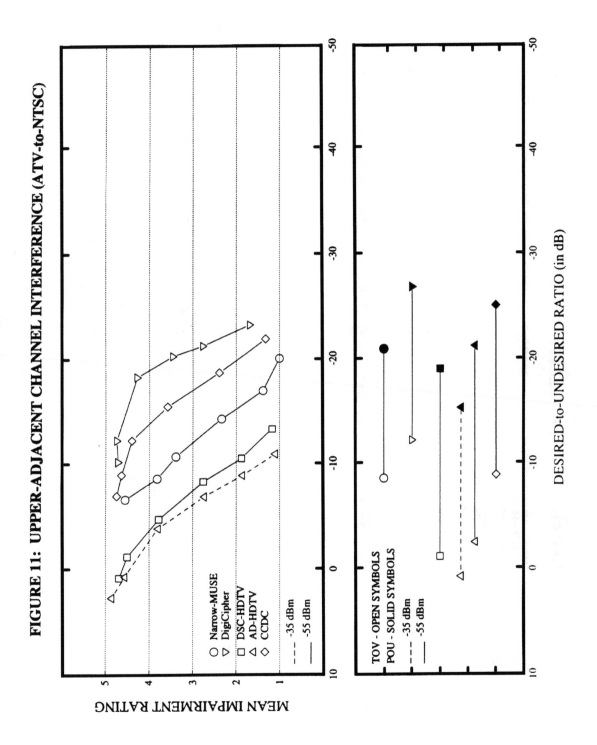

FIGURE 11: UPPER-ADJACENT CHANNEL INTERFERENCE (ATV-to-NTSC)

FIGURE 12: ATV CABLE RECEIVED QUALITY DIFFERENCE SCORES

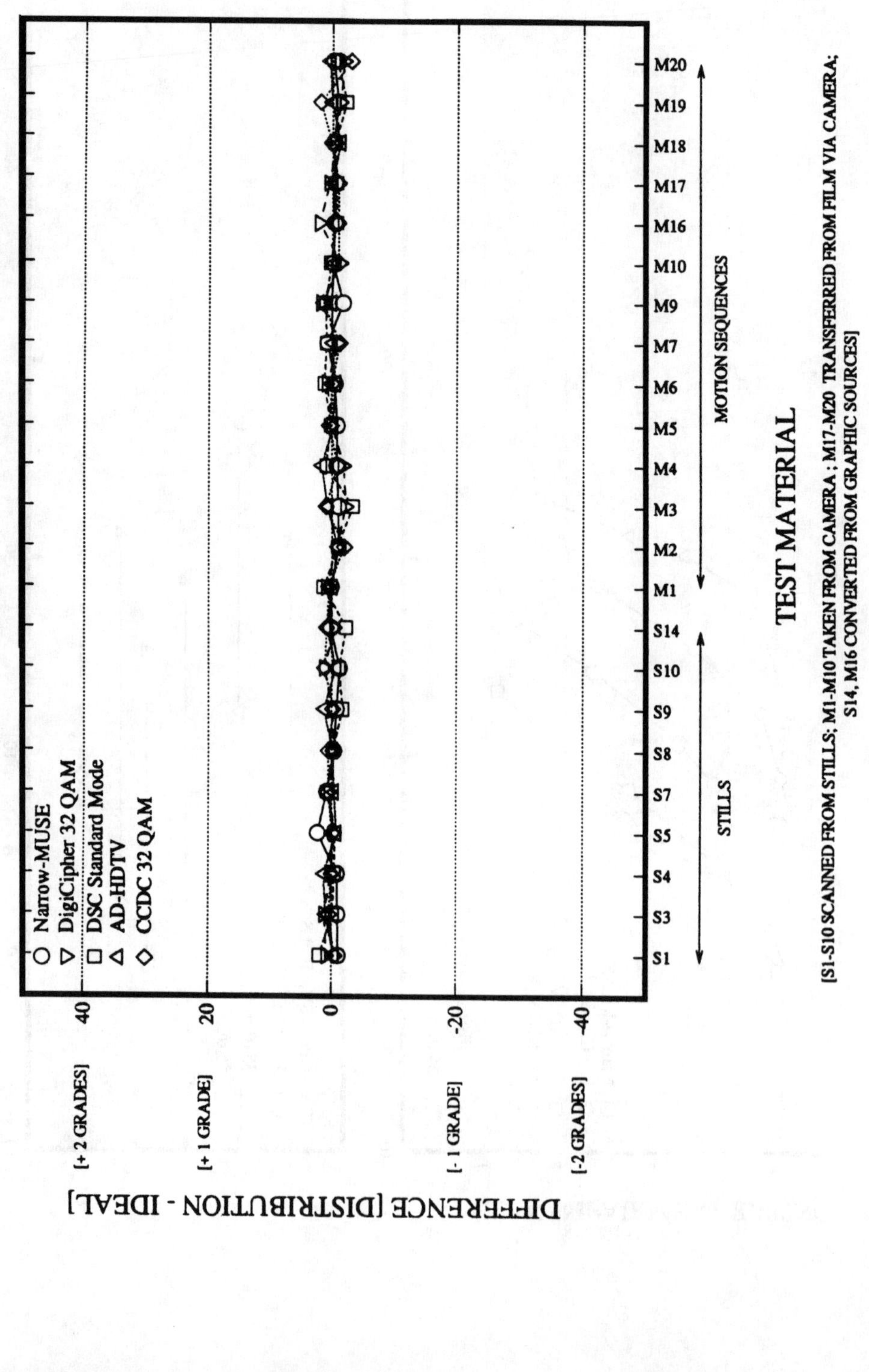

○ Narrow-MUSE
▽ DigiCipher 32 QAM
□ DSC Standard Mode
△ AD-HDTV
◇ CCDC 32 QAM

DIFFERENCE [DISTRIBUTION - IDEAL]

TEST MATERIAL

[S1-S10 SCANNED FROM STILLS; M1-M10 TAKEN FROM CAMERA ; M17-M20 TRANSFERRED FROM FILM VIA CAMERA; S14, M16 CONVERTED FROM GRAPHIC SOURCES]

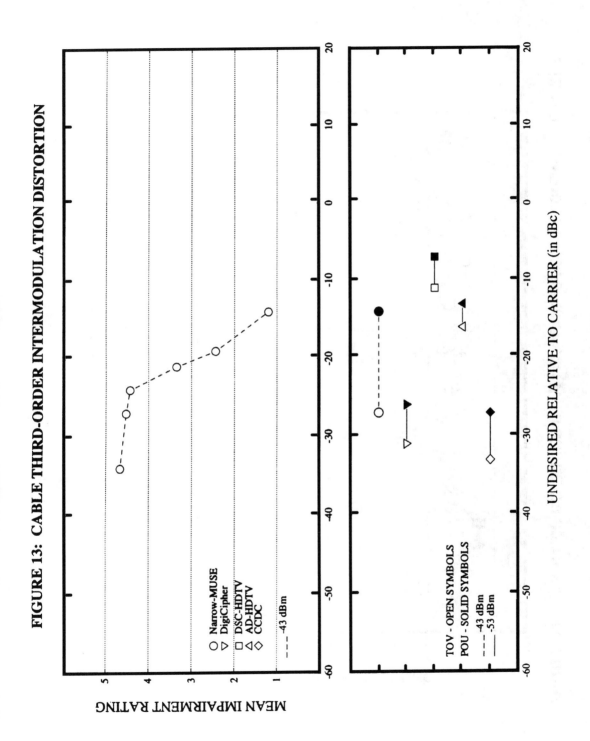

FIGURE 13: CABLE THIRD-ORDER INTERMODULATION DISTORTION

FIGURE 14: ATV BASIC RECEIVED QUALITY SCORES FOR REFERENCE PICTURES

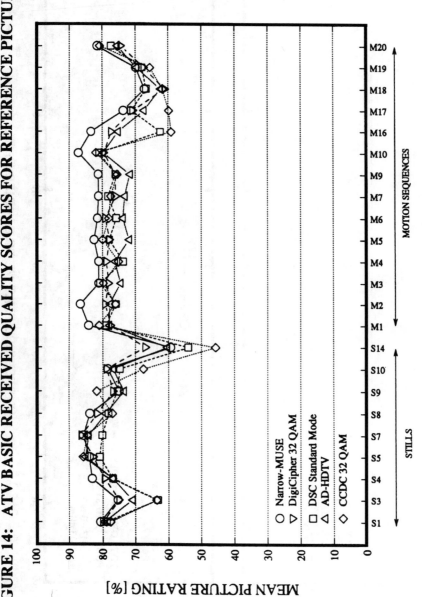

TEST MATERIAL

[S1-S10 SCANNED FROM STILLS; M1-M10 TAKEN FROM CAMERA ; M17-M20 TRANSFERRED FROM FILM VIA CAMERA; S14, M16 CONVERTED FROM GRAPHIC SOURCES]

13

The final HDTV
digital system proposed
by the Grand Alliance

As Desired by both ATV Chairman Wiley and the Federal Communications Commission, the surviving four system proponents had an ultimate meeting in May 1993. On May 24 they announced to undertake and produce a single high-definition television system consisting of the most acceptable portions of previous digital systems dutifully combined into one (Fig. 13-1).

System design approaches were to select best elements from all four, or at least "as good as the best of four systems": Modular design, multiple video formats, MPEG-2 syntax and extensions, packetization, and careful selection considerations.

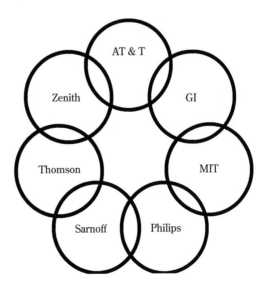

13-1 Grand Alliance individual members.

Block diagrams of the proposed transmitters and receivers are shown in Figs. 13-2 and 13-3, respectively. You see the variable video format selector, adaptive coder, transport multiplexer, and the transmission system with modulator. The receiver will tune and demodulate the incoming HDTV, the transport delivers decoder and demultiplexer, then on to video/audio decoders and the display format converter. There's also a data channel output from the transport that is derived from the transport transmitter data input. So, at least now you have a general outline of what broadcasts and receives in a system approach by the Grand Alliance.

During startup, the following scanning lines, progressive (1:1) and interlace (2:1) formats are supported, which are to develop eventually into a 1050-line progressive format having 60, 30, and 24 frames per second:

1050/1:1/30, 24
787.5/1:1/60, 30, 24
1050/2:1/60

Expectations are that the 1050 interlaced (2:1) format will eventually phase out leaving progressive scan (1:1) as the single-frame system. It's considered initially that 1050 lines at 30 and 24 frames will support film material best, and 787.5 progressive at 60 frames/sec are good for rapid action video and graphics. Square pixels (H/V pix. components) and progressive scans work well with computers and permit "significant portions of the total data capacity to be used for ancillary data services." Multiple formats via source adaptive coding deliver maximum source material as it progresses through the system.

Receiver display mediums—cathode ray tubes or otherwise—are expected to measure 34 inches diagonal or more at 60 frames/sec. and a line rate of 787.5 (or greater). Manufacturers will be asked for such commitments as additional specifications, development, and tests to show further necessary and desirable features with engineering progress. Probabilities are that the 1050/2:1/60 format will disappear shortly because noninterlace effectively negates interline flicker, apparent especially on larger display receivers. In addition, films respond better to compression when transmitted progressively, thereby allowing superior picture quality.

The Grand Alliance certainly will use the MPEG-2 syntax with field/frame coding, I and P frames. Subject to further investigation are B frames, coefficient selection coding, and nonuniform quantization with new VLCs.

Transmitter

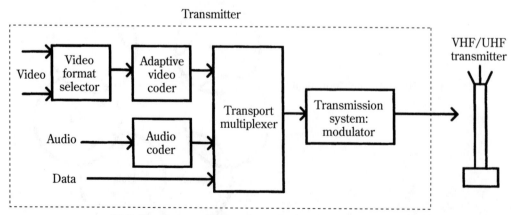

13-2 The proposed transmitter shown in the block diagram.

Receiver

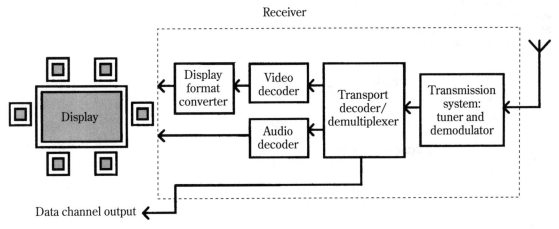

13-3 A block of the intended receiver and its display.

Additional issues involve transmission systems, such as vestigial sideband (VSB) or quadrature amplitude modulation (QAM). The 4 VSB, 32 QAM, and 32 SS-QAM featured in initial digital proponent systems are said to have worked well, and additional improvements have been included in the meantime. A 6 VSB trellis-coded transmission also is available. SS-QAM translates to spectrally shaped QAM.

In transport, a packetized, prioritized data format has been favored, and a final selection should be ready, at least on paper, by August 31, 1993. An audio format selection also has an August 31 due date with Dolby AC-3, Multichannel Musicam, and MIT-AC as competitors. Favored are front left, right, and center speakers, with two woofers in the rear, including surround sound.

Final 1993 date due specifications for the Grand Alliance unisystem are reported as follows:

Transport and audio: August 31
Format: September 15
Compression: September 30
Transmission: November 30

System integration is due February 1, 1994 with a complete system by March 1, 1994, operational verification by April 1, and ATTC testing by May 1, 1994.

Portions of the four original offerings might be added to the final system as units, additional hardware developed, and all should be operational by or before April 1, 1994.

Further developmental and engineering costs are to be borne by the four remaining proponents:

ATRC: Thomson, Philips and Sarnoff
G.I. and M.I.T. (2 systems)
Zenith and AT&T

Compression Labs and NBC, apparently, are not included, and DigiCipher, of course, is part of General Instrument. Financially, there's an even split among the main four groups, but there will be certain monetary divisions within the various units.

Decision making remains in the hands of highly qualified engineers appointed and selected by the technical subgroup of the FCC Advisory Committee identified as "expert groups." There are five, and the announcement is printed exactly as received so that members are readily identifiable.

**FCC Advisory Committee
Technical Subgroup**

Expert Groups

**Joseph Flaherty & Irwin Dorros
Co-chairmen**

**Alex Felker & Mark Richer
Vice-chairmen**

Scanning Formats/Compression Systems	Transmission	Transport
1. Paul Hearty	1. EBU, *ex officio*	1. Lyn Claudy
2. Robert Hopkins, Chair	2. John Henderson, Chair	2. EBU, *ex officio*
3. Richard Prodan	3. Brian James	3. Branko Gerovac
4. Victor Rojas, *ex officio*	4. Louis Libin	4. Craig Tanner, Chair
5. Robert Sanderson	5. Robert Niles	5. Michael Haley
6. Renn McMann	6. Charles Rhodes	
7. Peter Smith, EBU, ex officio	7. Victor Tawil	

Audio	Production & Receiver/VCR Impact
1. Kenneth Davies	1. Peter Fannon
2. Bernie Dayton	2. Reggie Gilliam
3. James Gaspar, Chair	3. George Hanover
4. Bronwen Jones	4. Howard Miller
5. Thomas Keller	5. Laurence Thorpe
	6. George Vrandenberg, Chair
	7. Werner Wedam

Final system makeup depends on both paper and final subsystems integration, as well as forthcoming field tests following full system delivery and laboratory approval. There could also be some field testing in parallel with laboratory testing so that problems may be quickly identified and resolved, thus saving time and money. The transmission subsystem should profit by such a procedure. In addition, there seems to be a problem with HDTV-loaned channel 6 near Charlotte finding its way into local cable runs. Causes should be found or circumvented during the two months of scheduled laboratory examination prior to probably three months of field testing.

If lab testing actually begins May 1, 1994, another five months will have elapsed before final ATV approval, with another relatively short delay before the FCC renders its blessing. Therefore, November or December 1994 appears to be the magic date for the U.S. entry into the HDTV world, which, good or otherwise, the remainder of our planet must follow and pay royalties to the famous foursome for many years to come. Besides

USA types, the Netherlands is represented by Philips and France by Thomson, owners of Magnavox and Philco, and Sylvania (Philips) and RCA (Thomson). The Japanese and their analog system departed early in 1993 because HDTV now is a wholly digital system and MUSE, plus its half-dozen versions, is decidedly analog, not digital. However, the Japanese will certainly enjoy a considerable part of HDTV with their cameras, video digital recorders, cathode ray tubes, and television receivers. Consequently, there seems to be adequate largess to satisfy even those not directly connected with system winners.

Video compression

Now that the general HDTV plan has already been outlined, further attention is due the Video Compression component which, after all, is fundamentally the main system entity. Without low power, low noise video, wide bandwidth, and other attributes all fitted into our regular NTSC channel envelope, there would probably be no satisfactory HDTV.

The international and motion picture contribution of MPEG-2 aids in establishing a global HDTV standard, contributes to integrated circuit development of very large scale integrated circuit video decoders, and allows greater flexibility of compressed digital bit streams.

MPsG-II

According to the ATR Consortium, MPEG-2 is a worldwide consensus standard due for considerable applications in computer, telecommunications, and consumer electronics. With periodic I-frame intraframe coded pictures, superior video displays are evident in both fast forward and reverse when used in VCRs, identified as forward-predicted P frames and backward-predicted B frames. Particular operations for ADTV MPEG involves fixed picture grouping of IBBPBBPBB in a following sequence of 9 frames repeated indefinitely, as analyzed by the Analysis Task Force of SS Working Party 1.

I-frame information is intra-frame coded independent of other frame content. P frames, however, are based predictably on prior I and P frame(s), and a B frame can be predicted on either bracketing I or P frames during the aforesaid sequence.

Prototype compensation ranges between -32 and +32 pels vertically and horizontally and the motion estimator is able to track 0.2X picture width/sec horizontally and 0.3X picture height/sec vertically.

Once codewords have been identified via two-tier transmission, higher and lower priority data is assigned and 8-8 macroblocks are Discrete Cosine Transformed (DCT) into 8-8 transform coefficients, which are also weighted and coded for eventual transmission. ac coefficients are quantized without a deadzone in an intra-frame coded macroblock, while ac coefficients in an inter-frame coded macroblock are. dc values move with an 8-bit quantizer and are differentially coded.

Variable run-length coding (VLC) appears in motion vectors and dc coefficients, as well as ac coefficients, where, in ac, lowest frequency coefficients are assigned zero runs and higher frequency coefficients appear as non-zeroes—this minimizes the bit numbers that are required to represent them.

All the above combines as prediction, DCT transforming, scaling, and variable length coding for format processing, organization and transmission. Data formatting allows higher layers to assume lower layer prior participation, followed by synchronizing, service-type identification, and coding as the video service level includes the actual encoded video information. Fixed-length cells of 148 bytes contain single-type data in the format sequence, followed by additional bytes for sync, service header, payload-cell service type and a 2-byte frame check trailer, plus an additional 20-byte forward-error correction trailer. A Reed-Solomon code corrects up to 10 error-containing bytes within 127 bytes protected by the code. Frame sync packet (in the prototype) affords less than one cell duration timing error.

The ADTV receiver operates with a double-conversion tuner and a first intermediate frequency (IF) at 611 MHz, with second IF centered at standard 44 MHz. A variable bandwidth tuner from 10 MHz at channel 2 to 41 MHz at channel 69 and adaptive equalizers permit 4 samples per symbol in 64 taps with channel changes of about 0.5 second.

Error receiver strategy discards error cells following Reed-Solomon processing. Errorless information is then accumulated and displayed pictures minimize any missing data.

This report is a paraphrase of available information and it might be changed somewhat when the final equipment appears. But it is invaluable for both background and basic design guidance.

Transmission

To be determined completely by November 30, 1993 is whether to use vestigial sideband or quadrature amplitude modulation. Both have attractive attributes: *QAM is a proven and widely used digital communications modulation system*, pilot tones and training sequences are not needed for equalizer beginning and carrier recovery, it has Trellis coding for low carrier-to-noise (C/N) threshold, high cable capacity, and simple receiver hardware. SS-QAM affords superior co-channel operations, Trellis coding for better threshold, dual-tier alternate mode for strong transmissions in addition to a high data rate. Further, 16 QAM can also be the alternate mode if either QAM or SS-QAM is selected.

For cable applications, highest data rates are greater than 37 megabits for either 16 VSB or 256 QAM, and 64 QAM is rated at 27 Mbps.

VSB strengths are strong signals, a pilot tone and training sequence, an interference NTSC rejection filter, 2/4 bi-level data mode, extended audio threshold, superior phase noise immunity, Trellis coding in the 6VSB version, and low cost.

Integration

Integration can occur at a selected location, and alliance members will make the determination, probably at one of their own activities—especially if this expedites the schedule. It might also be added that audio hardware is now available to add Philips, MIT, or Dolby and comparison testing of Musicam 5.1, MIT-AC, or Dolby AC-3 is to be completed by August 31, 1993. The format is defined as *multichannel surround sound*.

Although much of the foregoing becomes history in early 1994, it offers a rather detailed technical overview of the many considerations, problems, and electronic targets these members of the alliance must agree upon and solve before final laboratory and field testing prior to Federal Communications Commission approval late in the year or early 1995. Whatever the ultimate decisions, we should all profit in many ways in this country from the result, for once again the United States has taken the lead in consumer products lost so long ago to the Japanese. True, two European countries will also share in the proceeds, but the prime product is first and foremost American.

Overall considerations

Suggested and implemented formats deliver superb quality video for a great deal of source material, much of which is already available on film. They feature progressive scanning and square pixels to accommodate multimedia and computers.

All formats do not exceed the standard 6-MHz NTSC channels that are now in use. Early introduction of an HDTV standard is probable. Today's broadcast requirements, plus current and future telecommunications, multimedia and computer requirements are all taken into consideration.

For receivers, these are to detect and recognize the transmitted format, decode and decompress (expand) images, and to deliver to frame buffer, then reformat the images for a "native mode" single display for which the receiver is manufactured. Computers are likely to use multi-sync displays. Routinely, receivers will sync and demultiplex high-speed data, decode variable-length codewords, invert DCT coefficients, move image blocks having arbitrary vectors, and store images in frame memory. All this sounds somewhat complex, but proponents say that temporal repetition is simple, spatial filter in easy, no de-interlace for progressive scan, but de-interlace for small, less-expensive receivers.

There's more than considerable pressure on the appointed groups and sub-groups to move to a consensus as rapidly as possible so that projected system dates and anticipated costs are met. Consequently, meetings became essentially teleconferences—even though written inputs were welcome. However, proposals and engineering streamlining was of utmost importance to achieve these twin goals. In the meantime, the test site near Charlotte, NC neared completion before fall, where channels 6 and 53 are operated in terrestrial signal evaluations. Two-thirds of the Charlotte vicinity has been assigned as the field test area. Transmitters and signal originating equipment have been duly added, and a 30' receive antenna has gained approval when initial tests were scheduled for early August.

Cable HDTV

Alliance cable system testing occurred and is occurring in the same laboratories as terrestrial examinations using familiar equipment, ATTC personnel, CATV engineers, and a panel of expert viewers—at least that's what planning documents detailed.

Special attention was directed to possible distortions introduced by second-order (beat clusters) and third-order (composite triple beats) intermodulations. The former produce undesirable products offset +1.25 MHz above the video carrier, dominating single-ended amplifiers and fiberoptics nets. The latter cluster about the video carrier and are pronounced in push-pull amplifiers. The test uses 32 TV modulators and upconverters simulating typical cable headends.

Phase noise modulation enters the HDTV channels via phase modulating the test bed upconverting local oscillator. This is compared with an amplitude-modulated microwave link and cable, observing any changes in error rates or picture impairments.

Residual frequency modulation ordinarily surfaces inside frequency agile conversions as a result of power-supply frequency pickup. Once again, the test bed upconverter local oscillator is modulated, but this time with a quasi-rectangular 120-Hz signal. Levels are noted and unusual results recorded.

Fiberoptics is also an important test—especially when using distributed feedback lasers. These develop a knee on current-versus-light power curve. Operationally, second- and third-order intermodulations reflect the AM modulation percentage, determining by frequency cable signals that exceed this knee. Digital and analog carriers in the same spectrum will react unfavorably if the analogs exceed the knee and if impulse noise appears in digitals.

Channel changes with impairments are also notable tests, as are data channel bit-error rate examinations. There are also a number of receiver-impairment tests in the works, but because the receiver hasn't been manufactured, this portion of projected cable tests will not be offered; they may vary considerably from those previously included as a result of different designs and tradeoffs.

Local oscillator instability, moving secondary-image (ghosts) tracking, burst errors, data packets loss, and threshold determination—can appear, especially in a digital system as the "critical" error rate is exceeded.

Terrestrial testing

Whether prior tests and initiating procedures will be continued in part or whole will be determined by the ATTC and the various working parties in agreement with select members of the alliance. We already know, however, that such problems as multipath (secondary images called *ghosts*), broadcast signal acquisition at the threshold of visibility (TOV), impairments in slowly varying ranging tests, picture-quality ratings, transmission impairments, still and motion sequences, points of unusability (POU), as well as points of reception (POR), and points of failure (POF)—all of which have been executed previously in one form or another, but not restricted to a single, rigidly defined system approved by members of the alliance and the appropriate test and working parties. Therefore, there'll obviously be changes in substance and depths, depending on the eventual system, including specific tests and their contents.

As for multipath, this results in gain and frequency changes in channel reception and could require testing with relative carriers that are so phased that they deliver minimum signal levels at specified carrier frequency, as instrumented by a special Hewlett Packard Network Analyzer. Some engineers are declaring that multipath can reduce terrestrial coverage and that as many as five ghosts from an HP simulator can be used to generate even one or more pre-ghosts and one ghost equal to the longest specified delay. Propagation information as a result of sharp distance cutoff of digital broadcasts needs accurate coverage predictions, cross polarization for adequate discrimination between HDTV and NTSC signals, and the observation of changing seasons as trees lose their leaves.

If there's anything simple about this advanced television system and its huge promise of worldwide communications, little surfaces here. This is a tremendous effort coupled with more than considerable expense evident to put such broadcasts on the air. But wait until you see the results!

Meanwhile, the Service Systems Subcommittee Working Party 2 agreed in the May 5, 1993 meeting that all interference tests into ATV/HDTV should correspond to the following levels:

Weak: –68 dBm
Moderate: –53 dBm
Strong: –28 dBm

The major change here was an *increase* of 10 dBm from –38 to –28 dBm. Presumably, these levels will extend to the single system when final engineering parameters are published. There are still questions outstanding on the use of original tapes with 23 scenes, or should some images be superseded or deleted? Additionally, should most or all viewers be experts or nonexperts and should a second set of tapes be generated and compared with the first? Considering the amount of previous discussion, such questions might take a little longer to support a consensus.

And just for the record, preliminary investigations have already occurred using relatively low (1 kW) power into orthogonal (H/V) transmissions and receptions from the Charlotte test site, Ch. 53. These were to determine if digital transmissions would produce further reduced interference into NTSC. End-fire Yagis were used and signal samples in both planes were taken at as many as 120 sites. Will this produce a new series of transmit and receive antennas? It depends on test results, broadcast and receive antennas, and financial outlays obviously incurred. During the fall of 1993, such an investigation was primarily an experiment. But, as of now, UHF signals remain horizontally polarized and a good, UHF or dual U/V standard antenna with adequate directional mounting should be entirely adequate for the projected system until we're informed otherwise.

Costs and usage

In testifying before the Congressional House Telecommunications and Finance Subcommittee, John Abel, National Association of Broadcasters Executive Vice President/Operations, suggested additional usage for assigned HDTV broadcast channels. He requested the FCC permit additional flexibility for TV stations in transition, possibly based on market size and their ability to pay. Such ancillary services as data broadcasting to 30 million home computers (at rates considerably faster than modems) and personal digital assistants could combine computer, fax, and cellular phone technologies into a single service. All the foregoing and a network "pass through" is estimated to cost $1 million, and local originating facilities are estimated at anywhere from $10 to 14 million. Small broadcasters in the smaller communities, he said, would certainly be the hardest hit.

Whether such a proposal "has merit" in the eyes of the FCC, we don't yet know, but maximum HDTV broadcasting by nationwide TV stations will certainly increase its appeal and popularity considerably. The addition of data to some service areas just might do the trick.

Index